Farm Gas Engines and Tractors

McGraw-Hill Publications in Agricultural Engineering

The late Quincy C. Ayres was consulting editor of this series from 1939 until 1963.

Farm Gas Engines and Tractors

Fred R. Jones, M.S.

Formerly Professor and Head of Agricultural Engineering Department
Agricultural and Mechanical College of Texas
Fellow, American Society of Agricultural Engineers

FOURTH EDITION

McGraw-Hill Book Company, Inc. New York, San Francisco, Toronto, London

Preface

The first edition of "Farm Gas Engines and Tractors" was published in 1932. At that time the internal-combustion engine had become established as a dominant and reliable source of power for agricultural production in the United States, Canada, and other countries. It supplied power both as a stationary unit in various sizes and types and as an automotive machine better known as a tractor. Constant and rapid changes and improvements in the construction and design of these engines and tractors necessitated frequent revision of the text in order that the student, tractor user, design engineer, and others might have up-to-date information.

In the preparation and arrangement of the subject matter for each edition, three important considerations have been kept in mind: first, that the material should be presented in sufficient detail and in a clear and logical manner; second, that a thorough understanding of the fundamentals of gas-power generation and transmission and of internal-combustion engine construction and operation should precede a study of the more complex types of power units and tractor mechanisms; and third, that any publication of this nature should also treat of such related subjects as power-transmission methods, materials of construction, and the economics of power utilization. The material presented has been collected by the author as the result of nearly forty years of experience in teaching the subject of farm power to both collegiate and noncollegiate students.

In presenting a fourth edition of the text, the author has again attempted to bring the subject matter as completely up to date as possible and to stress the most significant changes and developments in farm tractor construction, design, operation, servicing, and maintenance, the basic objective being to provide college students, tractor owners, operators, dealers, and others with a comprehensive semitechnical treatment of the subject. In addition, considerable technical information is incorporated which can be utilized by tractor and farm-equipment design engineers.

Although some changes have been made in nearly every chapter, the most significant include complete up-to-date information relative to power measurement and testing equipment, engine design, fuels and carburetion, diesel engines, ignition, clutches and transmissions, hitches and stability, hydraulic principles and mechanisms, and the economics of tractor power. The lists of problems and references at the end of each chapter have been carefully revised and made more comprehensive. A special effort has been made to revise the illustrations by discarding those which were obsolescent and unsatisfactory and providing clearer and more up-to-date illustrations.

Again the author is greatly indebted to many manufacturers and others for supplying this illustrative material and other important and valuable information.

Fred R. Jones

Contents

1

Survey of Farm Power

The story of American agricultural progress from the colonial period to the present time is an interesting and spectacular one. At the beginning of the nineteenth century, industrial activities were limited, cities were relatively small, and a large part of the population of working age was engaged in the production of food and fiber products for self-subsistence. There was no appreciable incentive for an excess per capita agricultural production and output, because living standards were low as compared with present-day standards and the many conveniences and luxuries that now seem so commonplace did not exist. But, as the population increased, simple machines and processes were developed, new cities were established, factories were built, railroads and better transportation facilities were constructed, and American industry began to grow.

This slow but certain industrial expansion and a steadily increasing population created a demand for more land and a greater agricultural output, as well as for other basic and essential materials such as coal, iron and other metals, lumber, and oil. Consequently new agricultural areas were opened up, and individual farmers and farm families found themselves operating more acres and producing not only for their own needs and subsistence but for the needs of this constantly increasing number of people engaged in commerce and industry and in other non-agricultural enterprises. As the decades passed, this trend gained momentum. It was accelerated by many new inventions, by the discovery of petroleum and the great development of this industry, by such factors as the Civil War and the two world wars, and by normal technological progress. Not only is the United States today the most highly industrialized nation in the world, but its agricultural production and the efficiency and capacity of its farm workers are much greater than those of any other nation. This condition can be attributed largely to one

1

significant and spectacular development—mechanical power and modern farm machines.

Figure 1-1 shows the population and employment trends for the United States from 1820 to 1960 and the general relationship of the different kinds of farm power to population and industrial growth. According to this chart and Table 1-1, nearly 75 per cent of the working

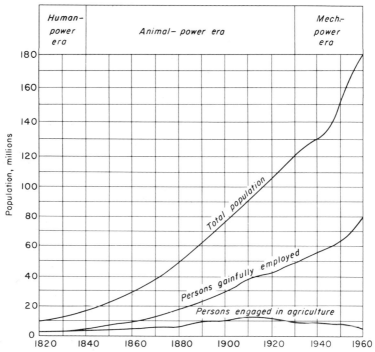

FIG. 1-1. *Total population, persons gainfully employed, and persons engaged in agriculture in the United States, 1820 to 1960.*

force of the United States in 1820 was employed in agricultural production and only about 25 per cent in nonagricultural activities. By 1880 farm employment had dropped to 50 per cent of the total number of persons or 17 per cent of the total population. In 1920 farm workers made up 27 per cent of the total labor force of the country or only 10.8 per cent of the total population. This decline has continued during recent decades, and it is now estimated that farm workers make up about 7 per cent of all employed persons or less than 3 per cent of the total population.

Farm-power progress and transition. Obviously, the first kind of power used in agriculture was human power, and all operations from land preparation through cultivation, harvesting, and processing of the final

Table 1-1. Relation of Agricultural Employment to Total Employment Force and Total Population of the United States, 1820–1960 [1]

Year	Total population, thousands	No. persons gainfully employed, thousands	Total farm employment, thousands	No. persons supported per farm worker	Farm workers, per cent of total population
1820	9,638	2,881	2,069	4.6	21.5
1840	17,069	5,420	3,720	4.6	21.8
1860	31,443	10,533	6,208	5.0	19.7
1880	50,156	17,392	8,585	5.8	17.1
1900	75,995	29,073	10,912	7.0	14.4
1910	91,972	37,371	11,592	7.9	12.6
1920	105,711	42,434	11,449	9.0	10.8
1930	122,775	48,830	10,472	11.7	8.5
1940	131,669	51,742	8,833	14.9	6.7
1950	150,697	59,015	6,838	22.0	4.5
1960 [2]	179,000	70,000	4,800	37.3	2.7

[1] 1954 Census of Agriculture.
[2] Preliminary estimate.

product were performed more or less by hand. Such was probably the situation in America during the Revolutionary period and the early part of the nineteenth century. But, as the need arose for increased crop production, the development and invention of heavier and more effective field tools and machines became imperative. Such tools and machines were necessary if farmers were to increase the acreage operated per farm worker, as the limit had already been reached using human power. Hence, heavier and larger plows and harrows, mechanical planters, cultivators, and harvesting devices were designed and introduced. But they required more and better power; therefore, the ox, the horse, and the mule entered the farm-power scene in appreciable numbers about 1820.

During the next fifty years numerous laborsaving machines were developed and introduced. These included the steel walking plow in 1837, the grain reaper in 1831, the thresher in 1842, and riding machines such as planters, cultivators, plows, mowers, and binders between 1850 and 1870. All these required one or more animals for power.

By 1850 the settlement of the fertile and expansive prairie area now known as the Middle West had started. Wheat was the predominating crop, and this area was ideal for its production. Hence the acreage of wheat and similar grains expanded rapidly. This expansion stimulated a need for an even better source of power than animals, particularly for harvesting and threshing. Consequently the steam engine came into use about 1870 and proved very popular for nearly half a century as a power medium for such heavy-duty operations as grain threshing, lumber and wood sawing, and corn shelling. The early steam engines were mounted on wheels and pulled about by horses. Later on they were made self-propelling, and with the development of the large wheat farms of the West and Northwest, steam tractors displaced animal power to a certain extent for preparing land and for sowing and harvesting the crop. The steam tractor for field work had its limitations. It was very heavy and slow-moving, the fuel was bulky and difficult to handle, and the matter of boiler-water supply and fueling meant constant attention on the part of one man, with a second man to handle and guide the machine. The manufacture of steam tractors was discontinued in the 1920's, and the steam engine is now obsolete as a source of farm power.

Mechanization and labor requirements. The data given in Table 1-2 depict very clearly how mechanization reduces the human-labor requirements for producing the major farm crops. In 1800, 56 man-hours were needed to grow an acre of wheat yielding 15 bushels. This was equivalent to 3.73 man-hours per bushel. By 1900, with the use of binders and threshers, this had been reduced to 15 man-hours per acre and 1.08 man-hours per bushel. Further mechanization, particularly of the harvesting operation, again reduced this labor requirement to 4.3 man-hours per acre and 0.26 man-hour per bushel.

In 1800, corn production required 86 man-hours per acre and 3.44 man-hours per bushel; in 1900, with the use of horse-drawn machines, the requirements were reduced to 38 man-hours per acre and 1.47 man-hours per bushel; in 1950, largely as a result of the use of row-crop tractors and mechanical pickers, the requirements were further reduced to 15 man-hours per acre and 0.40 man-hour per bushel.

Cotton has always been considered as a high-labor-consuming crop. But very definite progress is being made in reducing this hand-labor requirement through mechanization and improved planting and tillage methods. Again referring to Table 1-2, we find that, in 1800, 185 man-hours of labor were needed to produce an acre of cotton. With a yield of 154 lb. of lint per acre, this means a total labor requirement per 500-lb. bale of 601 man-hours. In 1900, with the use of improved methods and horse-drawn equipment, the requirements were 112 man-hours per acre and 283 man-hours per 500-lb. bale, with a yield of 198 lb. per acre. In 1950, with the use of row-crop tractors and modern equipment, the requirements dropped to 71 man-hours per acre and 132 man-hours per 500-lb. bale, with a yield of 269 lb. per acre. Continued progress in the mechanization of cotton-production operations, particularly harvesting, should result in a further pronounced reduction in the labor requirement of this crop in future years.

Table 1-2. Estimated Man-hours Used to Produce Wheat, Corn, and Cotton, for Designated Periods, United States Average [1]

Crop and item	Yearly average for						
	About 1800	About 1840	About 1880	About 1900	About 1920	About 1940	About 1950
Wheat:							
Man-hours per acre before harvest...	16	12	8	7	5.5	3.7	2.3
Harvest.........................	40	23	12	8	6.5	3.8	2.0
Total.........................	56	35	20	15	12.0	7.5	4.3
Yield per acre,[2] bushels............	15	15	13.2	13.9	13.8	15.9	16.5
Man-hours per 100 bushels..........	373	233	152	108	87	47	26.0
Corn for grain:							
Man-hours per acre before harvest...	56	44	28	22	19	15	9.8
Harvest.........................	30	25	18	16	13	10	5.2
Total.........................	86	69	46	38	32	25	15.0
Yield per acre,[2] bushels............	25	25	25.6	25.9	28.4	30.3	38.0
Man-hours per 100 bushels..........	344	276	180	147	113	83	40.0
Cotton:							
Man-hours per acre before harvest...	135	90	67	62	55	46	32
Harvest.........................	50	45	52	50	35	52	39
Total.........................	185	135	119	112	90	98	71
Yield of gross lint per acre,[2] pounds..	154	154	196	198	160	257	269
Man-hours per bale...............	601	439	304	283	281	191	132

[1] *U.S. Dept. Agr. Misc. Publ.* 630 and *U.S. Dept. Agr. Statist. Bull.* 144.

[2] Yields for 1800 and 1840 are estimates. Yields for the other years at 5-year averages of published data, centered on year shown.

Mechanization and labor output. Figure 1-2 shows the trend in respect to farm labor utilization and output during the period 1910 to 1960. It is noted that the output per man-hour remained relatively stable until about 1935. About that time all farm-equipment manufacturers were producing very reliable all-purpose tractors and equipment in numerous sizes to meet most crop needs. The accelerated purchase and use of mechanical power and equipment contributed directly to a sharp upturn in output per man-hour and this trend has continued in recent years because of additional mechanical improvements made in farm tractors and field machines.

Comparisons of farm-production equipment and other factors according to geographic divisions. According to the Bureau of Agricultural Economics [1] of the U.S. Department of Agriculture, the volume of modern production per worker varies greatly in different parts of the country, as shown in Table 1-3. Generally, productive soils and laborsaving ma-

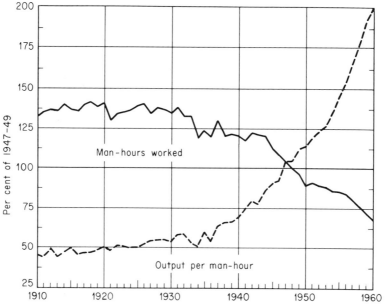

FIG. 1-2. *Trend in output per man-hour and total man-hours of work on farms in the United States, 1910 to 1960.*

chines go hand in hand with high production per worker. In some areas, volume of livestock production contributes considerably to production per worker.

In the fertile grain and livestock region of the West North Central States, for example, production per worker in 1944 was 168 per cent of the United States average, and the 1945 value of land and buildings, livestock, and equipment per worker was 170 per cent of the average. In the East South Central States, on the other hand, production per worker was only 51 per cent of the United States average, and the value per worker of the indicated capital items was 41 per cent of the average. The West North Central farmers had about 88 acres of cropland per worker in 1944, whereas the East South Central farmers had about 16 acres per worker. Equipment per worker averaged $926 in value in the

[1] *U.S. Dept. Agr. Misc. Publ.* 630.

Table 1-3. Gross Production per Worker and Amount of Specified Capital Items per Worker, by Geographic Divisions, 1944 and 1945 [1]

Geographic division	Gross production per worker, 1944 (U.S. average = 100)	Value of land, buildings, livestock, and equipment per worker, 1945 (U.S. average = 100)	Land and buildings per worker, 1945	Livestock per worker, 1945	Equipment per worker, 1945	Total cropland per worker, acres, 1944
West North Central.........	168	170	$7,668	$1,592	$926	88.1
Pacific...................	152	171	8,748	826	623	33.8
Mountain.................	143	151	6,470	1,820	719	66.5
East North Central.........	131	154	7,175	1,184	863	43.3
Middle Atlantic............	108	97	3,942	1,018	838	23.9
New England..............	96	88	3,960	745	529	15.6
West South Central.........	71	73	3,433	616	320	33.4
South Atlantic.............	61	46	2,212	343	187	14.6
East South Central.........	51	41	1,923	351	177	16.1
United States.............	100	100	$4,622	$ 844	$513	37.4

[1] *U.S. Dept. Agr. Misc. Publ.* 630; based on number of farm workers from Bureau of Agricultural Economics Farm Labor Reports, 1944, the production year reported in the 1945 census.

West North Central States, compared with $177 in the East South Central division. Most of these relationships among the regions probably have not changed greatly since the 1945 census was taken.

Although the total number of acres of cropland per worker in the South Atlantic and East South Central States is just about the same as the average for New England, production per worker in New England is nearly 60 per cent greater than production per worker in the South Atlantic States, and almost double the production per worker in the East South Central States. The value of equipment per worker in New England is also about three times the value per worker in the two Southern regions.

These differences are due in part to characteristics of the agricultural divisions that make them adaptable to different types of agriculture. These characteristics make the Southern division well suited for such cash crops as cotton, tobacco, and vegetables. Because of low yields of feed crops and pasture per acre, however, they are not so well adapted to specialized livestock and poultry production. New England farmers, on the other hand, are much less dependent on their cropland acres for production. Large permanent pastures and hay lands furnish roughage for dairy cattle during summer and winter. Grain and other concentrates with which to round out the dairy enterprise are brought in, principally from the Corn Belt. Large poultry enterprises, from which the great Eastern cities are supplied with fresh eggs and poultry meat, are fed by bringing in feed grown elsewhere. Thus, the resources per farm worker in buildings, machinery, and power are much less dictated by the crop-land acres per worker in New England than in the Southern division.

Westward from New England are the Central and Northern areas of less rugged topography, more productive land, and opportunities for operations on a larger scale, or for more diversity because of climatic conditions. Here even greater opportunities for great production per worker become apparent through the use of more machines and facilities for livestock production.

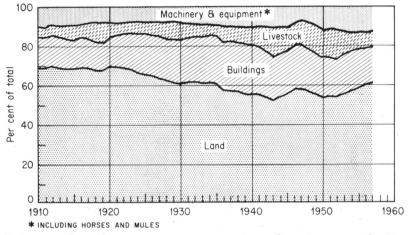

FIG. 1-3. *Trend in relative investment in major farm physical assets in the United States, 1910 to 1960.*

Value of farm physical assets. Figure 1-3 shows the trend since 1910 in the values of the principal physical assets as related to the agricultural industry in the United States. Since 1950, land has increased relative to other factors, and in early 1957, it represented 62 per cent of all assets. This is the highest proportion since the late 1920's. The relative value of buildings trended generally upward to 1940, but has since declined in most years. In early 1957, land and buildings together represented 79.5 per cent of all physical assets. The investment in livestock accounted for only 8 per cent of the total investment in 1957, the smallest proportion since 1937. Investments in machinery and equipment (including horses and mules) have held about steady relative to other assets since 1953, amounting to about 12.5 per cent of the total. Table 1-4 shows the changes and increases in the numbers of farm tractors and certain major farm machines since 1920. The figures show a pronounced acceleration and gain in the utilization of these machines since 1946.

Tractor and horse census and distribution. Figure 1-4 shows the num-ber of horses and tractors in the United States during the period from

Table 1-4. Tractors and Other Machines on Farms, 1920–1960 [1]

Year	Tractors, thousands	Motor trucks, thousands	Automobiles, thousands	Grain combines, thousands	Corn pickers, thousands	Pickup hay balers, thousands	Milking machines,[2] thousands
1920	246	139	2,146	4	10		55
1930	920	900	4,135	61	50		100
1940	1,545	1,047	4,144	190	110	15	175
1946	2,480	1,550	4,260	420	203	54	440
1950	3,394	2,207	4,199	714	456	196	636
1958	4,685	2,985	4,260	1,040	745	580	725
1960	4,770	3,100	4,260	1,065	780	640	725

[1] *U.S. Dept. Agr. Misc. Publ.* 630 and *Statist. Bulls.* and *Implement and Tractor,* statistical issues.

[2] Number of farms with milking machines.

1910 to 1960. The figures were prepared by the Bureau of Agricultural Economics of the U.S. Department of Agriculture and are based upon census figures and other reliable sources. They show that there has been a rapid increase in the number of farm tractors and a decrease in the number of horses and mules since the First World War. The first large increase in tractor numbers came after the end of the First World War, when agricultural and industrial production for peacetime consumption were at high levels. Development of the all-purpose type of tractor and its widespread adoption by farmers in the late 1920's were chiefly responsible for maintenance of the rapid upward trend in the number of tractors on farms. In the late 1930's, rubber-tired all-purpose tractors came on the market. These were bought freely by farmers, and the increase in tractor numbers, which had ceased during the depression years, was resumed. The present large postwar demand for farm tractors and tractor equipment points to a continuation of the strong upward swing in farm mechanization.

It is estimated that, of the total number of tractors on farms Jan. 1, 1960, about 89 per cent were wheel tractors, about 3.4 per cent were track-type tractors, and about 7.6 per cent were garden tractors. Perhaps 50 per cent or more of the track-type tractors used on United States farms will be found in the Pacific Coast and Mountain States. They are used largely in fruit and truck production and on the large hilly grain farms of the Northwest. The use of garden tractors has increased greatly in recent years, particularly in the truck-farming areas.

The distribution and utilization of tractors is affected by a number of factors, such as type of agriculture and crops produced, sizes of farms and fields, topography, availability and quality of labor, and soil fertility. Those regions having a relatively level topography with large fields and productive soil are most suitable for mechanization and laborsaving machines. The shift to mechanization began earlier and has been more pronounced in such regions. For example, in 1920, tractors were being used extensively on the grain and livestock farms of the Great Plains and the Corn Belt, in some parts of the Pacific Northwest, in the Eastern

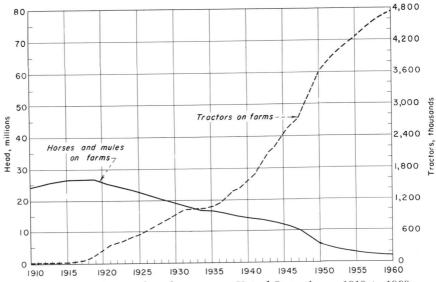

FIG. 1-4. *Work animals and tractors on United States farms, 1910 to 1960.*

States, and in the rice-, sugar-cane-, and fruit-growing areas of the South and West.

Mechanization of cotton production in some sections of the South has been retarded because of the relatively plentiful supply of labor, the small farms, the rolling or hilly topography, the nature of the crop, and the fact that tractors and equipment were not as well and as readily adapted to the successful handling of all production operations, particularly thinning and harvesting. Considerable progress has been made in recent years in the mechanization of these two high-labor-consuming operations.

REFERENCES

Implement and Tractor, annual statistical issue.
An Appraisal of Power Used on Farms in the United States, *U.S. Dept. Agr. Bull.* 1348.
Progress of Farm Mechanization, *U.S. Dept. Agr. Misc. Publ.* 630.

Statistical Abstract of United States, U.S. Bureau of the Census.
Changes in Farm Production and Efficiency, *U.S. Dept. Agr. Statist. Bull.* 233.
Selected Machines and Equipment on Farms, *U.S. Dept. Agr. Statist. Bull.* 258.

PROBLEMS AND QUESTIONS

1. Explain the trends in farm population, farm employment, and total agricultural production during the twentieth century.

2. Name the three major field crops, and discuss the trend in the labor requirements for producing each crop since 1800.

3. Discuss the variation in production per agricultural worker for the different geographic areas of the United States, and state the reasons for these variations.

4. What has been the trend in the total investment in farm equipment since 1910, and what were the principal general items of investment in 1910 and in 1960?

5. Assuming that the average work animal developed 0.5 hp. and was used 1,000 hr. per year and that the average tractor developed 30 hp. and was used 500 hr. per year, what was the total available horsepower-hours of power in 1910?

6. Assuming that the average work animal developed 0.5 hp. and was used 500 hr. per year and that the average tractor developed 25 hp. and was used 600 hr. per year, what was the total available horsepower-hours of power in 1960?

7. Discuss tractor distribution and use in the different geographic areas of the United States, and explain any variations in this distribution.

2

Farm Power Sources and Adaptability

Power is required on the farm for doing two kinds of work, namely, tractive work, requiring pulling or drawing effort, and stationary work, usually accomplished by means of a belt, gears, power take-off, or direct drive. Tractive jobs include (1) plowing and land preparation, (2) planting and seeding, (3) crop cultivation, (4) harvesting, and (5) hauling. Stationary jobs include (1) water pumping, (2) threshing, (3) feed grinding, (4) ensilage cutting, and (5) wood sawing, in addition to numerous other jobs of a like nature.

Sources of power. There are five possible sources of power for doing the various kinds of work. In other words, it can be said that there are five prime movers available for the farmer. These are (1) domestic animals, (2) wind, (3) flowing water, (4) electricity, and (5) heat engines. Some of these are necessarily limited in use, as will be mentioned later. In fact, up to this time only two of the five mentioned, namely, domestic animals and heat engines, have proved practical for supplying tractive power. Thus far wind, water, and electric power are confined entirely to stationary work.

Animal power. As shown in Fig. 1-4, the use of horses and mules for farm power in the United States reached a peak about 1918 and has shown a rapid decrease since about 1930. All farming operations in most sections of the United States are now carried on without the use or need for a single work animal. On the other hand, animals such as the horse, the mule, the ox, the water buffalo, and even the camel are still the principal source of farm power in many Latin American, European, and Asiatic countries. There are a number of reasons for this such as (1) size of farms, (2) topography, (3) kinds of crops grown, (4) lack of a suitable fuel at a reasonable cost, (5) high initial cost of mechanical equipment, and (6) plentiful supply of low-cost labor.

Power of horses and mules. The power and pulling ability of horses and mules are matters that are frequently debated but seldom understood. According to King,[1] a horse working continuously for several hours and walking at the rate of 2½ m.p.h. should not be expected to pull more than one-tenth to one-eighth of its weight. On this basis, a 1,000-lb. horse can develop 0.67 to 0.83 hp.; a 1,200-lb. horse, 0.80 to 1.00 hp.; and a 1,600-lb. horse, 1.07 to 1.33 hp.

Studies and tests made at the Iowa State College [2] demonstrated that:

1. It is possible for horses to exert a tractive effort of one-tenth to one-eighth of their own weight and travel a total of 20 miles per day without undue fatigue.

2. It is possible for horses weighing 1,500 to 1,900 lb. or over to pull continuously loads of 1 hp. or more for periods of a day or longer.

3. A well-trained horse can exert an overload of over 1,000 per cent for a short time.

4. For a period of a few seconds and over a limited distance of perhaps 30 ft. or less, a horse can exert a maximum pull of from 60 to 100 per cent of its actual weight. Under such conditions one horse may develop as much as 10 hp. or more, depending upon its size and pulling ability.

Domestic animals are not well adapted to the generation of power for stationary purposes. Prior to the introduction of steam and gas engines, horses and mules and, to a lesser degree, cattle and sheep and other common farm animals were used to operate certain stationary machines by means of a treadmill or a sweep. However, the power generated was extremely small unless a number of animals were used together. Hay balers, feed mills, and sirup mills are examples of sweep-power-operated machines.

Wind power. The energy of the wind, like that of flowing water, is more or less limited for farm use, chiefly because it cannot be controlled and is seldom available when needed. Consequently, the use of wind power on the farm is confined largely to water pumping, because whenever the wind blows, even if but once or twice a week, enough water can be pumped and conveniently stored to last several days, or until the wind blows again. The power of the wind is made available by means of the common windmill.

The power developed by this device depends primarily upon the size of wheel and the wind velocity. However, a number of other factors such as type of wheel, design of wheel and mill, and height of tower affect the performance of a windmill. The theoretical power of a stream of air passing through a circular area perpendicular to the direction of travel of the air is represented by the formula

[1] King, "Physics of Agriculture," published by the author, 1910.
[2] *Iowa State Coll. Agr. Exp. Sta. Bull.* 240.

$$\text{h.p.} = 0.00000525D^2W^3$$

where D = maximum diameter of wind wheel or circle, ft.

W = wind velocity, m.p.h.

Owing to certain reactions between the wind and the revolving wheel and to mechanical imperfections, it is usually considered that the actual efficiency of the common multisail type of farm windmill based upon this formula will be approximately 30 per cent for wind velocities up to 10 m.p.h., 20 per cent for wind velocities of 15 to 20 m.p.h., and 15 per cent for wind velocities of 25 m.p.h. or more. Table 2-1 gives the approximate

Table 2-1. Power of Windmills for Wheels of Different Sizes and for Different Wind Velocities

Wind velocity, m.p.h.	Diameter of wind wheel, ft.					
	6	8	10	12	14	16
6	0.01	0.02	0.03	0.05	0.07	0.09
10	0.06	0.10	0.16	0.23	0.31	0.40
15	0.13	0.23	0.35	0.51	0.70	0.91
20	0.30	0.54	0.84	1.21	1.65	2.15
25	0.44	0.79	1.23	1.77	2.42	3.15
30	0.77	1.36	2.12	3.06	4.16	5.45

horsepower developed by windmills of various sizes and at different wind velocities, based upon the above assumptions.

The airplane-type wind wheel, commonly used where high speed is desirable, as in the case of wind-driven electric plants, probably has a higher efficiency than the ordinary farm-windmill type of wheel.

Water power. In certain sections of the country are found many small streams, which can be harnessed up in such a manner as to develop useful power to be employed on nearby or conveniently located farms. Such sections of the country, however, are of course limited to comparatively rolling and hilly ground. Furthermore, a stream may furnish abundant power at one period of the year, but become so low in the driest season as to fail to supply sufficient power. The power developed by flowing water depends upon two factors, namely, the volume of water flowing per minute and the head or vertical distance the water drops at the point where the power installation is located. The former can be measured either by the float method or by a weir (Fig. 2-1). The head is determined by measuring the difference in surface level before the water falls and after.

For example, suppose that the following stream measurements have been made:

Ft.

Average width.............. 12
Average depth 2
Velocity per minute......... 15
Head..................... 4

Knowing that water weighs 62.4 lb. per cu. ft. and that 33,000 ft.-lb. per min. is equal to 1 hp., the theoretical power available from the stream is

$$\frac{12 \times 2 \times 62.4 \times 15 \times 4}{33,000} = 2.7 \text{ hp.}$$

Owing to frictional losses in the water wheel or other means used, the actual available horsepower would probably be somewhat less than 2.7.

FIG. 2-1. *Measuring the stream flow with a rectangular weir.*

Devices used for converting water power into useful form are generally classed as either water wheels (Fig. 2-2) or turbines (Fig. 2-3).

Electric power. The use of electricity on farms has increased tremendously in the past thirty years, and it is now playing a major part in farm mechanization. Electricity contributes directly to agricultural production by supplying heat, light, and power for lighting buildings and heating water, and for operating brooders, water pumps, and dairy and refrigeration equipment.

The greatest utilization of electricity will be found in the Eastern,

Middle Western, and Pacific Coast States. Most of the states in these regions show from 90 to 100 per cent of the farms as having central-station electric service. The Great Plains and the Southeastern cotton regions show the lowest utilization of electricity on farms.

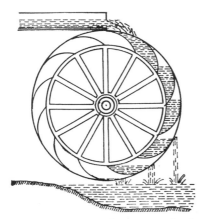

FIG. 2-2. *An overshot water wheel.*

Electricity is a very convenient and satisfactory source of power for operating various kinds of stationary equipment used in the farm home and about the farmstead. Electric motors are preferable to gas engines for operating most small stationary farm machines, but their utilization on farms is usually confined to machines not requiring more than 5 to $7\frac{1}{2}$ hp. The explanation for this is that most rural electric transmission lines are of the single-phase (two-wire) type. The maximum size of motor which is practical for use on a single-phase transmission line is $7\frac{1}{2}$ hp. If motors larger than this are needed, a three-phase (three-wire) line is required. Since high-voltage electric transmission lines require the use of very heavy wire and a suitable trans-

FIG. 2-3. *A water-turbine installation.*

former, a three-phase line is considerably more expensive to build than a single-phase line. Hence, unless there is a real need for a number of large motors on a line, it is difficult to justify this additional cost.

Electric motors for stationary power have a number of distinct advantages, such as: (1) they are relatively simple and compact in construction, (2) they are light in weight per horsepower, (3) they require little attention and limited care and servicing, (4) they start easily and readily, (5) they operate quietly, (6) they produce smooth, uniform power, and (7) they are adapted to uniform or variable loads.

Heat engines. Fortunately, when the demand arose for larger power-producing units for operating such stationary farm machines as the

FIG. 2-4. *A complete stationary steam-engine layout.*

thresher, the wood saw, the corn shredder, and the ensilage cutter, at about that time the steam engine and, later, the gas engine were invented. These engines are known to the engineer as *heat engines*. In either case, whether it is a steam engine or a gas engine, some kind of combustible material known as a fuel—particularly wood, coal, oil, or natural gas—is ignited, combustion takes place either slowly or rapidly, heat is produced and utilized in such a way as to create pressure, and the latter, when applied to certain movable parts of the apparatus, produces motion and therefore energy and power.

The steam engine (Fig. 2-4) and the ordinary gas engine (Fig. 2-5) are the two common types of heat engines. In the former, the heat of the burning fuel is applied to water in a closed receptacle called a boiler. As the water becomes heated, it is converted into steam. As the heating continues, more steam is formed and high pressure results. This steam, under pressure, when conducted by a pipe into a cylinder behind the piston, places the latter in motion and thus generates power. Since the fuel is ignited and burned outside the cylinder and its heat energy applied indirectly to the piston by an intermediate medium, namely, water vapor, the steam engine is called an *external-combustion engine.*

The gas engine resembles the steam engine in that the pressure is applied to a piston sliding back and forth within a cylinder, but it differs greatly in the combustion of the fuel and the application of the pressure resulting from the heat produced. In the case of the common gas engine

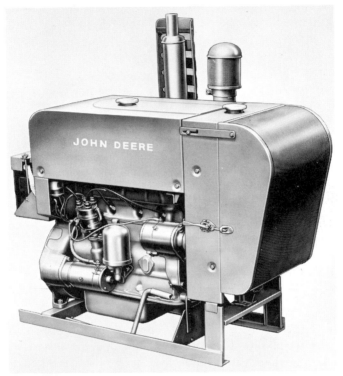

FIG. 2-5. *A stationary gasoline-engine power unit.* (Courtesy of Deere and Company.)

and engines of a similar type, the combustible fuel mixture is first placed inside the cylinder in a gaseous condition and compressed before it is ignited. The ignition of this compressed mixture causes very rapid combustion and an instantaneous application of pressure to the piston, more commonly known as an explosion. The piston is consequently set in motion and power is generated. Since the fuel is ignited and burned inside the cylinder, the gas engine and all engines that operate in a similar manner are known as *internal-combustion engines.*

Gas engine versus steam engine. The internal-combustion engine has completely replaced the steam engine for all types of farm power applications for the following reasons:

1. It is more efficient; that is, a greater percentage of the heat and energy value of the fuel is converted into useful power. The efficiency

of the internal-combustion engine varies from 15 to 30 per cent, whereas that of the external-combustion engine is often as low as 3 and seldom exceeds 10 per cent.

2. Weighs less per horsepower.

3. More compact.

4. Original cost less per horsepower.

5. Less time and work necessary preliminary to starting.

6. Less time and attention required while in operation.

7. Can be made in a greater variety of sizes and types and adapted to many special uses; that is, it has a greater range of adaptability.

REFERENCES

Testing Draft Horses, *Iowa State Coll. Agr. Expt. Sta. Bull.* 240.

Electric Energy from Winds, *Kansas State Coll. Eng. Expt. Sta. Bull.* 52.

Electric Light and Power Systems for the Farm, S. *Dakota State Coll. Agr. Expt. Sta. Bull.* 402.

PROBLEMS AND QUESTIONS

1. What are the sources of power most widely used in present-day farming, and what are the limitations, if any, of these particular kinds of power in performing the various field and stationary operations?

2. Explain the derivation of the formula for the theoretical horsepower of a wind wheel.

3. Compute the actual power output of a wind wheel having a 10-ft. (diameter) wheel, if the wind velocity is 18 m.p.h. and the efficiency is 20 per cent.

4. Name some common farm jobs that can be performed with electric power.

5. What are the principal factors which determine the power generated by a stream of water?

3

History and Development of the Internal-combustion Engine and Farm Tractor

The first ideas concerning the operation and construction of an internal-combustion engine were based upon the action of the ordinary rifle or cannon; that is, the barrel served as a cylinder and the bullet or cannon ball acted as a piston. The difficulty encountered, however, was in getting the piston to return to its original position, thus producing a continuous back-and-forth movement to ensure a continuous generation of power.

Early ideas and inventions. Nothing of consequence was accomplished in this field before the seventeenth century. In 1678, Hautefeuille, a Frenchman, proposed the use of an explosive powder to obtain power. He is said to have been the first man to design an engine using heat as a motive force and capable of producing a definite quantity of continuous work. Huygens, a Dutchman, is credited with having been the first man actually to construct an engine having a cylinder and piston. This device used explosive powder as fuel and was exhibited to the French minister of finance in 1680.

None of these early attempts was successful, however, and further efforts in the construction of an internal-combustion engine were abandoned for about a hundred years. During the eighteenth century the possibilities of utilizing steam for power were recognized and developed, and the energies of the engineers of that time were turned almost entirely toward applications of the steam engine. About 1800 the thoughts of these investigators were again directed toward the possible design of a gas engine. During the period from 1800 to 1860, a number of engines were constructed, none of which was really successful. Some notable steps were made, however, among which were the use of compression and an improved system of flame ignition by Barnett in 1838 and the actual construction and manufacture of an internal-combustion engine on a commercial scale by Lenoir in 1860. The Lenoir engine later proved to be impractical.

Beau de Rochas. Perhaps the individual making the first really important contribution toward the development of the present-day types of internal-combustion engines was Beau de Rochas, a French engineer. In 1862 this man advanced the actual theory of operation of all modern types of internal-combustion engines. He first stated that there were four conditions that were essential for efficient operation. These were as follows:

1. The greatest possible cylinder volume with the least possible cooling surface.
2. The greatest possible piston speed.
3. The highest possible compression at the beginning of expansion.
4. The greatest possible expansion.

These principles are still considered as fundamental and extremely important in gas-engine design. Beau de Rochas proposed further that a successful engine embodying these principles must consist of a single cylinder and a piston that made a stroke for each of the four distinct events constituting a cycle, as follows:

1. Drawing in of the combustible fuel mixture on an outward stroke.
2. Compression of the mixture on an inward stroke.
3. Ignition of the mixture at maximum compression producing an outward power or expansion stroke.
4. Discharge of the products of combustion on a fourth or inward stroke.

Otto and Clerk. Beau de Rochas never succeeded in constructing an engine based upon his theories, but they were promptly accepted as being essential. Although considerable effort was expended in the design of an engine during the next few years, it was not until 1876 that Dr. N. A. Otto, a German, patented the first really successful engine operating on this four-stroke-cycle principle. The engine was first exhibited in 1878. This cycle, although originally proposed by Beau de Rochas, is commonly known as the *Otto cycle.*

The invention of the four-stroke-cycle engine by Otto was soon followed by the issue of a patent, in 1878, to Dugald Clerk, an Englishman, on the first two-stroke-cycle engine, that is, an engine producing one power impulse for every revolution instead of for every two revolutions. This particular engine was not marketed at once, however, and was not really perfected until 1881.

Diesel. Another notable contribution to the development and varied application of the internal-combustion engine was the work of Dr. Rudolph Diesel, a German engineer, who conceived the idea of utilizing the heat produced by high compression for igniting the fuel charge in the cylinder. In 1892 he secured a patent on an engine designed to operate in this manner. This first machine proved unsatisfactory, however, and it was not until about 1898 that the first successful diesel-type engines were produced. During the past 35 years, rapid strides have been made in the development and utilization of the diesel principle in internal-combustion engines for both stationary and tractor applications.

We thus observe that the invention of the internal-combustion engine is a comparatively recent one and that the many finely constructed modern types of single- and multiple-cylinder engines have been designed and developed almost overnight. But when it is considered that petroleum, now the almost universal source of fuels and lubricants for these engines, was first discovered about 1858 and that very little was known concerning the application of electricity in the operation of internal-combustion engines previous to the latter part of the past century, we readily perceive the explanation of the retardation of this invention—now considered an indispensable device to modern life throughout the world.

HISTORY AND DEVELOPMENT OF THE FARM TRACTOR

A *tractor* is defined specifically as a self-propelled machine that can be used for supplying power for (1) pulling mobile machines and (2) operating the mechanisms of either stationary or mobile machines by means of a belt pulley or a power take-off. The two common types are the steam tractor, in which an external-combustion or steam engine supplies the power, and the gas tractor, in which an internal-combustion engine serves as the source of power.

Steam tractor. The invention and development of the steam engine preceded those of the internal-combustion engine by 100 years or more. Consequently, the earliest known tractors were of the steam type. They first came into general use for operating threshers (Fig. 3-1) in the wheat- and grain-growing sections of the country during the last two or three decades of the nineteenth century. Their self-propelling feature was utilized primarily for moving about from one threshing job to another. Later on, with the opening up of the large wheat farms of the West and Northwest, steam tractors displaced animal power to a certain extent for preparing the land and sowing and harvesting the crop.

The steam tractor for field work had its limitations. It was very heavy and slow-moving, the fuel was bulky and difficult to handle, and the matter of boiler-water supply and fueling meant constant attention on the part of one man, with a second man to handle and guide the machine.

Early gas tractors. Certain manufacturers, foreseeing a greater future demand for suitable mechanical power for field work, particularly in the wheat-growing sections of the country, started the construction of gas tractors even before the close of the nineteenth century. For example, Fig. 3-2 shows a machine that is said to have been built in 1892. Another tractor (Fig. 3-3) is reported to have been put into use in North Dakota in 1897, and Fig. 3-4 shows the first Hart Parr tractor, which

FIG. 3-1. *Steam tractor operating a grain thresher.*

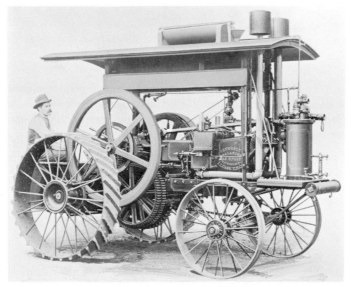

FIG. 3-2. *A gas tractor built in* 1892.

was sold in 1902. These heavy, cumbersome-appearing machines were the forerunners of the present-day tractor industry, which started soon after the opening of the present century and began to gain momentum about 1905.

According to Ellis and Rumely,[1]

By the spring of 1908 the builders of the first successful tractor had about 300 machines in the field and the sales of that year equaled those of the 5 years preceding. The following year the number in the field was again doubled and by the close of the year 1910 over 2,000 of these tractors were said to be in active service. Another company began to produce a small tractor

FIG. 3-3. *A gas tractor built in* 1897.

in 1907 and by the close of the decade was selling several thousand yearly. Dozens of gas tractor factories sprang up and practically every manufacturer of steam traction engines either went out of business or added an internal-combustion engine to his line.

These early tractors consisted usually of a large one-cylinder gas engine mounted on a heavy frame placed on four wheels. The two rear wheels were connected by a train of heavy, exposed cast-iron gears to the crankshaft of the engine, thus making the machine self-propelling. Like the steam tractors, they were heavy, cumbersome, and powerful, and in fact they seemed to be designed as a mere substitute for the former. They possessed certain advantages, however. The fuel was easier to handle, there was less water to haul, and less time and attention were required for starting and during operation. One man was usually able to handle the largest outfit.

The lightweight tractor. About 1910 the designers turned their attention toward the possibilities of a lighter weight gas tractor to meet the

[1] Ellis and Rumely, "Power and the Plow," Doubleday & Company, Inc., New York, 1911.

approaching demand of the smaller grain and livestock farmer for mechanical power. Consequently, about 1913, there began to appear on the
market a number of machines, comparatively light in weight and differing greatly in construction and appearance. In most cases, they were
equipped with two- and four-cylinder engines.

By 1915, the farmers were presented with an amazing array of types,
models, and sizes, ranging from the giant one- or two-cylinder four-
wheelers to a tractor attachment for a small automobile. No two ma-

FIG. 3-4. *A gas tractor sold in* 1902.

chines resembled each other. Some had two wheels, some three, and
some four. Some were driven from the front and others from the rear.
Some had the plows attached under the frame, while others pulled
them in the usual manner. Competition became very marked, and large
sums of money were spent for public demonstrations. Many of these
freak machines were sold. Some proved more or less successful, while
others gave unsatisfactory results and tended to destroy the faith of
their owners in the future value of the tractor. True it was that a few
of these first light-weight tractors were unreasonable in design and weak
in construction. On the other hand, many of them were not. Their failure in the hands of the farmer could be attributed largely to the lack
of knowledge of their operation and care.

The period of the freak tractor was short. By 1917, many of them had
disappeared from the market, and the more far-sighted designer observed that there were certain fundamentals of tractor design that had
to be adhered to.

The First World War and the tractor. The First World War had a
very pronounced effect upon farm-tractor development and use. Maxi-

mum agricultural production was urged. There was a shortage of labor and prices became abnormally high. All these factors meant an increased demand for laborsaving and timesaving machinery, especially small farm tractors. As a consequence, a large number of small tractor manufacturers sprang up overnight, so to speak, and placed upon the market between 200 and 300 different makes and models of machines. These ranged from the small two-wheel garden tractor to the larger four-wheel types. The average and most popular size seemed to be a machine rated at about 10 to 15 drawbar hp. and 20 to 30 belt hp. The tendency in design was toward a four-wheel rear-drive tractor with a four-cylinder engine. Most of these tractors seemed to give much better satisfaction and service than those of earlier manufacture.

Thus the First World War proved to be a great stimulus to the adoption of mechanical power by the farmer. Farm tractors were being used successfully in every nook and corner of the country.

Effect of agricultural depression of 1920. The tractor industry, like many others that were dependent upon the prosperity of the farmer, received a severe setback as the result of the unexpected agricultural depression in 1920. At this time more than 100 different companies were offering about 250 sizes, models, and types of machines. Many of these concerns were small and lacked the capital and the organization necessary to enable them to compete with the older, larger, and better established companies. They attempted to struggle along but, with little or no surplus to draw upon, soon fell by the wayside. Within 2 years' time practically every tractor company that had been organized during the 5 or 10 years preceding for the primary purpose of manufacturing and selling farm gas tractors was compelled to quit. Even some of the older and better established farm-equipment manufacturers, who had entered the tractor business, found little sale for their machines.

Those companies that were able to remain in the business realized that it was no longer a problem of convincing the small or average farmer that mechanical power, in the form of the gas tractor, was practical and economical. They saw that he was willing to pay the price for a well-built, sensibly designed machine that would actually do the work for which it was recommended. Consequently, in spite of the generally depressed and unprosperous condition of agriculture throughout the United States during the years 1921 to 1926, the demand for farm tractors continued to grow, as shown by the fact that the number in use on farms increased from about 250,000 in 1920 to over 500,000 in 1925. An analysis of the figures by states shows further that the greatest increase during this period was in the Middle Western, Eastern, and Southern states, indicating beyond a doubt that the small or average farmer, as well as the large grain raiser, was now a tractor convert.

The agricultural depression of 1930 to 1935 was even more pronounced than that of 1920. The prices of agricultural products dropped to the lowest point reached in many years. Consequently, there was little demand for farm tractors and equipment and sales were relatively small, particularly in 1932 and 1933. However, the small, low-priced, all-purpose tractor was introduced at this time, and as commodity prices improved, an immediate, widespread demand developed for such a tractor. As a result, tractor sales increased steadily and manufacturers were operating at capacity by 1935.

Design standardized. It is true that very few of the machines sold during this period, 1920 to 1926, were adapted to doing everything about the farm; that is, they were not of the all-purpose type. A really successful machine of this type was yet to appear on the market. Most of the machines were light-weight, two- or three-plow tractors that were used largely for plowing and land preparation and for belt work. The owners were satisfied to have something that would prepare the land quicker and better and likewise relieve the horse of this heavy work.

Another outstanding fact was that, during this period, the design of these tractors, as a whole, seemed more stable and uniform. In other words, there was less variation in design and construction than formerly, indicating that the manufacturers had now, after years of costly experience, settled upon many of the essentials of a successful farm tractor.

All-purpose tractors. The next and most logical step seemed to be the design of a light-weight, low-priced, all-purpose tractor that would do any kind of field or stationary work on the average farm, including plowing, harrowing, planting, cultivating, harvesting, threshing, or anything requiring similar power. Several machines of this type were designed and sold during the period 1917 to 1921, but few of them ever proved really successful. In other words, it appeared to be a difficult problem to construct a tractor that would be heavy and rugged enough to plow and harrow the heaviest soil and still be practical for such lighter jobs as planting and cultivating of row crops, mowing hay, and so on. Efforts were continued, however, by certain manufacturers to build a really successful and practical all-purpose farm tractor, and in 1924 one of these concerns introduced a machine that came nearer to meeting the requirements of such a tractor than any that had been previously built. Within a few years all the established manufacturers had designed and introduced one or more models of all-purpose tractors.

Power take-off—diesel tractors—pneumatic tires—power lifts and hydraulic controls—small tractors. Numerous other significant developments have taken place since 1925 which have accelerated the adoption of tractors for agricultural power, extended their range of utility, and improved their convenience and ease of operation. The first tractors supplying power directly to the mechanism of a field machine by means of a power take-off attachment appeared about 1927 and this device is now considered as standard equipment on all farm tractors and quite indispensable for many farm power applications.

Tractors equipped with diesel engines were introduced in 1931. In spite of their higher first cost, diesel-engined tractors have proved highly successful for certain kinds of work and for jobs requiring considerable power or operation under extremely adverse traction conditions.

Low-pressure pneumatic tires first appeared on farm tractors about 1932. In spite of their higher cost compared with steel-wheel tractors, it was soon discovered that rubber-tired tractors offered a number of definite advantages. By 1940 the demand was almost 100 per cent for this type of equipment. Many improvements have been made in rubber tires and tractor-wheel equipment in recent years.

During the late 1930's a few manufacturers introduced small one-row all-purpose tractors. Others followed with similar or even smaller tractors during or immediately following the end of the Second World War.

Other developments which have contributed to the popularity and more effective utilization of tractors, particularly the all-purpose types, are (1) improved hydraulic lifting and control devices, (2) special, direct-connected, and quickly attached implements and tools, (3) power steering, (4) a greater range of travel speeds, (5) electric starting and lighting, (6) better brakes, and (7) improved operator comfort.

REFERENCES

ELLIS, L. W., and E. A. RUMELY, "Power and the Plow," Doubleday & Company, Inc., New York, 1911.
Farm Power and the Post-war Tractor, *S.A.E. Journal*, Vol. 52, No. 10.
GRAY, R. B., "Development of the Agricultural Tractor in the United States," Parts I and II, American Society of Agricultural Engineers, St. Joseph, Mich.

PROBLEMS AND QUESTIONS

1. Discuss the development of mechanical power for agricultural use in the United States from 1800 to the present time, giving the principal significant events.

2. Discuss the development of the all-purpose tractor, naming the significant events involved.

4

Types of Farm Tractors

Classification of tractor types. Tractors as now manufactured can be classified as follows:

A. According to method of securing traction and self-propulsion:
    1. Wheel tractors
        a. Tricycle or three wheels
        b. Four wheels
    2. Track-type tractors
B. According to utility:
    1. General purpose or utility
    2. All-purpose or row-crop type
    3. Orchard
    4. Industrial
    5. Garden

Wheel tractors. The wheel-type tractor is the predominating type of machine, particularly for agricultural purposes. Wheel tractors are made either with three wheels (Fig. 4-1) or with four wheels (Fig. 4-2). With the established success of the row-crop type of tractor and its greater adaptability, the three-wheel tractor now probably predominates in agriculture. The usual arrangement consists of two rear-drive wheels and a front steering member. The drive wheels are, as a rule, spaced farther apart than in the ordinary four-wheel machine, to secure stability on sloping land. The steering member may consist of a single wheel or of two wheels placed very close together. The double steering-wheel arrangement provides greater front load support, better traction, and more positive steering under most conditions. Figure 24-19 shows an equalizing device used on one make of tractor which permits the two wheels to adjust themselves to uneven ground conditions.

Track-type tractors. The traction mechanism in the track-type tractor (Fig. 4-3) consists essentially of two heavy, endless, metal-linked devices known as tracks. Each runs on two iron wheels, one. of which bears sprockets and acts as a driver. The other serves as an idler (see Fig. 24-12). Steering is accomplished through the tracks themselves by reducing the movement of one track below the speed of the other.

FIG. 4-1. A *tricycle all-purpose tractor.* (Courtesy of Deere and Company.)

The use of the track-type tractor was quite limited up to the First World War period. The tanks that were developed at that time and proved so successful in traveling over the battle-swept areas did more perhaps than anything else to demonstrate the adaptability and utility of such a traction arrangement. Consequently, during the succeeding years, the development of successful track-type tractors in both small and large sizes for every known use was rather rapid. In fact, they have practically supplanted the wheel tractor for many heavy-duty, earth-moving, and industrial jobs requiring tractor power.

Track-type tractors have a limited use in agriculture. They are well adapted and extensively used for commercial orchard cultivation and maintenance; for grain and other crop-production operations in some hilly sections; for terracing, road maintenance, and special earth-moving jobs on large farms, particularly in irrigated areas; and for land clearing.

FIG. 4-2. *A four-wheel general-purpose tractor.* (Courtesy of Deere and Company.)

FIG. 4-3. *Track-type tractor pulling a subsoiler.* (Courtesy of Caterpillar Tractor Company.)

General-purpose or utility tractor. A general-purpose tractor is one of more or less conventional design such as an ordinary four-wheel machine (Fig. 4-2) or a track-type machine (Fig. 4-3). This type is also referred to as a utility tractor. It is made to perform only the usual tractor jobs, including both field and belt work such as plowing, harrowing, road grading, combining, feed grinding, and the like.

Orchard and industrial tractors. Orchard tractors are small or medium-size, general-purpose machines of either the wheel or crawler type (see Fig. 4-4), so constructed and equipped as to be operated to better ad-

FIG. 4-4. *Grove or orchard tractor.* (Courtesy of International Harvester Company.)

vantage around the trees. Such tractors are often built lower with as few projecting parts as possible and with special fenders.

Industrial tractors are machines of any size or type specially constructed for various industrial operations and for heavy hauling about

FIG. 4-5. *Industrial tractor.* (Courtesy of International Harvester Company.)

factories, freight depots, airports, and so on. They are equipped with rubber-tired wheels and may have hoisting, excavating, power-loading, and similar attachments built on them as shown in Fig. 4-5.

ALL-PURPOSE TRACTORS

An all-purpose or row-crop type (Figs. 4-1, 4-6, 4-7, and 4-8) is a tractor designed to handle practically all the field and belt jobs on the average farm, including the planting and intertillage of row crops. The most important requirements of such a tractor are (1) greater clearance,

FIG. 4-6. *Single-row four-wheel tractor.* (Courtesy of Deere and Company.)

FIG. 4-7. *Four-wheel four-row all-purpose tractor.* (Courtesy of Tractor and Implement Division, Ford Motor Company.)

both vertical and horizontal, (2) adaptation to the usual row widths, (3) quick, short-turning ability, (4) convenient and easy handling, (5) quick and easy attachment and removal of field implements and attachments, and (6) essential accessories such as hydraulic controls and power take-off. All-purpose tractors are made in several types and sizes to adapt them to the many kinds of crops and varying field and farm sizes and conditions.

FIG. 4-8. *A tricycle-type eight-row all-purpose tractor.* (Courtesy of International Harvester Company.)

General design—power—speed—capacity. Although there is considerable variation in the design and construction of the individual machines and equipment, the trend appears to be as follows:

1. Type: The majority of the machines used are wheel machines of either the tricycle or the four-wheel type.
2. Power: Seven sizes having power ranges of
    a. 8 to 12 drawbar hp., 10 to 14 belt hp.
    b. 15 to 20 drawbar hp., 18 to 25 belt hp.
    c. 21 to 24 drawbar hp., 27 to 30 belt hp.
    d. 25 to 30 drawbar hp., 32 to 38 belt hp.
    e. 31 to 40 drawbar hp., 40 to 50 belt hp.
    f. 41 to 50 drawbar hp., 51 to 62 belt hp.
    g. 51 to 70 drawbar hp., 63 to 85 belt hp.
3. Weight: 2,000 to 18,000 lb. depending on size, type, and wheel weighting.
4. Travel speeds: Four to twelve speeds forward ranging from a low of 1.2 m.p.h. to a high of from 12 to 17 m.p.h.
5. Field-tool and belt-power capacity:
    a. One 8- to 14-in. moldboard plow bottom or a one-disk plow; one-bottom lister plow; 4-ft. tandem disk harrow; 6- to 7-ft.

grain drill; one- or two-row planter; one-row cultivator; 4- to 5-ft. mower; small feed mill.

b. Two 12- or 14-in. or one 16-in. moldboard plow bottom or a two-disk plow; one-bottom lister plow; 6-ft. tandem disk harrow; 8- to 10-ft. grain drill; two-row planter or cultivator; 5- to 6-ft. mower; small feed mill.

c. Two 14-in. moldboard plow bottoms or a two-disk plow; two-bottom lister plow; 6- to 8-ft. tandem disk harrow; 12- to 14-ft. grain drill; two-row planter or cultivator; 7-ft. mower; 6-ft. combine; medium-size feed mill.

d. Three 14-in. moldboard plow bottoms or a three-disk plow; two- or three-bottom lister plow; 8- to 9-ft. tandem disk harrow; one 14-ft. or two 12-ft. grain drills; two- or four-row planter or cultivator; two 7-ft. mowers; two-row corn picker; 6- to 8-ft. combine; forage harvester; medium-size feed grinder.

e. Three or four 14-in. moldboard plow bottoms or four- or five-disk plow; four-bottom lister plow; 10-ft. tandem disk harrow; two 12-ft. grain drills; four- or six-row planter or cultivator; two 7-ft. mowers; two-row corn picker; 10- to 12-ft. combine; forage harvester; large feed grinder.

f. Five or six 14-in. moldboard plow bottoms or six- to eight-disk plow; four-bottom lister plow; 12- to 16-ft. heavy-duty disk harrow; two 14-ft. grain drills; six- or eight-row planter or cultivator; two-row corn picker; 12- to 20-ft. combine; large forage harvester or feed grinder.

g. Six to eight 14-in. moldboard plow bottoms or eight- to ten-disk plow; six-bottom lister plow; 16- to 24-ft. heavy-duty disk harrow; three 14-ft. grain drills; six- or eight-row planter or cultivator; two-row corn picker; 16- to 20-ft. combine; large forage harvester or feed grinder.

Load factor. Common sense as well as experience tells us that efficient results cannot be secured from a tractor that is not sufficiently loaded. On the other hand, topographic, soil, and crop conditions may serve as limiting factors with respect to the size of field tools that it is possible to use. For example, a tractor capable of pulling two 14-in. plows ought to handle a four-row cultivator in most soil conditions. However, the topography of the land, the size of fields, or the crop itself may make the use of a four-row cultivator impractical, although a two-row one will operate satisfactorily. This situation has led to the manufacture of both two-row and four-row equipment for the same tractor.

Row widths. In a paper entitled "The Requirements of the General-purpose Farm Tractor," [1] Heitshu states that:

[1] *Agr. Eng.*, Vol. 10, No. 5.

A major factor in the cultivating-tractor problem is the varying widths of row spacings used in different parts of the country. The distance between rows varies from 12 to 72 in. Crop, soil, climatic, and economic conditions allow but little argument in favor of changing the established widths.

An analysis of the data secured in relation to the width of rows (Fig. 4-9) indicates that the normal width of rows falls between 36 and 48 in. To adapt the tractor fully to interrow tillage operations, however, it is necessary that the

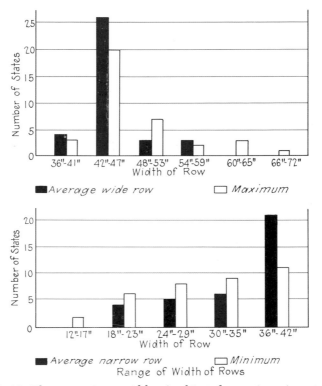

FIG. 4-9. *The range of row widths of cultivated crops in various states.*

tractor work in rows from 30 to 48 in. in width. For rows smaller than 30 in. or larger than 48 in., some combination of widths can be arranged to adapt the crop to tractor cultivation.

Clearance. With reference to clearance, Heitshu says:

The height and width of plants at the time of the last cultivation varies even more than does the width of row. The maximum height of the cultivated plants in the different states ranges from 24 to 72 in., the 36- to 41-in. classification covering the major group (Fig. 4-10). The average height of the time of the last cultivation is 41.1 in., with corn representing the major crop in this class. The maximum width is even less fixed, extending from 6 to 60 in. The average maximum width of plants is 28.6 in. In twelve states, potatoes have the maximum spread; in eight states, corn; and in eight other states, cotton.

That the majority of crops can be cultivated with less clearance than the actual size of a plant demands is shown in the average desirable clearance, which is 32.6 in. vertically, and 23.1 in. horizontally. The clearance necessary in row-crop cultivation can be chosen only by arbitration. All the data available show that 30-in. vertical clearance and 24-in., or even less, horizontal clearance should be sufficient for practically all crops.

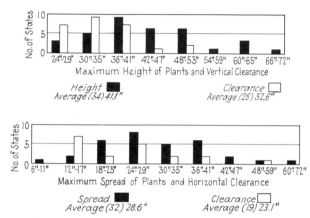

FIG. 4-10. *The range of plant heights and spreads and desired vertical and horizontal clearances in various states.*

Steering and control. Ease of handling and control of an all-purpose tractor and its attached field equipment are essential. The steering mechanism should (1) permit short, quick turning; (2) require the minimum of effort in its operation, regardless of whether the machine is moving or stationary; and (3) permit precise and accurate control of the attached units, particularly planters and cultivators. Tractors equipped with a hydraulically operated steering mechanism have a definite advantage in these respects.

Power take-off and hydraulic controls. A power take-off drive and shaft and hydraulic controls and lifts for the various attachments and machines operated by the tractor are essential accessories for any tractor. The power take-off is needed to operate mowers, combines, hay balers, corn pickers, stalk shredders, forage harvesters, and other field machines. Positive, conveniently operated hydraulic mechanisms are required for lifting or other adjustment and control of such machines as plows, harrows, cultivators, planters, and other similar machines.

Trend in farm tractor sizes. It was explained in Chap. 1 that there has been a pronounced transition in agricultural production methods in the United States since about 1940 because of the adoption of mechanical power and the development of new and larger types of machines for crop production and processing. As a consequence, the trend has been toward larger farms operated with less labor. Other factors contributing to the situation are (1) the development of higher-yielding crop varieties; (2) the more extensive use of commercial fertilizers; (3) better seedbed preparation, planting, and cultivation practices; (4) more effective disease and insect control; and (5) faster and more efficient harvesting and processing methods.

A concurrent but significant effect of this revolution in American agriculture has been the shift from smaller to larger sizes of tractors and power machines. This is clearly shown in Tables 4-1 and 4-2. According to the U.S. Department of Agriculture,[1]

In the early forties, when workstock was used for a good share of the farm work, three-fourths of the 1.6 millions of wheel tractors on farms were under 25 belt horsepower. Less than five per cent were 35 belt horsepower or above. By 1956, besides the increase in numbers of tractors, average horsepower had increased also. About three-fourths of the wheel tractors on farms were over 25 belt horsepower.

Farmers now have a wider choice with respect to size of tractor than they had in earlier periods. Wheel tractors made in 1940 ranged from 10 to 45 belt horsepower, whereas those made in 1958 ranged from 10 to 70 belt horsepower. Wheel tractors produced for farm use in 1958 and 1959 averaged 45 to 47 belt horsepower or 70 per cent more than those made in 1940.

During the last two decades, the number of farms has decreased materially, but the average size of farm has increased. Usually larger farms have more than one tractor. New tractors bought, as either additions or replacements, are usually larger than the ones replaced, or than those still on the farm. From 1950 to 1954, the number of farms with two tractors increased 45 per cent, and those with three or more tractors increased over 90 per cent. During this period, the average horsepower of tractors shipped for farm use increased by more than 20 per cent.

The trend toward larger farms has been a factor in the trend toward larger tractors. The larger tractors tend to be found on the larger farms. In 1956, for example, farms of 220 acres and over had more than 40 per cent of the large wheel tractors (35 horsepower and over), whereas farms of less than 100 acres had only about 11 per cent of the large tractors.

Type-of-farming operation also influences tractor size. For example, the average cash-grain farm contained 380 acres in 1954. Approximately one-half the tractors on these farms in 1956 were large units. Dairy farms, however, averaged under 180 acres in 1954, and in 1956 only one-fourth of the tractors on these farms were 35 belt horsepower or more.

Even more important in bringing about larger tractors has been the increasing need to reduce farm costs by substituting machinery for labor. A farmer can multiply his efforts several fold by operating a four-plow instead of a one-plow tractor. Some farmers like a more powerful tractor than is needed for most of their operations in order to have a reserve of power for special

---

[1] *U.S. Dept. Agr., Agr. Infor. Bull.* 231, ARS.

Table 4-1. Wheel Tractors on United States Farms According to Size and Annual Use [1]

Tractor size	1941	1948	1957	1940	1947	1956
	Tractors on farms, thousands			Average annual use, hr.		
Small (18–20 drawbar hp.)	1,147	1,717	1,197	459	587	513
Medium (21–29 drawbar hp.)	370	726	1,906	550	708	565
Large (30 drawbar hp. or larger)	65	257	1,329	670	752	745
United States	1,582	2,700	4,432	488	634	605

[1] *U.S. Dept. Agr., Agr. Infor. Bull. 231, ARS.*

Table 4-2. Distribution of Wheel Tractors on United States Farms According to Tractor Size and Farm Size [1]

Size of farm, acres	Farms, per cent	Tractors on farms, Jan. 1957, thousands	Tractor size,[2] per cent		
			Small	Medium	Large
Less than 100	53.6	886	46.8	42.6	10.6
100 to 219	25.3	1,538	27.4	48.0	24.6
220 and over	21.1	2,008	18.6	38.3	43.1
United States	100.0	4,432	27.0	42.5	30.5

[1] *U.S. Dept. Agr., Agr. Infor. Bull. 231, ARS.*

[2] Maximum belt horsepower: small, under 25; medium, 25 to 34; large, 35 and over.

occasions. This preference may be more significant than it was earlier, because of the trend toward specialized, highly intensive farming and the consequent importance of timeliness in getting certain jobs done.

Figure 4-11 shows a very large, heavy-duty, four-wheel-drive tractor which is particularly adapted to large-scale grain farming and other similar field operations.

GARDEN TRACTORS

Garden tractors are the smallest machines manufactured. Their use is limited to garden and truck farms or similar small farms. They are made in three general sizes: (1) a small light size (Fig. 4-12), (2) a medium size (Fig. 4-13), and (3) a large size (Fig. 4-14). The rotary tiller (Fig. 4-15) is a special type of garden tractor which is used primarily for preparing a well-pulverized seedbed and for shredding and mixing organic matter with the soil.

FIG. 4-11. *Heavy-duty four-wheel-drive tractor.* (Courtesy of Deere and Company.)

Classification of garden tractors. Concerning garden-tractor types, A. A. Stone, in a booklet entitled "Garden Tractors on Long Island," states as follows: "The term 'garden tractor,' although not a well-chosen

FIG. 4-12. *A small lightweight garden tractor.* (Courtesy of Bolens Products Division, Food Machinery and Chemical Corporation.)

expression, has come to be widely used. This class of tractors includes three sizes or types, although the limits of each are difficult to define." Stone suggests the following classification:

    A. Large garden tractors (Fig. 4-14). The capacity of machines of this class is indicated by the following approximate specifications and ratings, which are the result of observation of their use under Long Island conditions:

1. Five- to twelve-horsepower motors.
2. Riding models.
3. Pull one 12-in. plow to a depth of 7 in. at the rate of about two acres per day under favorable conditions.
4. Operate three 30-in. lawn mowers.

FIG. 4-13. *A medium-size garden tractor.* (Courtesy of Bolens Products Division, Food Machinery and Chemical Corporation.)

5. Operate 5-ft. field mower.
6. Operate 5-ft. single-disk harrow.
7. Gasoline consumption 4 to 6 gal. per day (approximate).

B. General-purpose garden tractors (Fig. 4-13).
1. Three- to four-horsepower motor, usually single-cylinder.
2. Walking models usually.
3. Pull 8-in. plow at rate of one acre per day (approximate).

    4. Operate 3½-ft. field mower and cut at rate of 3 to 4 acres per day.

    5. Operate 20- to 22-in. wood saw.

    6. Operate 30- to 36-in. lawn mower.

    7. Gasoline consumption 2 to 3 gal. per day (approximate).

C. Small power cultivators (Fig. 4-12).

    1. One- to two-horsepower motors; usually single-cylinder.

    2. Walking models.

    3. Operate 22- to 30-in. lawn mower.

    4. Pull 4- to 6-in. plow (used mostly for hilling up or opening rows for

FIG. 4-14. *A large-size garden tractor.* (Courtesy of Bolens Products Division, Food Machinery and Chemical Corporation.)

seed, although some models do light garden plowing in a very creditable manner).

    5. Pull one section (3-ft.) spike-tooth harrow.

    6. Pull one 3-ft. Acme harrow.

    7. Gasoline consumption 1½ to 2 gal. per day (approximate).

A wide variety of types and sizes of garden tractors are available. In general, they conform to Stone's classification. Recent improvements include (1) well-enclosed working mechanisms, (2) two- and three-speed transmission with a reverse gear, (3) power take-off shaft, and (4) adjustable tread wheels. Available attachments and tools include plows, planters, cultivators, various kinds of harrows, hillers, hay and lawn mowers, grader blades, and wood saws.

Make-up of a tractor. Any tractor is made up of three distinct parts or assemblies as follows:

1. Power unit—engine and all accessories necessary for its operation.

2. Power-transmitting system—clutch, change-speed gears, differential, final-drive mechanism, belt pulley, power take-off, power lift or control.

3. Chassis—frame, wheels, and steering mechanism.

Power unit. The power unit of a tractor consists of the engine and all essential parts and accessories, such as ignition system, fuel-supply and

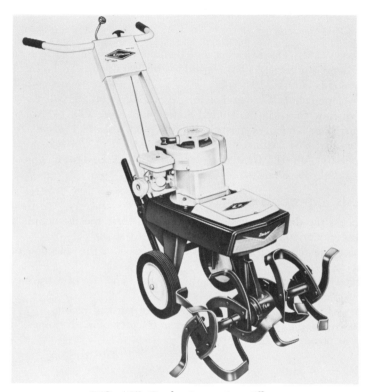

FIG. 4-15. *Garden-type rotary tiller.*

carburetion system, cooling system, lubrication system, governing mechanism, and starting and lighting equipment. The various types of engines and their construction and operation, as well as the detailed operation and construction of the related systems mentioned above, are discussed in detail in the succeeding chapters.

Power-transmitting system. Certain parts and units are necessary for the transmission of the engine power to the rear wheels, to the belt pulley, to the power take-off shaft, and to the implement-control device. The arrangement, construction, and operation of the different units and parts making up the complete transmission system in the various makes and types of tractors are discussed fully in succeeding chapters.

Tractor chassis. An automobile is said to consist of two main parts, the chassis and the body. The chassis consists of the entire mechanical make-up of the car, including the engine, transmission, frame, wheels, and steering mechanism. Tractors do not have a body. Therefore, the tractor chassis is considered as including only the frame, wheels, and steering mechanism. A more complete discussion of these parts will be found in Chap. 24.

REFERENCES

FAIRBANKS, W. M., The Selection and Use of Tractors for Gardens and Small Acreages (bulletin), Long Island Agricultural and Technical Institute, Farmingdale, N.Y., 1949.
New Developments in Garden Tractors, *Agr. Eng.*, Vol. 29, No. 1.
Spacing of Row Crops in the United States, *Agr. Eng.*, Vol. 14, No. 9.
Trends in Farm Tractor Types, Sizes, Age, and Use, *U.S. Dept. Agr., Agr. Infor. Bull.* 231, ARS, 1960.
WORTHINGTON, W. H., Contemporary British and European Tractors, *Agr. Eng.*, Vol. 35, Nos. 3–6.

PROBLEMS AND QUESTIONS

1. Discuss the different types of tractors and their specific adaptability and utilization for agricultural power.

2. Name the principal factors to be considered in the selection of a row-crop tractor.

3. Under what conditions would the purchase and use of a track-type tractor be justified by a farmer?

4. Discuss the adaptability and utilization of garden tractors.

5. Name the principal sizes of garden tractors, and distinguish between them as to power and utility.

5

Power and Its Measurement—
Fuel Consumption—Engine Efficiency

In the study of farm power it is important to have a clear and definite understanding of the exact technical meaning of such terms as horsepower, energy, efficiency, inertia, and other terms as applied to mechanical devices. To obtain such an understanding, one must consider, first of all, certain fundamental physical terms, definitions, and units.

Mass. Mass is defined as the quantity of matter a body contains irrespective of the kind of material of which it is composed. The unit of mass in the metric system is the gram or kilogram and in the English system it is the pound.

Inertia. Inertia is defined as that property of matter by virtue of which a body tends to remain at rest or continue in motion in a straight line.

Momentum. Momentum is a term applied to a body which is in motion and is defined as the product of its mass and the velocity at any instant. For example, the momentum of a mass of 1 kg. moving with a velocity of 10 cm. per sec. would be 10 kg.-cm. per sec.

Force. A *force* is an action, exerted upon a body, that changes or tends to change its natural state of rest or uniform motion in a straight line. It is thus observed that a force may or may not be effective in producing motion in the body acted upon. Likewise, if a body is in motion, a force may be applied that may or may not change its direction of movement. The unit of measurement of a force is the pound weight.

The force required to move a body may not be the same as the weight of the body. Only when the latter is moved vertically, with respect to the earth's surface, will this be true. Under certain conditions the force required to move an object might be greater than its weight.

Work. If a force is applied to a body and its state of motion is changed —that is, it is made to move from a condition of rest or, if it is already in motion, its rate or direction of travel is changed—then *work* is done. In other words, if a force acts on a stationary body but does not produce motion, no work is done. Work is measured by determining the force in pounds and the distance through which it acts in feet. The product of the two gives the work done in foot-pounds. That is, the unit of work is the foot-pound.

Energy. The energy possessed by a body is defined as its capacity for doing work. The energy possessed by an object or body by virtue of its position is known as *potential energy*. The energy possessed by the body by virtue of its motion is called *kinetic energy*. For example, the water stored in an elevated tank possesses potential energy. If this water is now discharged through a pipe, that water which is in motion in the pipe possesses kinetic energy.

Energy, like work, is measured in foot-pounds. The potential energy of a body, with respect to a given point or surface, is equal to the product of the weight in pounds and the vertical height in feet through which it has been lifted above this point or surface.

The kinetic energy of a body is dependent upon its weight and its velocity or rate of travel. For a body moving at a uniform velocity,

$$\text{Kinetic energy} = \frac{WV^2}{2g}$$

where W = weight of body, lb.

V = velocity, ft. per sec.

g = acceleration of a freely falling body

= 32.2 ft. per sec. per sec.

Torque. Torque is defined as a turning or twisting effort or action. For example, when a wrench is attached to a bolt or nut and the bolt is turned by a pull on the handle of the wrench, a torque action is produced. Likewise, turning a machine with a hand crank requires torque and when the pistons and connecting rods of an engine react on the crankshaft, the torque effect produces rotation. The unit of torque is the pound-foot; that is, torque is equal to the applied force in pounds and its perpendicular distance in feet from the axis of rotation of the crank or lever arm.

Power. Power is defined as the rate at which work is done. In other words, power involves the time element. For example, if a force of 100 lb. acts through a distance of 50 ft., 5,000 ft.-lb. of work is done. If, in one case, this 100-lb. force requires 1 min. to move the object 50 ft., and, in another case, the same force consumes 2 min. to move the object this distance, then twice as much power is required in the first case as in the second because the same work is done in one-half the time.

Horsepower. The term *horsepower* is defined as a unit of measurement of power, and 1 hp. is equal to doing work at the rate of 33,000 ft.-lb. per min. or 550 ft.-lb. per sec. There is no real reason why this unit should have this particular value. However, it was fixed some time during the eighteenth century as a result of observations made of the work done by a horse in England in hoisting freight. It was estimated from these observations that the average horse was able to lift vertically a load of 150 lb. when traveling at the rate of 2½ m.p.h. Calculate as follows:

$$\frac{150 \times 2.5 \times 5{,}280}{60} = 33{,}000 \text{ ft.-lb. per min.}$$

Therefore, 33,000 ft.-lb. per min. was chosen as the rate at which the average horse could work and, consequently, was termed 1 hp.

In calculating the horsepower developed or required by a machine, it is only necessary to determine the total foot-pounds of work done or required per minute and divide this total by 33,000.

RELATION BETWEEN MECHANICAL AND ELECTRIC POWER UNITS

Electrical work. Electrical work is measured in joules, a *joule* being defined as the amount of work done by a current of 1 amp. flowing for 1 sec. under a pressure of 1 volt; that is,

Electrical work = volts × amperes × seconds = joules

Electric power—the watt. Since power is the rate of doing work, the power of an electric current would be the electrical work it is capable of doing per time unit (second). In other words,

$$\text{Electric power} = \frac{\text{electrical work}}{\text{time}}$$

$$\text{Electric power} = \frac{\text{joules}}{\text{seconds}}$$

$$= \frac{\text{volts} \times \text{amperes} \times \text{seconds}}{\text{seconds}}$$

The unit of electric power, known as the watt, is the power required to do 1 joule of electrical work per second; that is,

$$1 \text{ watt} = 1 \text{ joule per sec.}$$

$$= \frac{1 \text{ amp.} \times 1 \text{ volt} \times 1 \text{ sec.}}{1 \text{ sec.}}$$

$$= 1 \text{ amp.} \times 1 \text{ volt}$$

or
$$\text{Watts} = \frac{\text{joules}}{\text{seconds}}$$

$$= \frac{\text{amperes} \times \text{volts} \times \text{seconds}}{\text{seconds}}$$

$$= \text{amperes} \times \text{volts}$$

It has been found by experiment that if mechanical work is done at the rate of 1 ft.-lb. per sec., then 1.356 watts of electric power will be required to do the same work; that is,

$$1 \text{ ft.-lb. per sec.} = 1.356 \text{ watts}$$

but
$$1 \text{ hp.} = 550 \text{ ft.-lb. per sec.}$$

Therefore
$$1 \text{ hp.} = 550 \times 1.356$$

$$= 746 \text{ watts}$$

and
$$\text{Horsepower} = \frac{\text{watts}}{746}$$

$$= \frac{\text{volts} \times \text{amperes}}{746}$$

Since
$$1 \text{ kw.} = 1{,}000 \text{ watts}$$

then
$$1 \text{ kw.} = \frac{1{,}000}{746}$$

$$= 1.35 \text{ hp.}$$

HORSEPOWER OF ENGINES

Indicated horsepower. The indicated horsepower (i.hp.) of an engine is the power generated in the cylinder and received by the piston.

Belt or brake horsepower. The belt or brake horsepower (b.hp.) of an engine is the power generated at the belt pulley and available for useful work. Several methods are used for measuring brake horsepower, as described later.

Friction horsepower. The friction horsepower of an engine is the power that it consumes in operating itself at a given speed without any load. That is, it is the power required to overcome friction in the moving parts of the engine plus pumping losses on the intake and compression strokes.

$$\text{i.hp.} - \text{b.hp.} = \text{friction hp.}$$

Drawbar horsepower. The drawbar horsepower of a pulling machine such as a tractor is the power developed at the hitch or drawbar and available for pulling, dragging, or similar tractive effort. In a tractor, for example, the drawbar horsepower would be equal to the b.hp. less the power consumed in moving the tractor itself. Methods of measurement are described later.

Rated horsepower. The rated horsepower may be the amount of power that the engine will generate at some designated crankshaft speed (r.p.m.) or it may be designated as a certain percentage of the maximum power output as determined by tests. For example, in the Nebraska tractor tests (see Chap. 26) the rated belt power tests are based on a load equal to 85 per cent of the maximum belt power test at the specified engine speed. In general, manufacturers recommend that for continuous operation, the load on the engine should not exceed 80 to 85 per cent of the maximum power output, but for intermittent operation, the load may be as much as 90 per cent of the maximum output.

Tractors are usually given both a brake horsepower and a drawbar horsepower rating. In the Nebraska tests, the rated drawbar tests are based on a load equal to 75 per cent of the maximum drawbar power tests.

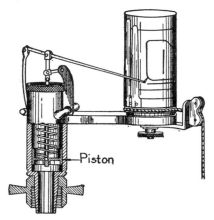

FIG. 5-1. *Indicator for determining the mean effective pressure of an engine.*

Measurement of horsepower. In the measurement of the power of an engine it must be kept in mind that the fundamental problem is to determine specific values for the physical factors involved, namely, the force acting, the distance through which the force acts, and the time it is acting. Knowing these, the rate of power generation in foot-pounds per minute can be calculated, and by dividing by 33,000, the generated horsepower is obtained.

Measurement of indicated horsepower. The power generated in the cylinder of an engine owing to the explosion pressure acting on the piston is termed the *indicated horsepower*, because a device known as an *indicator* (Fig. 5-1) is necessary in determining it. The indicator is attached to the cylinder at the closed end. The combustion chamber is connected to the small indicator cylinder by means of a small passage so that the pressure existing in the engine cylinder at any time reacts upon the indicator piston and spring. As this piston moves, it actuates a recording arm bearing a pencil point, and the latter records the pressure graphically on the paper-covered drum. This drum is connected to the crankshaft of the engine so that it revolves back and forth with the crank and piston movement. The pencil, therefore, will have a tendency to make a vertical line on the paper due to the pressure reaction and a horizontal line due to the drum movement. The result of the two movements will be what is known as an *indicator diagram* (Fig. 5-2). A specially prepared indicator form or card is used.

Referring to the diagram, the vertical line *OY* represents the pressure, and the horizontal line *PX* represents the piston movement and corre-

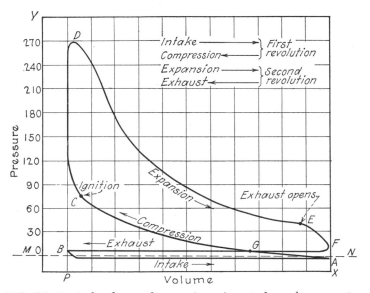

FIG. 5-2. *Typical indicator diagram for a four-stroke-cycle gas engine.*

sponding volume. The horizontal line *MN* represents atmospheric pressure. Examining the curve, the irregular line *BA*, representing the action in the cylinder on the suction or intake stroke, shows that the existing cylinder pressure is slightly below atmospheric. This, of course, is natural because the cylinder volume is increasing. At the end of the intake stroke, the piston starts back on compression and the pressure increases rather uniformly to about 90 lb., as shown by the curve *AC*. At the point *C*, slightly before the completion of the stroke, the spark ignites the charge and the pressure jumps quickly to about 270 lb., as shown by the curve from *C* to *D*. The curve *ACD*, therefore, represents the action during the entire compression stroke, with *C* indicating the point of ignition. The curve *DE* represents the action on the expansion or power stroke. As the piston moves outward, the cylinder volume increases and the pressure drops rapidly. The exhaust valve opens at *E* just before the expansion stroke ends and the pressure drops nearly to atmospheric pressure. The exhaust stroke, shown by the horizontal line *FB*, indicates that there is little change of pressure during this event. At *B*, the piston is back at its starting point and ready to begin the intake stroke again.

It is thus observed that two irregular closed areas are described by the indicator pencil during one complete cycle. The one is the area *FCDE* and the other the area *ABG*. The first or larger area represents the energy applied to the piston in producing power and might be called the positive area. The second or smaller area represents energy tending to retard the movement of the piston, or negative energy. Since this latter area is extremely small, it can be neglected in making calculations.

The next step is to determine, from this indicator diagram, the average working pressure existing in the cylinder during the cycle. This is known as the mean effective pressure (m.e.p.). The procedure consists first in determining the exact area of *FCDE* in square inches. For this purpose a special device, known as a *planimeter*, is used. Then, dividing the area by its length—horizontal distance *PX*—in inches will give the average height in inches. The height multiplied by the scale of the indicator spring (pounds required to deflect the spring 1 in.) will give the average or m.e.p. per square inch of cylinder cross-sectional area.

In order to calculate the i.hp. of an engine, its operating r.p.m., bore of cylinder in inches, and length of piston stroke in feet must be known, in addition to the m.e.p. just explained. With these values determined, the power may be calculated by means of the following formula:

$$\text{i.hp.} = \frac{PLANn}{33{,}000 \times 2} \quad \text{for four-stroke-cycle engine}$$

or

$$\text{i.hp.} = \frac{PLANn}{33{,}000} \quad \text{for two-stroke-cycle engine}$$

where P = m.e.p.

L = length of piston stroke, ft.

A = area of cylinder, sq. in.

  $= (\text{bore})^2 \times 0.7854$

N = r.p.m.

n = number of cylinders

For multiple-cylinder engines, the i.hp. of one cylinder is multiplied by the number of cylinders, because it is assumed that the m.e.p. of all cylinders is alike.

Example. What is the i.hp. of a four-cylinder four-stroke-cycle engine if the m.e.p. is 90 lb., cylinder dimensions 4 by 5 in., r.p.m. 1,200?

$$\text{i.hp.} = \frac{90 \times \frac{5}{12} \times 4^2 \times 0.7854 \times 1{,}200 \times 4}{33{,}000 \times 2}$$

  $= 34.27$

The device (Fig. 5-1) was originally designed for determining the indicated horsepower of slow-speed, reciprocating steam engines but gave reasonably satisfactory results with the old types of slow-speed gas engines, that is, engines with a rated r.p.m. of 500 or less. However, it cannot be used on modern high-speed engines, and special, complex types of indicators have been developed. Nevertheless the principle involved is the same, namely, to obtain a diagram of the pressure reactions in the engine cylinder during a complete cycle of events, which in turn will enable one to compute the mean effective pressure.

Measurement of belt horsepower. Devices used for the determination of the belt or brake horsepower of engines are known as *dynamometers.*

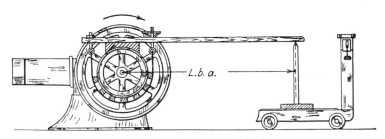

FIG. 5-3. *Use of a prony brake in determining the horsepower of an engine.*

Dyna or *dynamo* means force or power, and a *meter* is a measuring device; therefore, a dynamometer is a power-measuring device. There are a number of different types of dynamometers, such as the prony brake (Fig. 5-3), the electric type (Fig. 5-6), and the hydraulic type. Of these, the first two named are used most extensively.

Prony-brake dynamometer. The prony brake consists of an adjustable friction band, which fits on the belt pulley or a special pulley keyed to the engine crankshaft, and an arm from 2 to 5 ft. in length, which rests on or is supported by scales (Fig. 5-3). To explain its operation more clearly, let us assume that the engine crankshaft is locked so that it cannot turn and that a pair of spring scales is fastened to the outer end of the brake arm (Fig. 5-4). Now suppose that the brake band is tightened on the pulley but that the brake is rotated on the latter by grasping the scales and applying the rotative force at the outer end of the brake arm. The scales will register a certain number of pounds, depending upon the tension of the brake in addition to the weight of the arm itself. Likewise, as the arm rotates, the point of application of the rotating force will describe a circle whose circumference is equal to $2\pi r$ (Fig. 5-4). The work done in one turn in foot-pounds is equal to the product of the force in pounds registered by the scales (less the weight of the brake arm) and the circumference in feet of the circle described. By counting the total revolutions made in 1 min., the total foot-pounds of work per minute can be calculated. Dividing by 33,000 gives the horsepower developed. In other words,

$$hp. = \frac{\text{force on scales due to friction only (lb.)} \times 2\pi r \text{ (ft.)} \times \text{r.p.m.}}{33,000}$$

In actual practice, the brake arm is held in a fixed position as shown by Fig. 5-3, and the engine pulley turns in the band. This will not alter

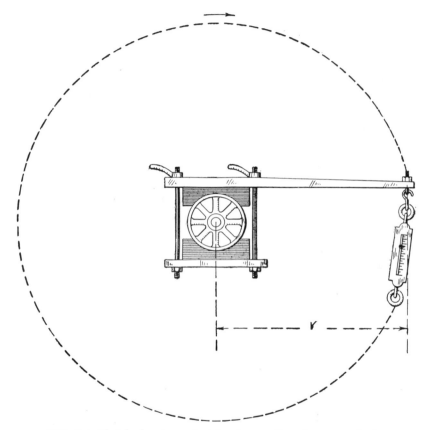

FIG. 5-4. *Sketch showing principle of operation of a prony brake.*

conditions for the reason that the friction contact will still be the same and will, therefore, create a like pressure on the scales. By measuring the distance *r* in feet, better known as the length of brake arm (l.b.a.), and obtaining the engine r.p.m., the horsepower output can be calculated as follows:

$$hp. = \frac{\text{net load (lb.)} \times \text{l.b.a. (ft.)} \times 2\pi \times \text{r.p.m.}}{33,000}$$

The net load on the scales is determined by first weighing the brake arm and support, with the brake loose and engine not running, and then subtracting this so-called tare load from the total load on the scales when engine is running under test; that is, the gross load minus the weight of arm and stand (tare load) equals the net or friction load.

FIG. 5-5. *Revolution counter or speed indicator.*

The crankshaft r.p.m. is determined by means of a speed counter or indicator such as that shown in Fig. 5-5.

The prony brake is an inexpensive apparatus to construct and is simple and easy to operate compared with other types of brake dynamometers. However, the friction between the brake and the pulley surface generates considerable heat, depending upon the size and speed of the pulley. This heat has a tendency to cause the frictional contact and the resulting brake load to increase or vary. To eliminate or remedy this undesirable load variation it is often necessary to apply some cooling medium such as water or oil to the surfaces. It is better to apply the cooling liquid continuously in small quantities than intermittently in large amounts.

Electric dynamometer. For precise power measurements of large, or multiple-cylinder, variable-speed engines, the electric dynamometer is preferred. The complete outfit consists of the generating unit (Fig. 5-6), the resistor unit (Fig. 5-7), and the control and instrument board (Fig. 5-8).

The outer field frame of the direct-current generator is mounted with ball bearings on two heavy iron pedestals as shown, so that it is possible for the entire generator unit to rotate. This rotation is prevented, however, by the torque arm and scales. The generator armature rotates independently in the field frame as in any other generator. The engine to be tested is mounted beside the generator and its crankshaft connected directly to the armature; or, where that is impractical, a pulley and belt drive may be used as in testing a tractor. The load or pressure on the scales is created by the electromagnetic action between the field frame and the armature, which exists in any such machine. That is, as the armature rotates, the electromagnetic field set up tends to cause the field frame to rotate with the armature. This pulling or torque action, as it is called, does make the frame rotate a certain amount and creates a pressure on the scales attached to the torque arm. The electromagnetic field can be closely adjusted so as to increase or decrease the load on the engine by any desired amount. In other words, the stronger the current supplied to the field windings, the greater the load on the engine and the resulting pull or torque. In other respects this device is very much like the prony brake. That is, by observing the r.p.m. of the arma-

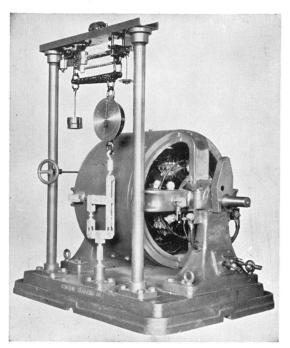

FIG. 5-6. *Electric-type dynamometer for determining belt horsepower.*

ture, the length of the torque arm, and the net load on the scales, the power output can be calculated by the same formula, namely,

$$\text{hp.} = \frac{\text{net load (lb.)} \times \text{l.b.a. (ft.)} \times 2\pi \times \text{r.p.m.}}{33,000}$$

The electric dynamometer is much more expensive to install than the prony brake and requires more experience and care in operation. However, where a large amount of accurate and precise engine testing is done, it is the most desirable apparatus to use.

A second type of electric dynamometer (Fig. 5-9) utilizes the effect of eddy currents in developing magnetic flux between the stator and the rotor. The stator or outer frame member contains an exciter coil which is energized by a small externally mounted generator. The opposing magnetic reaction between the magnetic fields in the stator and the rotor as the latter is rotated results in a torque reaction on the stator. Hence, if the entire unit is cradled on antifriction bearings, this torque can be measured and the applied power determined just as it is with the electric dynamometer. In the eddy-current dynamometer, the power is converted into heat which accumulates in the stator. Therefore, it is necessary to circulate cool water at a high velocity through suitable channels in the stator inductor ring.

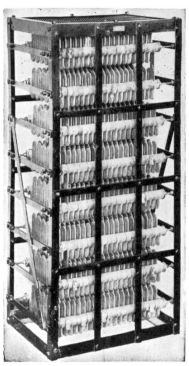

FIG. 5-7. *Current absorber or resistor for electric dynamometer.*

FIG. 5-8. *Control unit for electric dynamometer.*

Hydraulic dynamometer. The dynamometer (Fig. 5-10) operates very much like the electric eddy-current type except that the torque action on the outer housing or stator is produced by a hydraulic reaction created by water contained in the housing and surrounding the rotors. The rotation of the rotors imparts motion to the water, and this water movement in turn tends to cause rotation of the stator. The energy applied to the rotors and the resultant action on the water heats the latter. Hence, the load is adjusted and controlled by controlling the temperature and the rate of flow of the water through the stator.

A second type of hydraulic dynamometer is shown in Fig. 5-11. This is a special portable power take-off-driven device designed particularly for tractor service shops. The power-absorbing unit consists of a constant-volume hydraulic pump operated by a geared take-off shaft. Oil contained in a small reservoir serves as a hydraulic fluid. The oil pressure is controlled by a valve, and a large pressure-gauge dial gives a reading which can be correlated with horsepower. The oil reservoir con-

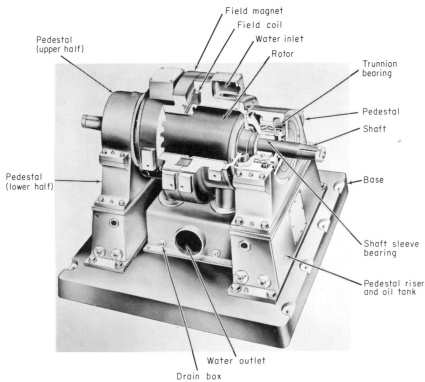

FIG. 5-9. *Eddy-current type of electric dynamometer.* (Courtesy of Dynamatic Division, Eaton Manufacturing Company.)

tains cooling coils through which cold water is circulated to dissipate heat and maintain the desired oil temperature.

Drawbar dynamometers. Drawbar dynamometers are of (1) the spring type, (2) the distortion type, (3) the hydraulic type, or (4) the electrical strain-gauge type. The spring type (Fig. 5-12) utilizes either a heavy spiral spring or an elliptic spring to absorb the pull. The depression or elongation of the spring actuates an indicating needle on a dial showing the magnitude of the load. The distortion dynamometer (Fig. 5-13) consists of a special alloy steel beam which deflects in some manner under tension. This limited movement is multiplied and trans-

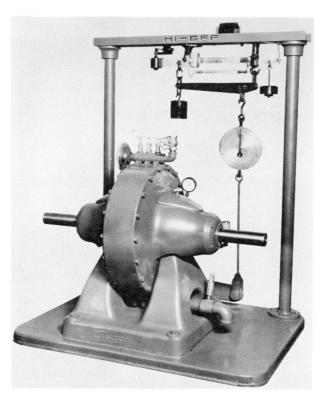

FIG. 5-10. *Hydraulic-type dynamometer.* (Courtesy of Taylor Dynamometer and Machine Company.)

FIG. 5-11. *Portable hydraulic power take-off-driven dynamometer.* (Courtesy of M & W Gear Company.)

FIG. 5-12. *Spring-type indicating drawbar dynamometer.*

FIG. 5-13. *Distortion-type indicating drawbar dynamometer.* (Courtesy of W. C. Dillon and Company.)

mitted by a special linkage to an indicating dial. The hydraulic dynamometer (Fig. 5-14) uses an oil-filled cylinder and piston arrangement
by which the tension or pull creates hydraulic pres-
sure. This pressure is read on a dial indicator and
converted to pounds of draft.

The operation of the electrical strain-gauge dynamometer is based upon the principle that if a piece
of fine wire of a certain composition is subjected to
some degree of strain, there will be a change in its
length and resistance. Hence, if such a wire is properly bonded to some structural member or material
and the latter is subjected to a strain or tension, the
wire will also experience a like strain, which, in turn,
changes its electric resistance. Furthermore, it has
been found that there is a definite relationship between the strain applied to the structural member and
the change in the electric resistance of the fine wire
bonded to the material.

A strain-gauge unit (Fig. 5-15) consists of a grid
or a series of loops of small-diameter wire mounted
in an insulating material such as paper or bakelite.
One or more of these units are bonded securely at
proper locations on the specimen to be tested or subjected to tension or strain. If the two ends of the
gauge wire are connected to a suitable source of electricity and the test specimen is subjected to a strain,
the wire will be compressed or elongated, as the case
may be, and a change in its resistance can be measured

FIG. 5-14. *Hydrau-
lic-type indicating
drawbar dynamom-
eter.* (Courtesy of
V e g o r s Enter-
prises.)

with appropriate instruments including
a Wheatstone bridge and a galvanometer. Figure 5-16 shows one style of
drawbar dynamometer using four strain-
gauge units. Units *A* and *B* are located
so as to react in tension, while *C* and *D*
are in compression.

*Determination of drawbar horse-
power.* It is often desirable to know
the pulling power of a tractor under
various conditions. The usual procedure is to hitch the machine to some
heavy object or load to be pulled or
dragged, which will require not more

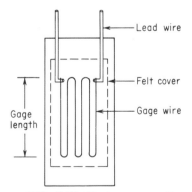

FIG. 5-15. *Strain-gauge unit.*

than the maximum pulling power of the tractor. Between the tractor
and the load is placed the dynamometer, which must at least record

or indicate the pulling effort in pounds required to drag the load at a certain rate of travel. The rate of travel can be determined by observing

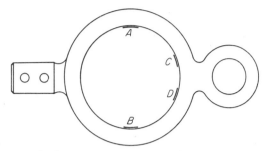

FIG. 5-16. *Strain-gauge-type dynamometer.*

the time required to cover some definite measured distance, such as 500 ft. Then, the horsepower developed can be calculated as follows:

$$\text{hp.} = \frac{\text{average pull (lb.)} \times \text{rate of travel (ft. per min.)}}{33,000}$$

ENGINE OPERATING CHARACTERISTICS

Mechanical efficiency. The mechanical efficiency of an engine is the ratio of its brake horsepower to its indicated horsepower, that is,

$$\text{Mechanical efficiency (per cent)} = \frac{\text{b.hp.}}{\text{i.hp.}} \times 100$$

The principal factors affecting the mechanical efficiency of an engine are losses due to friction in the moving parts such as the crankshaft and connecting-rod bearings, pistons and cylinders, valve mechanism, and cooling fan and pump, and losses involved in the induction of the fuel mixture and the exhaust of the residue. The most practical method of measuring these losses, that is, the engine friction horsepower, is to motor the engine under normal operating conditions with an electric dynamometer or an electric motor and thereby check the actual power requirement. The mechanical efficiency of an internal-combustion engine varies from 75 to 90 per cent, depending upon the load, speed, and other factors.

Volumetric efficiency. Volumetric efficiency refers to the relationship of the quantity of fuel mixture actually drawn into the cylinder by the piston on the intake stroke and producing power to the actual volume of the space displaced by the piston on this stroke and, therefore, the theoretical amount of combustible mixture which would have been taken in under ideal conditions. The principal factors affecting volumetric efficiency are (1) atmospheric pressure and temperature; (2) manifold design, such as length, size, and smoothness; (3) intake manifold temperature; (4) air-filter design and operation; (5) fuel characteristics; (6) piston speed; (7) compression ratio; (8) valve size, opening, and timing; (9) engine-operating temperature.

The volumetric efficiency of automotive-type engines should fall within a range of 75 to 85 per cent, depending on their design and existing operating conditions and factors. Two methods of increasing the volumetric efficiency of high-speed multiple-cylinder engines are by the use of (1) the supercharger and (2) multiple-barrel carburetors, as described in Chap. 12.

Thermal efficiency. The thermal efficiency of an engine is the ratio of the output in the form of useful mechanical power to the power value of the fuel consumed; that is,

$$\text{Thermal efficiency (per cent)} = \frac{\text{b.hp.}}{\text{power value of fuel}} \times 100$$

In order to determine the thermal efficiency of an engine, the quantity of fuel consumed and the power generated in a given time must be measured. Then this power and fuel must be converted into a common form; that is, the power must be converted into heat-energy units, or the fuel into mechanical-power units. The heat unit used is the British thermal unit (B.t.u.). It has been determined that 1 B.t.u. of heat is equivalent to 778 ft.-lb. of work. This is known as the mechanical equivalent of heat. Since 1 hp. equals 33,000 ft.-lb. per min.,

$$1 \text{ hp.} = \frac{33,000}{778}$$

$$= 42.42 \text{ B.t.u. per min.}$$

and 1 hp. generated for 1 hr. is equal to 60×42.42, or 2,545 B.t.u.

Again the heat value in B.t.u. has been determined for the various engine fuels. Gasoline, kerosene, and other petroleum fuels contain approximately 20,000 B.t.u. per lb. (see Table 11-2). A gallon of gasoline (6.2 lb.) contains $6.2 \times 20,000$ or 124,000 B.t.u. Therefore, if an engine were 100 per cent efficient in its operation, that is, if the entire heat value of the fuel burned were converted into useful power, then 1 gal. of gasoline would produce 124,000/2,545 or 48.7 hp. for 1 hr.

Such power production, however, is obviously impossible, because every engine wastes a large quantity of heat through the exhaust, through the cylinder walls and the piston, by friction, and so on.

The thermal efficiency of internal-combustion engines varies from 15 to 35 per cent, depending upon the type of engine, speed, load, design, and other factors.

For example, the ordinary stationary gasoline engine uses about 0.7 lb. of fuel per hp. per hr. The input is

$$0.7 \times 20,000 = 14,000 \text{ B.t.u. per hr.}$$

The output is

$$1 \text{ hp. per hr.} = 2545 \text{ B.t.u.}$$

Then

$$\text{Thermal efficiency} = \frac{\text{output}}{\text{input}}$$

$$= \frac{2545}{14,000} \times 100$$

$$= 18.2 \text{ per cent}$$

Certain diesel-type engines often burn as low as 0.45 lb. of fuel per hp. per hr. Calculating as above,

$$0.45 \times 19,000 = 8550 \text{ B.t.u. per hr.}$$

$$\text{Thermal efficiency} = \frac{2545}{8550} \times 100$$

$$= 29.8 \text{ per cent}$$

Brake mean effective pressure. The brake mean effective pressure of an engine is that portion of the total or indicated mean effective pressure which is actually consumed in generating the useful or brake horsepower. Therefore it is equal to the indicated mean effective pressure multiplied by the mechanical efficiency and is calculated by making the necessary substitutions for b.hp. and i.hp. and solving the formula

$$\text{Brake mean effective pressure} = \text{indicated mean effective pressure} \times \frac{\text{b.hp.}}{\text{i.hp.}}$$

Torque. The torque of an engine refers to the turning or twisting effort developed through its crankshaft and applied to the belt pulley or power-transmitting mechanism. Figure 5-17 shows torque curves for heavy-duty engines—one a diesel type and the other using electric ignition and gasoline. It will be noted that the torque varies considerably with engine speed and falls off appreciably at high speeds. This is probably due to less effective fuel-mixture induction and reduced volumetric efficiency. It is also noted that the diesel-torque curve is higher and somewhat more uniform than the spark-ignition curve. This explains the better lugging characteristic of a diesel engine.

Factors affecting fuel consumption and efficiency. One of the fundamental objectives in the design, construction, and operation of any internal-combustion engine is to secure the greatest possible efficiency without interfering with other considerations involved in practical adaptability to a particular purpose. As already explained, efficiency in an engine means obtaining the greatest possible power out of it with the lowest possible fuel cost—not necessarily the lowest fuel consumption. For example, an engine might burn either of two fuels satisfactorily but use slightly less of one than of the other, indicating that the first fuel is

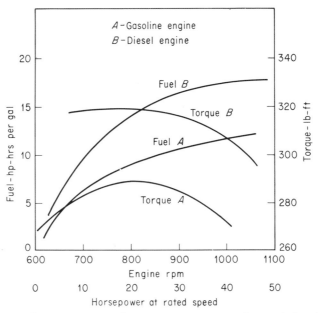

FIG. 5-17. *Fuel-consumption and torque curves for gasoline and diesel engines.*

the better to use. However, if the second fuel costs considerably less per gallon, it might be the more economical one to use in the engine.

The actual fuel consumption of engines is usually expressed in pounds per horsepower-hour or in horsepower-hours per gallon. The total fuel consumption of engines varies, of course, according to the size, the power generated, and the length of time in operation. However, when reduced to the basis of pounds per horsepower-hour, the fuel consumption of two engines of entirely different size and type may be very nearly the same.

In general, the fuel consumption of all gasoline-burning engines, such as automobile, truck, and tractor engines, is about the same when reduced to the basis of pounds per horsepower-hour, provided they are all operated under a one-half to full load. Such engines seldom burn less than 0.55 lb. of fuel per hp.-hr. The average is around 0.60 lb., and the rate may run as high as 0.70 lb. Diesel-type and similar high-compression heavy-duty oil-burning engines often show a fuel consumption of 0.4 to 0.5 lb. per hp.-hr. and seldom use more than 0.55 lb.

Given a certain type of engine burning a given fuel, the most important factors affecting its economical and efficient operation are:

1. Normal operating compression pressure
2. Operating load: light, medium, or heavy
3. Mechanical condition:
   - *a.* Ignition correctly timed
   - *b.* Valves correctly timed
   - *c.* Fuel mixture properly adjusted
   - *d.* Piston rings and cylinder not badly worn
   - *e.* Bearings properly adjusted
   - *f.* Properly lubricated

Compression and efficiency. Referring to Table 6-1 and Fig. 6-9, it is observed that, theoretically, the greater the compression pressure, the

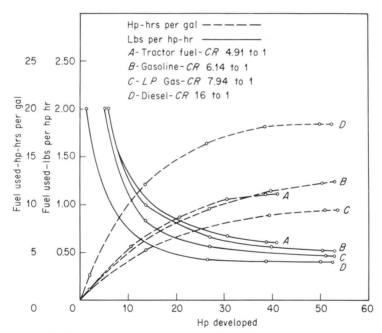

FIG. 5-18. *Fuel-consumption curves for different kinds of fuels.*

higher the thermal efficiency. It is difficult and impractical to take advantage of this, however, in the carbureting type of engine, such as the farm, automobile, or tractor engine, for the reason that too high a compression causes detonation of the fuel mixture. In other words, the high compression produces a higher cylinder temperature and the mixture ignites and burns rapidly and explodes too early. In the diesel and similar types of heavy-duty oil engines, high compression is practical because the fuel charge does not enter the cylinder until the piston is ready to receive the explosion. Engines of this type, therefore, are somewhat more efficient than carbureting engines.

Effect of load on efficiency. The curves (Fig. 5-18) show that any engine, when operating at a very light load, will use more fuel per horsepower-hour. As the load increases, the fuel consumption decreases until, at about nine-tenths of the maximum power developed by the engine, it gives the most economical results. It is obvious that a certain amount of fuel is required to operate the engine itself, that is, to supply the power necessary to overcome friction. Furthermore, this friction and the amount of fuel required to overcome it remain practically constant, regardless of the load on the engine. Therefore, as the load increases, this quantity of fuel required to overcome friction becomes less and less in proportion to the total amount burned.

This characteristic of engines to give the best fuel economy at medium to heavy loads means that it is important always to use an engine that fits the job. That is, a 20-hp. engine should not be used to operate a machine requiring only 5 hp. On the other hand, it is not good practice to use an engine that is too small and will be overloaded.

REFERENCES

A Discussion of Present Day Dynamometers: Their Application, Operation, and Control, *Gen. Motors Eng. J.*, Vol. 4, No. 4.

A Drawbar Dynamometer and Its Use in Soil Tillage Experiments, *Univ. Missouri Agr. Expt. Sta. Research Bull.* 226.

CLYDE, A. W., Drawbar Dynamometer Using Strain Gages, *Agr. Eng.*, Vol. 36, No. 8.

Design and Construction of a Torsion Dynamometer, *West Va. Univ. Agr. Expt. Sta. Bull.* 419T.

Effect of Full Load on Farm Machine Operating Economies, *Agr. Eng.*, Vol. 24, No. 4.

Electrical Dynamometer for Testing Tractor Uses, *Agr. Eng.*, Vol. 30, No. 9.

HELDT, P. M., High-speed Combustion Engines, 16th ed., Chilton Company, Philadelphia, 1956.

LARSON, G. H., A Low Cost Hydraulic Dynamometer, *Agr. Eng.*, Vol. 34, No. 10.

Power Requirements of Tillage Implements, *N. Dakota State Coll. Agr. Expt. Sta. Bull.* 415.

RICHEY, C. B., PAUL JACOBSON, and CARL W. HALL: "Agricultural Engineers' Handbook," McGraw-Hill Book Company, Inc., New York, 1961.

Testing Draft Horses, *Iowa State Coll. Agr. Expt. Sta. Bull.* 240.

Transmission Dynamometer for Traction and Power Take-off Measurements *Agr. Eng.*, Vol. 28, No. 1.

PROBLEMS AND QUESTIONS

1. Distinguish between the terms inertia, momentum, and kinetic energy.

2. Distinguish between the terms torque and work.

3. Define the term horsepower and explain the origin of the unit's actual value.

4. What size of engine (horsepower rating) would you recommend to operate a 120-volt, direct-current electric generator having a maximum output of 75 amp. and an operating efficiency of 80 per cent?

5. A four-cylinder, four-stroke-cycle engine with 3- by 4-in. cylinders develops 19 hp. at 1,650 r.p.m. Assuming a mechanical efficiency of 85 per cent, compute the i.hp. and m.e.p.

6. Compute the thermal efficiency of the engine (Prob. 5) if it used 47 lb. of gasoline in a 4-hr. test.

7. A tractor with a 9-in. pulley is belted to a prony brake having a 24-in. pulley. If the engine-pulley speed is 950 r.p.m., the brake arm length is 54 in., and the net load on the scales is 60 lb., what is the value of the brake constant and what horsepower is developed?

8. Calculate the drawbar horsepower required to pull a plow with three 14-in. bottoms at a rate of 3.25 m.p.h. if the draft is 8 lb. per sq. in. of furrow section and the depth of cut is 7 in.

9. Calculate the gallons of gasoline needed to fill a 1,000-gal. tank from a well whose water level is 200 ft. below the tank, if the over-all efficiency of the power unit and pump is 15 per cent.

10. A drawbar dynamometer shows that the average pull required for a certain machine is 2,800 lb. If the tractor travels 1,000 ft. in 3½ min., what is the horsepower developed and rate of travel in miles per hour?

11. If an engine shows an average output at the crankshaft of 35 hp. at 1,650 r.p.m., what torque is exerted?

12. Referring to the curves (Fig. 5-18), compare the cost per 10-hr. day of operating a tractor on LP gas, gasoline, and diesel fuel if the average load is 30 hp. and the fuel cost per gallon is 12, 20, and 15 cents for the respective fuels.

6

Thermodynamic Principles and Applications
Engine Cycles and Efficiencies

The following symbols are used in this chapter (and throughout the text):

A	area	k	the ratio c_p/c_v
C	a constant	P	pressure or total pressure
c	specific heat	p	unit pressure (p.s.i.)
c_p	specific heat at constant pressure	Q	transferred heat
c_v	specific heat at constant volume	R	specific gas constant (pv/T)
D	distance or diameter	T	absolute temperature (°F.)
e	thermal efficiency	V	volume
F	force or total load	W	work
J	Joule's constant (778)	w	weight of substance

Since an internal-combustion engine generates power from the heat energy of certain gaseous fuels, its operation is based specifically upon certain physical principles and theories as applied to gases. The basic factors entering into the energy and power generated by a combustible gaseous mixture are (1) volume, (2) pressure, and (3) temperature. Scientists have been able to establish certain definite relationships and reactions between these. An understanding of the relationship of these factors to each other is important in establishing a clear understanding of the fundamentals involved in the design and efficient operation of an internal-combustion engine.

Thermodynamics. Thermodynamics is defined as that phase of physical science which is related to the conversion of heat into mechanical force or energy, or vice versa, and the specific factors and relationships involved. Two basic principles known as the two laws of thermodynamics have been evolved and must be well understood in any discussion of heat and its relationship to mechanical energy. The first law, basically, is the law of the conversion of energy and states that "when heat energy is transformed into mechanical energy, the work done is equivalent to the quantity of heat involved." Joule, an English scientist, made extensive studies of this hypothesis and established the presently accepted value of 778 ft.-lb. of work as being equivalent to 1 B.t.u. This is known as the mechanical equivalent of heat or Joule's constant.

The second law of thermodynamics states that heat will, of itself, pass from a hot to a cold substance, but external work is required to transfer heat from a cold substance to a hot substance. For example, the operation of the heat engine is based upon a flow of heat from a hot to a cold substance, but a mechanical refrigerating machine requires external energy because it transfers heat away from a cold material and into a hotter substance.

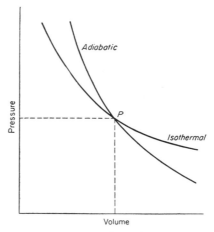

FIG. 6-1. *Pressure-volume diagram showing adiabatic and isothermal changes and relationships.*

Boyle's law. Suppose a cylinder is filled with a gas such as air or natural gas or some common fuel vapor and then a piston is inserted in the cylinder which compresses the gas into one end of the cylinder without leakage or loss. The volume of the gas is decreased and there is an increase in its pressure. Likewise its temperature is increased on account of the energy expended in producing compression.

Not only is there an increase in pressure with a decrease in volume of a gas, but there is a definite pressure-volume relationship for any gas. This relationship was first expressed by Boyle and is known as *Boyle's law* as applied to gases. It states that, if the temperature of a gas is kept constant, its volume will vary inversely as the pressure to which it is subjected. That is, $PV = C$, C being a constant depending upon the kind of gas, initial pressure, temperature, and other factors. Or if V_1 represents the volume of a gas at a pressure P_1 and V_2 represents the volume of the same gas when the pressure is P_2, it follows that

$$P_1 V_1 = P_2 V_2 = C$$

The change of state of a gas with respect to pressure and volume, the temperature remaining constant, is known as an *isothermal change*. If a curve is drawn showing this *PV* relationship of a gas at any time, it is called an *isothermal curve* (Fig. 6-1).

Charles' law. Normally heat is generated when a gas is compressed and heat is released when its volume is increased. Or we can say that the volume of a gas increases when its temperature is raised and decreases with a drop in temperature. Again, let us assume that a free-moving piston is inserted in a tight cylinder containing a gas and that heat is applied to the gas. Increased pressure will be developed and the piston will move outward. Now if the piston is allowed to move in such a manner that there is no actual increased pressure built up behind it, it will be found that there is a definite relationship between the increase in the volume of the gas and the rise in temperature. In fact, experiments show that when a quantity of gas is heated or cooled while the pressure to which it is subjected remains constant, the volume will change $\frac{1}{492}$ of its volume at 32°F. or $\frac{1}{273}$ of its volume at 0°C. for each degree of temperature change. Therefore, if a mass of gas were cooled to $-273°$C. (273 degrees below 0°C.), the gas would contract to zero volume, provided the same law held true to this point. This we may assume to be the case with a perfect gas, although any known gas would change its state before this temperature were reached.

In the study of gases it was also found that if a gas were heated without allowing it to expand, that is, with its volume remaining constant, then the pressure increased $\frac{1}{273}$ of its value for each degree rise in temperature above 0°C. If the pressure of the gas is measured at 0°C. and this rate of decrease in pressure continues as the temperature is gradually lowered, it is clear that when the temperature has become $-273°$ the pressure will disappear and the gas will no longer be able to exert a pressure. From the standpoint of the kinetic theory of gases, a gas must always exert a pressure as long as the molecules are in motion. Hence, the temperature at which the molecules cease to exert a pressure is the temperature at which these molecules cease to move. The temperature at which the molecules have no motion is known as absolute zero and is $-273°$C. or $-460°$F. Temperatures when measured from these points as zero are known as *absolute temperatures*.

This temperature-volume-pressure relationship of a gas is known as *the law of Charles* and is stated as follows: The pressure remaining constant, the volume of a mass of gas is directly proportional to its absolute temperature. It may also be stated in the following way: The volume remaining constant, the pressure of a gas is directly proportional to its absolute temperature.

From the above, if the volume V_1 of a gas changes to the volume V_2 when the absolute temperature T_1 changes to the value T_2, the pressure remaining constant, Charles' law may be expressed as

$$V_1 T_2 = V_2 T_1$$

and if the pressure P_1 of a gas changes to the pressure P_2 with a change of absolute temperature from T_1 to T_2, the volume remaining constant, the law may be expressed as

$$P_1T_2 = P_2T_1$$

Boyle's and Charles' laws combined. We have seen that according to Boyle's law $P_1V_1 = P_2V_2$ (T being constant) and according to Charles' law $V_1T_2 = V_2T_1$ (P being constant). Now if the volume V_1 of a gas changes to a new volume V_2, while at the same time the pressure P_1 and the absolute temperature T_1 change to new values P_2 and T_2 respectively, the final relation between the volume, the pressure, and the absolute temperature of the gas may be determined by conceiving that the

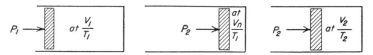

FIG. 6-2. *Boyle's and Charles' laws functioning independently and successively.*

change of volume due to the change in pressure and the change in volume due to the change in absolute temperature take place independently and successively. Referring to Fig. 6-2, let us assume that the initial pressure P_1 is changed to P_2 while the volume V_1 changes to V_n with no change in temperature. Then, according to Boyle's law,

$$P_1V_1 = P_2V_n \tag{1}$$

But now suppose the temperature changes from T_1 to T_2 and the volume V_n changes to V_2, with no change in pressure. Then, according to Charles' law,

$$V_nT_2 = V_2T_1 \tag{2}$$

Combining Eqs. (1) and (2), we find that

$$\frac{P_1V_1}{T_1} = \frac{P_2V_2}{T_2}$$

and

$$\frac{PV}{T} = R \qquad \text{a constant}$$

or

$$PV = RT$$

That is, the product of the pressure and the volume of a gas is always proportional to its absolute temperature.

If P = absolute pressure, lb. per sq. ft.
$\quad$ V = volume of gas, cu. ft.
$\quad$ W = weight of gas, lb. per cu. ft.
$\quad$ T = temperature, °F. abs.
$\quad$ R = gas constant
then, for any gas,

$$PV = WTR$$

and for air, if

$$P = 144 \times 14.7$$

$$V = 1$$

$$W = 0.0807$$

$$T = 492°F. \text{ abs.}$$

then $\qquad R = \dfrac{144 \times 14.7}{0.0807 \times 492} = 53.3$

Heat and energy. Ordinarily heat is thought of as something created by the rapid combustion or burning of some material. However, it was discovered many years ago that there was a definite relationship between heat and mechanical energy. For example, when friction is developed by two objects rubbing against each other, the work done in breaking down the irregularities between the two surfaces is transformed into an increased kinetic energy of the particles, and the heat thus produced is a measure of the work done against friction. When flint and steel are used to "strike fire," the work done by the flint in tearing away little particles of the steel is so great that these particles are heated to a temperature at which they burn in the air. These and other simple experiments prove that heat is produced as a result of work performed; therefore, it is a form of energy. It is now considered that the heat of a body is the kinetic energy of its ultimate particles, that is, of its electrons and its molecules, and that the temperature of the body is simply a measure of this kinetic energy.

Unit quantity of heat—the calorie and the British thermal unit. Temperature is a measure of the kinetic energy of the molecules of a body but is entirely independent of the number of these molecules, that is, of the mass of the body. On the other hand, the quantity of heat a body contains denotes the total kinetic energy of its particles and depends upon the mass of the body.

It has been found that the quantity of heat required to raise the temperature of a given mass of one substance to a certain degree will raise the temperature of the same mass of another substance to an entirely different degree. Therefore, in choosing the unit quantity of heat, water was selected as the standard material. The unit is known as a *calorie* and is defined as the quantity of heat that will raise the temperature of 1 gm. of water 1°C. In the English system, the unit is called the *British thermal unit* (B.t.u.) and is defined as the quantity of heat required to raise the temperature of 1 lb. of water 1°F.

Specific heat. The *specific heat* of a substance is defined as the ratio between the quantity of heat required to raise the temperature of any mass of that substance one degree and the quantity required to raise the temperature of an equal mass of water one degree.

In the case of gases, the specific heat is affected by the conditions of pressure and volume when heating takes place. For example, if the gas is confined in a tight vessel and the volume remains constant, the effect of the heat is confined to increasing the kinetic energy of the molecules of the gas, which in turn raises its temperature. The number of B.t.u. required to raise the temperature of 1 lb. of gas 1°C. at constant volume is called its *specific heat at constant volume* or c_v. If the heat applied to a gas causes expansion and an increase in its volume but the pressure remains constant, external work is done. If 1 lb. of gas is thus heated and its temperature is increased 1°C., the amount of heat supplied is known as the *specific heat at constant pressure* c_p. The ratio of these two specific heats, which increases with the pressure, is constant for all diatomic gases at atmospheric pressure. That is, for such gases at atmospheric pressure,

$$\frac{c_p}{c_v} = 1.4(k)$$

The difference between these two specific heats for any given gas must be equal to the heat equivalent of the external work done when a unit weight of the gas is raised one degree at a constant pressure.

Adiabatic compression. Boyle's law states that, the temperature remaining constant, the volume of a gas varies inversely as the pressure to which it is subjected. This is known as *isothermal compression or expansion*. However, as previously explained, according to Charles' law, an increase in the temperature of a gas at a constant volume gives an increase in pressure. Conversely a change in the volume of the gas results in a change of temperature. For example, let us assume that a gas is enclosed in a cylinder provided with a piston and that the walls of the cylinder, as well as the piston, are absolute nonconductors of heat so that, whether the temperature of the gas is high or low, no heat can pass through the walls. If, therefore, the gas is compressed in such a cylinder, the heat produced by the compression remains in the gas itself and so raises its temperature, and if the gas expands, the cold produced by the expansion lowers the temperature of the gas. The compression or expansion of a gas when enclosed in such a cylinder is known as *adiabatic*.

In general, adiabatic changes are possible only when the system is enclosed by a non-heat-conducting material. Rapid changes of condition are approximately adiabatic, since time is required for conduction and radiation of heat; thus the compression of air in an "air-cooled" compressor cylinder is practically adiabatic, as the time is so short that little heat can escape through the cylinder walls.

According to Boyle's law, $PV = C$ (temperature remaining constant). However, if a gas is subjected to adiabatic compression, the change in temperature also affects the pressure produced and an additional factor must be introduced. This factor k depends upon the specific heat of the material, that is, $k = c_p/c_v$. Therefore, for adiabatic compression, $PV^k = C$. The exponent k varies with the initial pressure and the kind of gas.

For example, for air,
If initial pressure is 11½ psi (abs.), $k = 1.21$.
If initial pressure is 13 psi (abs.), $k = 1.29$.
If initial pressure is 14 psi (abs.), $k = 1.34$.
If initial pressure is 14.7 psi (abs.), $k = 1.40$.

For other gases, as those used in internal-combustion engines, the value of k may be lower because the ratio of the specific heats is different from what it would be for air and because of losses from leakage past the pistons and valves and heat loss through the cylinder walls. In general practice, the equation of a curve representing the adiabatic change of a gas is

$$P_1V_1{}^k = P_2V_2{}^k \qquad \text{etc.}$$

and

$$P_2 = P_1\left(\frac{V_1}{V_2}\right)^k$$

Also, if

$$P_1V_1{}^k = P_2V_2{}^k$$

then

$$TV^{k-1} = C$$

or

$$\frac{T_1}{T_2} = \left(\frac{V_2}{V_1}\right)^{k-1}$$

Compression ratio and pressure. The compression ratio of an engine is equal to the total cylinder volume divided by the clearance volume, or $V_1/V_2 = r$. The greater this ratio the higher the compression pressure in the cylinder; that is, $P_2 = P_1V_1/V_2$, or, for adiabatic conditions, $P_2 = P_1(V_1/V_2)^k$. By the use of this formula we may compute the theoretical maximum compression pressure of an engine for certain assumed conditions.

For example, if $P_1 = 14.7$ lb. (atmospheric pressure)
$$V_1 = 18 \text{ cu. in.}$$
$$V_2 = 3 \text{ cu. in.}$$
$$k = 1.4$$

then $P_2 = 14.7(18/3)^{1.4} = 180.7$ lb. per sq. in.   absolute pressure

or $180.7 - 14.7 = 166$ lb. per sq. in.   gauge pressure

Under most conditions in an engine the initial pressure would be less than the normal atmospheric pressure of 14.7 lb. and the exponent k would be about 1.3.

Work and gas pressure. If a volume of gas is enclosed in a cylinder behind a piston whose area is A and the total gas pressure is P, then $P = Ap$ (p is unit of force per unit area). If the piston is forced inward a distance D and the gas is compressed, the value of p increases. Assuming that the average pressure exerted on the piston during its movement through D is pA and that p is the average unit pressure of the gas, the work done is pAD. But AD represents the decrease in volume of the gas. Letting V equal this volume, $pAD = Vp$; that is, the work done in compressing a gas equals the product of the change in volume and the average unit pressure of the gas during compression, or work done is equal to $p(V_1 - V_2)$.

We have also observed that when a gas is heated at constant volume the increase in internal energy is in proportion to the heat supplied and is equal to $c_v(T_2 - T_1)$ B.t.u. If the gas is heated at a constant pressure, the total heat supplied is equal to $c_p(T_2 - T_1)$ B.t.u. and includes the heat needed to raise the temperature at a constant volume plus an additional quantity of heat which is expended in doing external work because the pressure remains constant. Therefore, $c_p(T_2 - T_1)$ B.t.u. is greater than $c_v(T_2 - T_1)$ B.t.u., and the net energy output is equal to

$$(c_p - c_v)(T_2 - T_1) \text{ B.t.u.}$$

Furthermore, for any gas, $778(c_p - c_v) = R$ (gas constant).

The work done by a gas under pressure can also be represented by graphs (Figs. 6-3 and 6-4). In Fig. 6-3 it is assumed that P is constant at all volumes and the volume changes from V_1 to V_2 as represented by line CD. The product of P and CD is represented by area $ABCD$, which, in turn, represents the work done by the gas when it expands and moves the piston.

In the operation of most heat engines the gas pressure P is variable, as shown by Fig. 6-4; that is, the P curve drops from B to A as the volume increases. Again, the work done during the stroke is represented by the area $ABCD$, which, in turn, is the product of CD and the mean height of curve AB.

Carnot cycle. In 1824, Sadi Carnot, a French physicist, proposed an operating cycle for what may be considered as the ideal heat engine. Referring to Fig. 6-5, let us assume the following:

1. The cylinder and piston assembly C are made of a material which will not conduct heat with the exception of the base which is a perfect conductor.

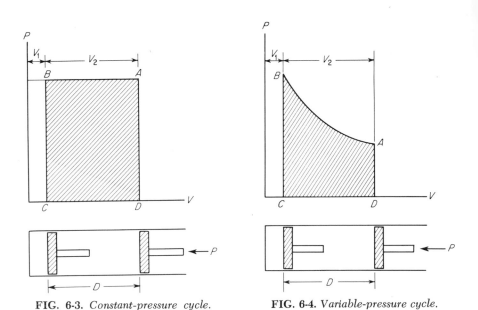

FIG. 6-3. *Constant-pressure cycle.*   FIG. 6-4. *Variable-pressure cycle.*

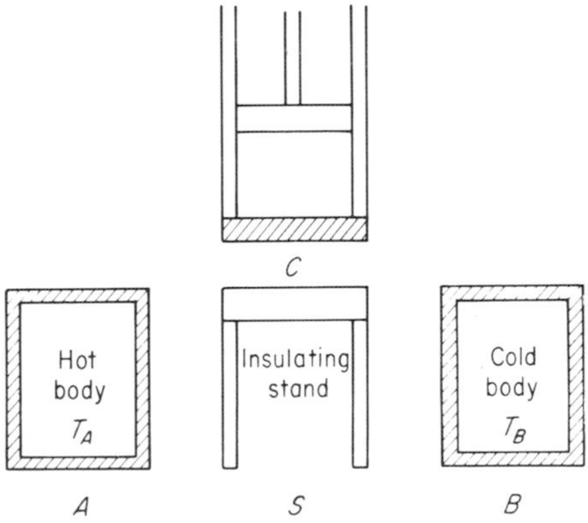

FIG. 6-5. *Carnot-engine principles.*

2. The cylinder contains a perfect gas as the working substance.

3. A and B are heat reservoirs whose temperatures are maintained constant, but T_A is relatively high and T_B relatively low.

4. S is an insulating stand which is completely non-heat-absorbing or transmitting.

5. The engine parts are without friction.

Theoretically, the cycle would function as follows: With cylinder C sitting on heat source A and the piston near the bottom, the gas at temperature T_A occupies a small volume at a relatively high pressure, as indicated on the PV diagram (Fig. 6-6). Now, if the pressure is reduced slightly so that the gas can expand, a quantity of heat Q_1 flows into it from A and maintains a constant temperature. Therefore, isothermal expansion occurs, as indicated by curve AB. Now, if the cylinder is placed on insulating stand S, the gas will expand further adiabatically, as indicated by curve BC, C being the point at which the gas temperature reaches the value T_B. At this instant, if the cylinder is placed on B and the gas pressure is increased by a slight pressure increase on the piston, the resultant heat Q_2 will flow into the cold body B. Again, the gas temperature remains constant and the pressure as indicated by curve CD is isothermal. If at point D the cylinder is again placed on stand S, there is a further increase in pressure which is adiabatic because the heat cannot escape. This pressure is indicated by curve DA, and the cycle is completed.

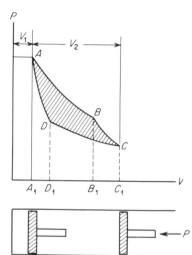

FIG. 6-6. *Carnot-engine cycle.*

As explained previously, the areas under the PV curves represent work. Therefore, referring to Fig. 6-6, areas ABB_1A_1 and BCC_1B_1 represent the work done by the expansion of the gas (positive work) and areas CDD_1C_1 and DAA_1D_1 represent the work required for compression (negative work). Hence, the net work output of the cycle is represented by area $ABCC_1A_1$ − area $ADCC_1A_1$, or $ABCD$.

During the cycle a quantity of heat Q_1 was absorbed by the gas during isothermal expansion along curve AB at T_A and a quantity of heat Q_2 was rejected by isothermal compression along line CD at T_B. Therefore, during the cycle, $Q_1 - Q_2$ heat units have been transformed into mechanical energy (W) and

$$W = J(Q_1 - Q_2)$$

where J is the number of units of work produced from one unit of heat.

The efficiency of the Carnot cycle depends only upon the temperatures between which it operates. Since the efficiency of any engine has been defined as the ratio of the heat applied to it and the heat equivalent of its energy output, we can say

$$\text{Efficiency} = \frac{Q_1 - Q_2}{Q_1}$$

Furthermore, in the case of the Carnot engine, it may be shown that

$$e = \frac{T_A - T_B}{T_A}$$

where T_A is the temperature (absolute) of the hot body supplying the heat and T_B is the temperature (absolute) of the cold body which absorbs the heat not converted into useful work.

ENGINE CYCLES AND EFFICIENCIES

The operation of any internal-combustion engine is based upon the theoretical thermodynamic principles previously discussed. However, actual operating results may vary somewhat from theoretical values because of such factors as (1) variation in the specific heats of the gases at different temperatures, (2) variation in air-fuel ratio, (3) exchanges and losses of heat to the cylinder walls and piston, (4) leakage and resistance to gas flow, (5) lapse of time between ignition and complete combustion of mixture, and others. It is possible to analyze some of the common engine cycles by using a gas such as air and making certain assumptions, namely, that the specific heat remains constant and that there is no loss or transfer of heat to the working parts. Such analyses will aid in showing the effect of changing operating conditions and provide a better understanding of the basic factors involved in engine design and the part that they play in operating efficiency.

The two cycles used in present-day engines are known as the *Otto cycle* and the *diesel cycle*. Either may be subdivided into two- and four-stroke-cycle types, depending upon the number of piston strokes required to complete a cycle of events in the cylinder.

Ideal Otto cycle (air standard). Figure 6-7 is a *PV* diagram of the Otto cycle as it would function under ideal and air-standard conditions. V_1 represents the total cylinder volume, V_2 the clearance or compression volume, and $V_1 - V_2$ the piston displacement.

The line *MN* represents atmospheric pressure, and *AB* represents the admission of the gas, with the pressure dropping slightly below atmospheric. *BGC* represents compression under adiabatic conditions, with ignition occurring at *C*. It is assumed that combustion is instantaneous and that the rise in pressure *CD* occurs at a constant volume V_2. *DE* represents adiabatic expansion or the working stroke. Exhaust takes place at *E*, and the pressure drops nearly to atmospheric and remains so during the exhaust stroke *FA*.

In examining Fig. 6-7, it will be observed that areas represent work because horizontal distances are volumes in cubic feet and vertical distances are pressures in pounds per square inch. Since work equals FD, vertical distances multiplied by horizontal distances equal some area which, by means of suitable units and values, can be converted into units of work. Furthermore, the area ABG is relatively very small and can be neglected. The area $ADEB$ represents the gross work of the expansion stroke, and area ACB represents the negative work done during the com-

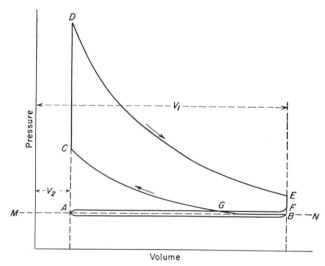

FIG. 6-7. *Ideal* PV *diagram for a four-stroke-cycle electric ignition engine* (*air standard*).

pression stroke. The difference between these two areas is $CDEB$ and represents the net work of the cycle.

Analyzing the heat and energy reactions of the cycle, we find that heat is added along CD and lost along EB; that is,

$$Q_1 \text{ (heat added)} = c_V(T_D - T_C) \tag{1}$$

$$Q_2 \text{ (heat lost)} = c_V(T_E - T_B) \tag{2}$$

The theoretical thermal efficiency e of the cycle is given by the equation

$$e = \frac{Q_1 - Q_2}{Q_1} \tag{3}$$

Substituting,

$$e = \frac{c_V(T_D - T_C) - c_V(T_E - T_B)}{c_V(T_D - T_C)} \tag{4}$$

or

$$e = 1 - \frac{T_E - T_B}{T_D - T_C} \tag{5}$$

From the laws of gases,

$$\frac{P_B V_B}{T_B} = \frac{P_C V_C}{T_C} = \frac{P_D V_D}{T_D} = \frac{P_E V_E}{T_E} \tag{6}$$

and $\qquad P_B V_B{}^k = P_C V_C{}^k \qquad$ and $\qquad P_D V_D{}^k = P_E V_E{}^k \tag{7}$

eferring to Fig. 6-7 and combining Eqs. (6) and (7),

$$\frac{T_B}{T_C} = \left(\frac{P_B}{P_C}\right)^{(k-1)/k} \tag{8}$$

$$\frac{T_B}{T_C} = \left(\frac{V_C}{V_B}\right)^{k-1} \tag{9}$$

and $$\frac{T_E}{T_D} = \left(\frac{V_D}{V_E}\right)^{k-1} \tag{10}$$

but (Fig. 6-7)
$$V_D = V_C \qquad \text{and} \qquad V_E = V_B$$

Hence $\qquad \dfrac{T_B}{T_C} = \left(\dfrac{V_C}{V_B}\right)^{k-1} \qquad$ and $\qquad \dfrac{T_E}{T_D} = \left(\dfrac{V_C}{V_B}\right)^{k-1} \tag{11}$

Therefore $\qquad \dfrac{T_B}{T_C} = \dfrac{T_E}{T_D} \qquad$ or $\qquad \dfrac{T_E}{T_B} = \dfrac{T_D}{T_C} \tag{12}$

Then $\qquad \dfrac{T_E}{T_B} - 1 = \dfrac{T_D}{T_C} - 1 \qquad$ and $\qquad \dfrac{T_E - T_B}{T_B} = \dfrac{T_D - T_C}{T_C} \tag{13}$

or $$\frac{T_E - T_B}{T_D - T_C} = \frac{T_B}{T_C} \tag{14}$$

Substituting Eq. (14) in Eq. (5),

$$e = 1 - \frac{T_B}{T_C} \tag{15}$$

From Eq. (8),

$$e = 1 - \left(\frac{P_B}{P_C}\right)^{(k-1)/k} \tag{16}$$

and from Eq. (9),

$$e = 1 - \left(\frac{V_C}{V_B}\right)^{k-1} \tag{17}$$

Equations (15) to (17) show that the air-standard thermal efficiency of an Otto-cycle engine is dependent upon (1) the ratios of the absolute temperatures before and after compression, (2) the increase in the compression pressure, and (3) the relative initial and final volumes.

Ideal diesel cycle (air standard). The diesel-cycle engine differs from the Otto-cycle one in that the heat of compression instead of an electric spark is utilized to produce ignition. The air and fuel are not premixed by a carburetor and introduced as a gaseous mixture; instead, air alone is taken in and compressed, and the fuel is injected into the highly compressed and heated air at the end of the compression stroke. It is assumed

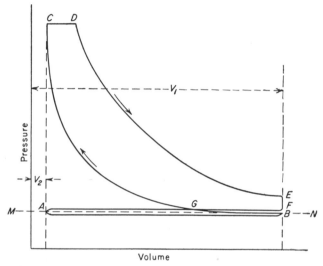

FIG. 6-8. *Ideal PV diagram for a four-stroke-cycle diesel engine (air standard).*

that the rate of admission of the fuel is so regulated that the pressure remains constant during this injection interval and until combustion is complete.

Figure 6-8 is a *PV* diagram of the diesel cycle as it would function under ideal and air-standard conditions. The line *MN* represents atmospheric pressure, and *AB* represents the admission of the air. *BGC* represents adiabatic compression with a compression ratio of about 15:1 and a maximum pressure of approximately 500 lb. per sq. in. Injection of the fuel charge begins at *C* and stops at *D*. Combustion takes place during this interval, and a condition of constant pressure is assumed. The ratio of the volumes at *D* and *C* (V_D/V_C) is known as the *cutoff ratio*. Adiabatic expansion occurs from *D* to *E*, with the exhaust valve opening at *E* and the pressure dropping nearly to atmospheric and remaining so during the exhaust stroke *FA*. The area *ACDEB* represents the total work of the expansion stroke, and area *ACB* represents the negative work done during the compression stroke. The difference between these two areas is *BCDE* and represents the net work of the cycle.

In analyzing the heat and energy reactions of the cycle, the following assumptions are made:

1. The air pressure during the stroke AB is atmospheric.
2. Compression is adiabatic and the cylinder walls are nonconductors.
3. Fuel enters the cylinder at the temperature T.
4. Combustion takes place at constant pressure during the interval CD.
5. Expansion is adiabatic.
6. Exhaust takes place at atmospheric pressure.
7. Specific heat remains constant during the entire cycle.

With the above assumptions in mind, we find that heat is added along CD and lost along EB; that is,

$$Q_1 \text{ (heat added)} = c_P(T_D - T_C) \tag{1}$$

$$Q_2 \text{ (heat lost)} = c_V(T_E - T_B) \tag{2}$$

The theoretical thermal efficiency e of the cycle is given by the equation

$$e = \frac{Q_1 - Q_2}{Q_1} \tag{3}$$

Substituting,

$$e = \frac{c_P(T_D - T_C) - c_V(T_E - T_B)}{c_P(T_D - T_C)} \tag{4}$$

or

$$e = 1 - \frac{c_V(T_E - T_B)}{c_P(T_D - T_C)} \tag{5}$$

Since

$$\frac{c_P}{c_V} = k \tag{6}$$

then

$$e = 1 - \frac{T_E - T_B}{k(T_D - T_C)} \tag{7}$$

From the laws of gases,

$$\frac{P_B V_B}{T_B} = \frac{P_C V_C}{T_C} = \frac{P_D V_D}{T_D} = \frac{P_E V_E}{T_E} \tag{8}$$

and

$$P_B V_B{}^k = P_C V_C{}^k \quad \text{and} \quad P_D V_D{}^k = P_E V_E{}^k \tag{9}$$

Since CD is at constant pressure and EB is at constant volume, from Eq. (8),

$$T_D = T_C \frac{V_D}{V_C} \tag{10}$$

and

$$T_E = T_B \frac{P_E}{P_B} \tag{11}$$

and, from Eq. (9),

$$\frac{P_B}{P_C} = \left(\frac{V_C}{V_B}\right)^k \quad \text{and} \quad \frac{P_D}{P_E} = \left(\frac{V_E}{V_D}\right)^k \tag{12}$$

But

$$P_C = P_D \quad \text{and} \quad V_B = V_E$$

Hence

$$\frac{P_E}{P_B} = \left(\frac{V_D}{V_C}\right)^k \tag{13}$$

and, substituting Eq. (13) in Eq. (11),

$$T_E = T_B \left(\frac{V_D}{V_C}\right)^k \tag{14}$$

Substituting Eqs. (10) and (14) in Eq. (7),

$$e = 1 - \frac{T_B}{T_C} \frac{[(V_D/V_C)^k - 1]}{k(V_D/V_C - 1)} \tag{15}$$

From Eqs. (8) and (9),

$$\frac{T_B}{T_C} = \left(\frac{V_C}{V_B}\right)^{k-1} = \left(\frac{P_B}{P_C}\right)^{(k-1)/k} \tag{16}$$

Hence

$$e = 1 - \left(\frac{V_C}{V_B}\right)^{k-1} \frac{[(V_D/V_C)^k - 1]}{k(V_D/V_C - 1)} \tag{17}$$

and

$$e = 1 - \left(\frac{P_B}{P_C}\right)^{(k-1)/k} \frac{[(V_D/V_C)^k - 1]}{k(V_D/V_C - 1)} \tag{18}$$

A study of the preceding theoretical analysis of the diesel cycle shows that its efficiency is dependent upon the compression ratio and the cutoff ratio; that is, the efficiency is increased by a high compression ratio and a decrease in the cutoff ratio.

Comparison of ideal cycles. Table 6-1 and Fig. 6-9 show the comparative efficiency values for ideal Otto and diesel cycles. It will be noted that, at first, the efficiency increases rapidly with the increase in compression but the rate of increase is less as the compression ratio becomes high. It will also be noted that the Otto cycle gives a higher theoretical efficiency than the diesel cycle. However, in actual practice, it is not higher, because the compression ratio of the Otto-cycle engine is limited by the fuel characteristics, particularly with respect to ignition and detonation. Diesel engines normally use considerably higher compression pressures than Otto-cycle engines and, therefore, give a higher fuel-utilization efficiency.

Table 6-1. Theoretical Thermal-efficiency Values for Otto and Diesel Cycles (Air Standard)

Compression ratio, V_1/V_2	Clearance vol., per cent of piston displacement	P_2, lb. per sq. in. abs.	Thermal efficiency, per cent	
			Otto cycle	Diesel cycle
3.0	50.0	69	35.6	34.3
4.0	33.3	102	42.6	41.0
4.5	28.9	121	45.2	43.6
5.0	25.0	140	47.4	45.8
5.5	22.3	160	49.5	47.5
6.0	20.0	180	51.1	48.9
6.5	18.2	202	52.7	50.4
7.0	16.7	224	54.1	51.2
7.5	15.4	247	55.3	52.7
8.0	14.5	270	56.4	53.5
9.0	12.5	318	58.5	55.2
10.0	11.1	369	60.2	56.9
11.0	10.0	422	61.7	58.3
12.0	9.1	477	63.0	59.4
13.0	8.3	533	64.2	60.6
14.0	7.7	590	65.2	61.2
15.0	7.1	651	66.1	62.0
16.0	6.6	713	67.0	62.8

It should be made clear that engines cannot be made to perform under the ideal cycle conditions just explained. This is true for a number of reasons, namely, (1) compression and expansion cannot be completely adiabatic; (2) the fuel is not a perfect gas; (3) heat cannot be supplied to the gaseous material at either an exact constant volume or constant pressure; and (4) losses from heat, mechanical imperfections, and other sources are unavoidable. A knowledge of the theoretical efficiency and performance of an ideal-cycle engine does make possible a more intelligent analysis of the actual performance of any engine and whether or not it is well designed.

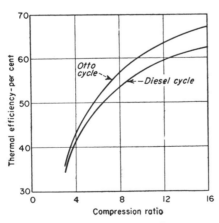

FIG. 6-9. *Theoretical relationship of compression ratio and thermal efficiency for electric-ignition and diesel-engine cycles.*

REFERENCES

BARGER, E. L., W. M. CARLETON, E. G. MCKIBBEN, and ROY BAINER, "Tractors and Their Power Units," John Wiley & Sons, Inc., New York, 1952.

HELDT, P. M., "High-speed Combustion Engines," 16th ed., Chilton Company, Philadelphia, 1956.

LICHTY, L. C., "Internal Combustion Engines," 6th ed., McGraw-Hill Book Company, Inc., New York, 1951.

OBERT, EDWARD F., "Internal Combustion Engines," 2d ed., International Textbook Company, Scranton, Pa., 1950.

POLSON, J. A., "Internal Combustion Engines," 2d ed., John Wiley & Sons, Inc., New York, 1942.

PROBLEMS AND QUESTIONS

1. What is meant by the absolute temperature of a substance?

2. Define calorie, B.t.u., and specific heat.

3. Distinguish between isothermal and adiabatic expansion.

4. An engine has a compression ratio of 7.5. Compute P_2 (gauge) if P_1 is 13.5 lb. per sq. in. and k is 1.3.

5. What is the compression ratio of an engine if P_1 is 14.0 lb. per sq. in., P_2 is 190 lb. per sq. in., and k is 1.4? What is the percentage change if k is 1.2?

6. Calculate the theoretical thermal efficiency for an ideal Otto-cycle engine if $V_B = 51$ cu. in., $V_c = 8.3$ cu. in., and $k = 1.35$.

7. Calculate the theoretical thermal efficiency for a diesel-cycle engine if $V_B = 180$ cu. in., $V_C = 12$ cu. in., $V_D = 14.5$ cu. in., and $k = 1.35$.

8. Make sketches of typical PV diagrams for ideal Otto- and diesel-cycle engines (air standard), and explain the P, V, and T reactions for the different events in the cycles.

9. Compare the Otto and diesel cycles as to efficiency from both a theoretical and a practical standpoint.

7

Engine Construction and Design

All gas engines, regardless of size, type, and number of cylinders, are made up of certain basic and essential parts and assemblies. A thorough knowledge of the correct terminology, function, and specific characteristics of these parts is important.

Principal engine parts. The parts and systems making up a simple internal-combustion engine are as follows:

1. Cylinder
2. Cylinder head
3. Piston
4. Piston rings
5. Piston pin
6. Connecting rod
7. Crankshaft
8. Flywheel
9. Valve system
    a. Valves—intake and exhaust
    b. Cam gear and cam or camshaft
    c. Tappet
    d. Push rod
    e. Rocker arm
10. Fuel-supply and carburetion system
    a. Fuel tank
    b. Fuel line
    c. Fuel pump
    d. Carburetor
    e. Manifold
    f. Air cleaner

11. Ignition system
   a. Battery or magneto
   b. Coil
   c. Sparking device
   d. Timing mechanism (breaker points, distributor)
   e. Switch and wire connections
12. Cooling system
   a. Tank, radiator, or water hopper
   b. Pump (in forced-circulation system only)
   c. Water jacket
   d. Fan
   e. Thermostat
   f. Pipes and connections
13. Lubrication system
   a. Oil pump
   b. Oil lines
   c. Oil gauge
   d. Oil filter
   e. Grease fittings
14. Governing system
   a. Weights and springs
   b. Detent arm or finger (in hit-and-miss system only)
   c. Throttle butterfly (in throttle system only)

Cylinder. The cylinder (Fig. 7-1) or cylinder block (Fig. 7-2) of an engine constitutes the principal basic and supporting portion of the engine power unit. Its major function is to provide the space in which the piston operates to draw in the fuel mixture, compress it, and allow it to expand and generate power. The design and construction of the cylinder are dependent upon such factors as power required, exact purpose of engine, compression ratio, valve arrangement, method of cooling, arrangement of cylinders (if multiple-cylinder), and manufacturing and production operations.

Multiple-cylinder, automotive engines usually have all cylinders cast together; that is, the cylinders are arranged side by side or in line in a single unit. Exceptions are a few large, heavy-duty engines with six or more cylinders. In such cases, the cylinders may be cast in two groups. Special cylinder arrangements such as the V arrangement and the radial arrangement, in most cases, have the cylinders cast singly or in groups.

Casting the cylinders in a single block offers a number of advantages. It gives a more compact and rigid construction, simplifies manufacturing and assembly operations, and provides better enclosure of engine mechanisms. Hollow spaces in the block provide for the circulation of the cooling medium for liquid-cooled engines.

Cylinders are usually made of high-grade cast iron. This material has the necessary strength, machines and grinds readily, withstands extreme pressures and temperatures without distortion, and is low in cost. The trend in recent years has been to mix some scrap steel with the pig iron

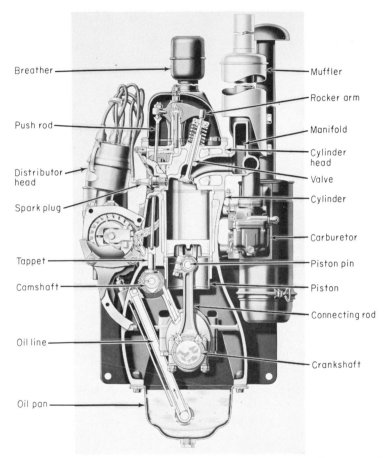

FIG. 7-1. *Basic design and parts of typical automotive-type engine.* (Courtesy of Allis-Chalmers Manufacturing Company.)

in casting cylinder blocks. This provides additional strength and better wearing qualities. In some cases such metals as chromium, nickel, and molybdenum are added to the cast iron to give an alloy that has greater strength and wear resistance with less weight.

Air-cooled engines usually have the cylinders cast separately and equipped with fins to provide better air circulation and more rapid escape of the excess heat.

Cylinder head. Nearly all engines and particularly liquid-cooled engines have removable cylinder heads. This head is attached to the block with a number of bolts and a copper-asbestos gasket provides a seal between it and the block. The cylinder head contains the pocket or space above the cylinder and piston known as the *combustion chamber.* It contains passages that match those of the cylinder block and allow the coolant to circulate to provide effective cooling. If the engine is of the valve-in-head type, all valves with their guides, springs, and retainers are mounted in the head.

Cylinder heads are usually made of the same material as the block. However, in some special cases, a cast-aluminum alloy has been used to provide better heat dissipation and control. The principal objection to such an alloy is that it is subject to corrosion if pure clean water or a special cooling liquid is not used.

Cylinder manufacture. In manufacturing cylinders and cylinder blocks, a number of distinct steps are involved, as follows:

1. Melting and casting
2. Cleaning the rough casting
3. Machining: planing and milling
4. Boring, drilling, and tapping
5. Grinding the wall
6. Honing and polishing the wall

The grinding process consists in removing a thin layer of metal and producing an absolutely true bore by means of a somewhat coarse abrasive grinding wheel revolved at high speed. Honing

FIG. 7-2. *Cylinder block showing removable liner.*

is a finishing and polishing operation performed by a very fine-grained revolving stone. This operation produces a bore of exact dimensions and a mirror-smooth surface, which will provide the most efficient lubrication and the least possible wear.

Removable cylinder liners. Some stationary engines, most tractor engines, and even some truck engines are equipped with removable cylinder liners or sleeves (Fig. 7-2). The possible advantages are that (1) overhauling and rebuilding the engine is rendered relatively simple, easy, reliable, and satisfactory at a reasonable cost, since, by inserting new liners with new factory-fitted pistons, rings, and piston pins, the engine is practically restored to its original new condition so far as the cylinders and pistons are concerned; (2) in case one cylinder is scored or damaged, it can be easily repaired and the original bore and balance retained; and (3) a higher grade of cast iron or an alloy with better wear-resisting properties can be used for these liners, whereas to make the entire block of such material would be too expensive; special bore-finishing operations such as heat-treatment and honing to provide better oil control and longer wear are readily accomplished.

Cylinder liners may be classified as the "dry" type and the "wet" type. The latter serves as the entire cylinder wall and comes into direct contact with the coolant. Special sealing rings are placed at the top and bottom to prevent leakage of the coolant. "Dry" liners are usually much thinner and easier to replace and merely serve as the inner lining and cylinder wearing surface.

Crankcase and oil pan. The crankcase is that part of the engine which supports and encloses the crankshaft and camshaft and provides a reservoir for the lubricating oil. It may also serve as a mounting for such accessories as the oil pump, oil filter, generator, starter motor, and ignition parts. Normally the upper portion of the crankcase is cast with or is integral with the cylinder block. The lower part of the crankcase is commonly called the *oil pan* and may be made of cast iron, cast aluminum, or pressed steel. This pan is securely bolted to the block and the joints sealed with suitable gaskets and oil seals.

Pistons. The piston of an engine is the first part to begin movement and to transmit power to the crankshaft as a result of the pressure and energy released by the combustion of the fuel. Pistons are of the trunk type, that is, closed at one end and open at the other to permit direct attachment of the connecting rod and its free action. They are usually somewhat longer than their diameter, and they are made as light as possible consistent with necessary strength, heat dissipation, and wearing qualities.

Materials used for pistons are gray cast iron, cast steel, and aluminum alloy. Cast iron or cast steel is ordinarily used in heavy-duty engines such as tractors, where high speeds and quick acceleration are not involved. Most automobile engines use aluminum-alloy pistons, because the lighter weight material permits higher operating speeds and greater speed flexibility. On the other hand, there are a few cases where heavy-duty engines use aluminum-alloy pistons because of this alloy's heat-conducting characteristic; that is, its use permits better control of the heat in the combustion chamber and therefore better control of the ignition and combustion of the fuel mixture.

Cast-iron pistons are more wear-resistant and require slightly less clearance in the cylinder than aluminum-alloy pistons. Cast-steel pistons are sometimes thinly coated with tin or a special metal to provide a smoother finish and a more wear-resistant surface.

The approximate composition of a common piston alloy is:

Element	Per cent
Aluminum	78.00–86.00
Silicon	11.25–15.00
Nickel	1.00– 3.00
Iron, max	1.30
Copper	0.50– 1.50
Magnesium	0.70– 1.30

The principal characteristics of this alloy are (1) low coefficient of expansion as compared with other aluminum alloys, (2) hardness and resistance to wear, and (3) good mechanical properties at high temperatures.

Another piston alloy especially adapted to high-temperature conditions consists of:

Element	Per cent
Aluminum	90.00–92.00
Copper	3.75– 4.25
Nickel	1.80– 2.30
Magnesium	1.20– 1.70
Iron, max	1.00
Silicon, max	0.70
Other impurities, max	0.20

The principal disadvantage of aluminum alloy for pistons is that it has a high coefficient of expansion. This means that the piston must be given slightly more clearance when fitted in the cylinder than is given one of cast iron. However, this problem has been partly overcome by the use of the so-called "split-skirt" or "T-slot" piston (Fig. 7-3) and by embedding devices of steel or a special metal called *invar* at certain points in the piston when it is cast. These devices are called *struts*. They control the expansion by controlling the heat-flow path as well as strengthening the piston structure. Reinforcing ribs on the inside of pistons also provide greater strength and better heat dissipation.

Figure 7-4 shows a special heavy-duty aluminum-alloy piston used in one make of diesel tractor. An iron band is built into the upper part and bears the top-ring groove. This is done to make the top ring and its groove more wear-resistant, because they are exposed to higher temperatures, carbon deposits, and other factors that induce more rapid wear. Note also the chrome-nickel steel plug in the top of the piston which provides heat resistance in the high-temperature area.

Pistons and piston rings are frequently given a special surface treatment to make them more wear-resistant. For example, some aluminum-alloy pistons are subjected to a process known as anodizing. This is an electrolytic process which converts a thin outer layer of the metal into

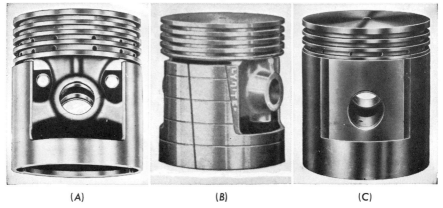

FIG. 7-3. *Common piston types.* (A) *Strut-type aluminum alloy.* (B) *Split-skirt aluminum alloy.* (C) *Plain cast iron.*

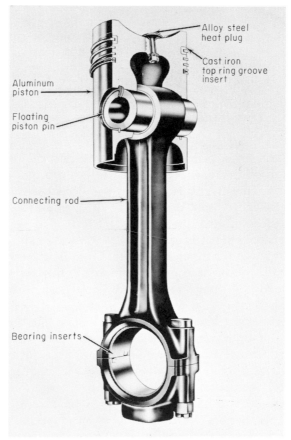

Alloy steel
heat plug

Cast iron
top ring groove
insert

Aluminum
piston

Floating
piston pin

Connecting rod

Bearing inserts

FIG. 7-4. *Piston and connecting-rod assembly for diesel tractor engine.* (Courtesy of Caterpillar Tractor Company.)

aluminum oxide. This oxide is harder than the original metal and also more heat-resistant. Tin plating is another method of providing a smoother and better-wearing surface for both cast-iron and aluminum-alloy pistons.

The term *piston clearance* is applied to the space between the piston wall and cylinder wall. For cast-iron pistons, this clearance, at the closed end, when the engine is cold, should be about 0.0005 in. for each inch of cylinder diameter. Most pistons are slightly tapered and larger in diameter at the open end and may have less clearance at this end, since this portion of the piston is not exposed to as much heat as the closed end and therefore expands less. Aluminum-alloy pistons require about twice as much clearance as cast-iron pistons; but, as previously explained, most aluminum-alloy pistons are now so constructed that they require no more clearance than other types. Some pistons are said to be *cam-ground;* that is, the skirt is not a true circle but has an elliptical shape. The variation is possibly 0.005 to 0.010 in., and the greatest diameter is across the surfaces of greatest wear, namely, at right angles to the piston pin. Too much piston clearance will cause loss of compression, oil pumping, and piston slap. Too little clearance will cause the piston to stick or seize in the cylinder as the engine gets hot. However, a piston may seize in a cylinder even though it has the proper clearance, as a result of improper action of the cooling system or lack of cylinder lubrication.

Piston rings. The primary function of the piston rings is to retain compression and, at the same time, reduce the cylinder-wall and piston-wall contact area to a minimum, thus preventing friction losses and excessive wear. Other important functions are the control of the oil and cylinder lubrication and the transmission of heat away from the piston and to the cylinder walls.

Piston rings are made of cast iron because it retains its wearing qualities and elasticity indefinitely. Furthermore, it is simpler and cheaper to replace the rings than the cylinders or liners. Hence, the rings should absorb the wear if possible, and this makes cast-iron rings more desirable. The top ring in some heavy-duty and automotive-type engines is chromium plated to improve its performance and wearing qualities. The number of rings per piston varies from three to five, depending upon the type of engine and the compression desired. The ordinary types of engines seldom have more than three or four rings, but diesel-type engines usually have five rings per piston.

Piston rings are classed as compression rings and oil rings (Figs. 7-5 and 7-6), depending upon their specific function and location on the piston. Compression rings are usually plain one-piece rings and are always placed in the grooves nearest the piston head. Oil rings are grooved or slotted and are located either in the lowest groove above the piston pin or in a groove near the piston skirt. Their function, obviously, is to control the distribution of the lubricating oil to the cylinder and piston surfaces and to prevent unnecessary or excessive oil consumption. The ring groove under an oil ring is provided with holes through which the excess oil returns to the crankcase.

When removed from the cylinder, piston rings are always slightly larger in diameter than the cylinder itself, and they must be compressed

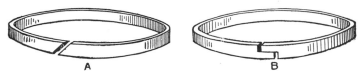

FIG. 7-5. *Plain compression rings showing* (A) *bevel joint and* (B) *straight joint.*

when inserted. Two kinds of joints are found (Figs. 7-5 and 7-6): the bevel joint and the plain butt joint.

Piston-ring clearance is the distance or space at the joint of the ring when it is in the cylinder (Fig. 7-7). This clearance is necessary to allow for the expansion of the ring as it gets hot. Without such clearance

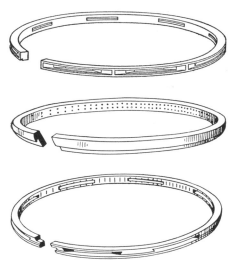

FIG. 7-6. *Oil-control piston rings.*

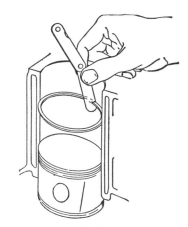

FIG. 7-7. *Checking piston-ring clearance.*

the ring would buckle and break and consequently injure the cylinder and piston of the engine. Too much piston-ring clearance is apt to produce leakage of compression and possible waste of lubricating oil. Table 7-1 gives the SAE recommended end clearance for piston rings.

Special thin, flexible, spring-steel bands called inner rings (Fig. 7-8) or expanders are sometimes placed in the ring grooves under the regu-

Table 7-1. Piston-ring End Clearances

Cylinder diameter, in.	End clearance, in.
1–1$^{31}/_{32}$	0.005–0.013
2–2$^{31}/_{32}$	0.007–0.017
3–3$^{31}/_{32}$	0.010–0.020
4–4$^{31}/_{32}$	0.013–0.025
5–6$^{31}/_{32}$	0.017–0.032
7–8	0.023–0.040

lar rings in reconditioned engines for the purpose of creating better contact between ring and cylinder wall.

In fitting and replacing piston rings, care should be taken to see that (1) the grooves are free of carbon deposits, (2) each ring is free in its groove and has the correct end and side clearance, and (3) the joints of the rings are not in line when the piston is inserted in the cylinder.

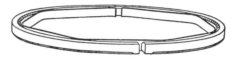

FIG. 7-8. *Piston-ring expanders.*

Piston pin. The function of the piston pin is to join the connecting rod to the piston and, at the same time, provide a flexible or hinge-like connection between the two.

The pin passes through the piston-pin bosses and through the upper end of the connecting rod that rides within the piston on the middle of the pin. Piston pins are made of casehardened alloy steel with a precision finish. The hollow construction gives maximum strength with minimum weight. They are lubricated by splash from the crankcase or by pressure through passages bored in the connecting rods.

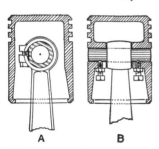

A **B**

FIG. 7-9. *Methods of fastening piston pins. (A) Pin clamped to connecting rod. (B) Pin fastened to piston.*

Three different methods are used to anchor piston pins so that they cannot work sideways and score the cylinder. The first is to clamp the pin to the connecting rod by means of a clamp screw or setscrew (Fig. 7-9A), so that the bearing will be at each end of the pin where it fits in the piston. In the second case, the pin is anchored to the piston by means of setscrews and the bearing is in the connecting rod (Fig. 7-9B). In the third, or most common, method (Fig. 7-10), the piston pin is allowed to float, so to speak, or move in both the piston and connecting rod but is held in place by means of snap rings at each end of the pin.

Some kind of removable bushing, usually bronze, is placed either in the connecting rod or in the piston to receive the wear. When the piston-pin bearing becomes badly worn, this bushing can be removed readily and replaced. Frequently, however, it is necessary to replace both the

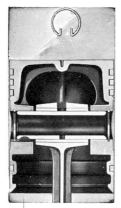

piston pin and the bushing. The floating piston pin gives more uniform wear distribution. For this type, the connecting rod uses a removable bronze bushing, but bushings are not used in the piston bosses.

Connecting rod. Connecting rods are made of what is known as *drop-forged* steel. They must be of some material that is neither brittle nor ductile; that is, they must stand a twisting strain but should not break or bend when subjected to such a strain. The I-beam type is the prevailing connecting-rod shape. It gives strength with less weight and material. That end of the rod fastened to the piston pin

FIG. 7-10. *A floating piston pin.*

is known as the small end, and the other end, which is attached to the crankshaft, is spoken of as the large end of the connecting rod. The large end ordinarily has what is known as a split bearing held together by two bolts. Four bolts are often used in large engines.

Connecting-rod and crankshaft bearings. One of the outstanding achievements in automotive engineering has been the remarkable improvement and progress made in the design of engine crankshaft and connecting-rod bearings whereby those bearings wear much longer even under excessively high speeds and loads. This exceptional bearing performance can be attributed to a number of factors, such as (1) the use of better bearing alloys, (2) greater precision in bearing and crankshaft manufacture, (3) the use of harder and more wear-resistant crankshaft steels, and (4) better engine lubrication and improved engine oils.

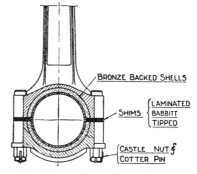

FIG. 7-11. *A shim-adjusted connecting-rod bearing.*

For many years preceding the development of the high-speed, high-compression engine, all bearings were of the thick, heavy, tin-base babbitt type (Fig. 7-11). The bearing metal either was cast into the connecting rod and cylinder block or was backed by a heavy bronze shell. The babbitt was usually melted and cast in place by pouring. Later on a method was developed whereby the molten babbitt was spun into the cast-iron or bronze shell by centrifugal action. This produced a much smoother and truer bearing surface. The replacement and fitting of this old-type

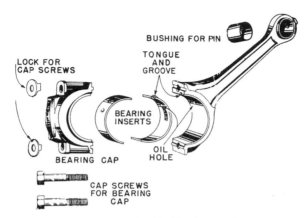

FIG. 7-12. *Connecting-rod assembly showing bearing inserts.*

bearing involved careful hand scraping of the surfaces until proper bearing and journal contact was obtained. As wear occurred and adjustment became necessary, the bearing cap was separated and a certain number of thin shims removed until the desired fit was again obtained. In time the crank journal will probably wear smaller or out of round, and an entirely new undersize bearing must be installed.

With the development of higher speeds and compression pressures, greater bearing pressures were produced, and it was found that these older types of thick babbitt bearings would not stand up as satisfactorily as desired. Consequently, it became necessary to develop new bearing materials and designs, provide the crankshaft journals with a smoother and harder finish, and maintain precision construction throughout. The result was the introduction of thin-shelled

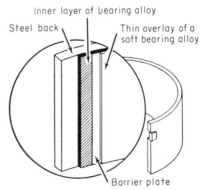

FIG. 7-13. *Three-layer bearing construction.*

precision or insert types of bearings and the use of new types of bearing alloys, such as lead-base babbitt, copper-lead, and aluminum.

The general construction of an insert bearing is shown in Figs. 7-12 and 7-13. The two-layer insert consists of a thin layer (0.010 to 0.030 in.)

of the bearing alloy bonded to a thicker bronze or steel back. A mild
steel is used and is preferable to bronze from the standpoint of cost,
strength, and general bonding characteristics. The three-layer insert is
similar to the two-layer except that a very thin layer—about 0.001 in.
thick—of babbitt or other lead alloy is bonded to the usual bearing-
alloy layer. This third layer, called an overlay or overplate, provides a
cushion between the shaft journal and the bearing during the "run-
ning-in" period as they conform to each other. The overplate usually
wears away, but, in doing so, leaves a smooth fitting journal and bearing surface.

To give satisfactory results, a bearing alloy must have a number of
specific characteristics such as (1) sufficient strength including load-
carrying capacity, resistance to fatigue, high impact and compressive
strength, and high-temperature strength; (2) good antifriction and surface characteristics so that it will adjust itself to the journal without any
bonding action or surface failure and damage; (3) resistance to corrosion by combustion products or motor-oil contaminants; (4) high thermal
conductivity to provide rapid frictional heat dissipation; (5) reasonable
cost.

The principal bearing alloys and their approximate composition are:

Tin-base babbitt. Copper, 3.50 per cent; antimony, 7.50 per cent; tin, 89.00
per cent.

Lead-base babbitt. Copper, 0.25 to 0.50 per cent; tin, 5.00 to 10.00 per
cent; antimony, 9.00 to 16.00 per cent; lead, 75.00 to 85.00 per cent.

Copper-lead alloy. Lead, 25.00 to 40.00 per cent; copper, 60.00 to 75.00
per cent.

Aluminum alloy. Copper and nickel, 0.50 per cent; silicon, 2.50 per cent;
tin, 7.50 per cent; aluminum, 90.00 per cent.

Table 7-2. Properties of Metals

Metal	Brinnell hardness number	Melting point, °F.	Relative thermal conductivity
Tin................	4.5–7.0	450	0.16
Lead..............	4.2	621	0.083
Antimony..........	....	1,167	0.045
Aluminum.........	25–40	1,220	0.53
Silver.............	59	1,761	1.00
Copper (cast).......	35	1,981	0.94
Nickel.............	90–110	2,651	0.22
Wrought iron.......	69–75	2,600	0.18
High-carbon steel....	190–220	2,500	
Chromium..........	91	3,430	0.16

Tin-base babbitts have been used for many years for automotive engine bearings. However, as compression pressures and operating speeds and temperatures increased, it was found that tin-base babbitts lacked the necessary mechanical strength to meet reasonable service requirements. This was particularly true if the bearing temperatures were unusually high. Therefore other alloys were developed. At the present time the copper-lead alloys appear best adapted to heavy-duty engines and are widely used. Aluminum bearing alloys in the form of heavy solid bushings are also proving satisfactory for this heavy-duty service.

A most important consideration is the proper servicing and replacement of precision insert bearings. First of all, shims are never used with insert bearings, and bearing caps and inserts should never be filed under any conditions. The primary factor in insert-bearing replacement is correct oil clearance. This is the space allowed between the bearing surface and the journal surface for the oil film. If this space is too small, the film will be too thin to prevent metal-to-metal contact between the bearing and the journal. If the clearance is excessive or greater

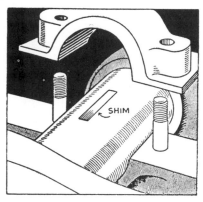

FIG. 7-14. *Use of shim in fitting precision bearing for correct oil clearance.*

than necessary, oil will flow too freely and may result in a reduction in pressure and some increased oil consumption and wastage.

The oil-film clearance depends on the thickness of the bearing insert and the journal diameter, and suggested clearances are indicated in Table 7-3. The best method of checking oil clearance is to use a strip of brass shim stock of the proper thickness (see Fig. 7-14). A shim 0.001 in. thicker than the recommended oil clearance should lock the shaft.

Antifriction bearings for engines. Antifriction bearings—particularly ball bearings—have been used in a few cases for some main bearings of crankshafts. They give less power loss and require little maintenance, but the first cost is higher and installation is more difficult, particularly when intermediate main bearings are necessary.

Crankshaft. The crankshaft, by means of its cranks and the connecting rods, converts the reciprocating movement of the piston into the necessary rotary motion. Most crankshafts are made of medium-carbon steel or a chrome-nickel alloy steel by the drop-forging process. A few high-speed, multiple-cylinder engines use a cast crankshaft, the material having a relatively high carbon and copper content. The casting process is simpler and less expensive because these crankshafts require

Table 7-3. Recommended Oil Clearance for Various Types of Bearings for Pressure Lubrication

Diameter of crankshaft journal or crankpin, in.	Lead or tin-base babbitt, in.		Copper-lead, in.		Plated copper-lead, in.		Aluminum, in.	
	Connecting rod	Main journal	Connecting rod	Main journal	Connecting rod	Main journal	Connecting rod	Main journal
2–2.75	0.0008–0.0025	0.0010–0.0030	0.0015–0.0035	0.0020–0.0040	0.0008–0.0030	0.0010–0.0035	0.0015–0.0035	0.0020–0.0040
2.81–3.50	0.0010–0.0030	0.0015–0.0035	0.0020–0.0040	0.0025–0.0045	0.0010–0.0035	0.0015–0.0040	0.0010–0.0035	0.0015–0.0040
3.56–4.00	0.0020–0.0035		0.0030–0.0045		0.0020–0.0040		0.0035–0.0050	

heavy integral counterweights which make the forging method quite difficult.

The size of the crankshaft, the number of main bearings, and the number and arrangement of the cranks are dependent upon the type, size, and speed of the engine. Figures 7-15 to 7-21 inclusive show a number of typical crankshaft designs. The angle of the cranks with re-

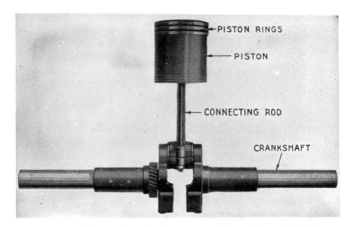

FIG. 7-15. *Single-cylinder counterbalanced crankshaft.*

spect to each other for the crankshaft of a multiple-cylinder engine is determined by the number of cylinders and their arrangement. A symmetrical or balanced arrangement of cranks about the shaft provides better balance and reduces vibration. Crankshafts for high-speed multiple-cylinder engines are equipped with counterweights throughout their length to provide complete balance and to reduce bearing stresses and

FIG. 7-16. *Plain two-cylinder opposed crankshaft.*

wear at high speeds. These weights are usually made integral with the shaft.

The number of main crankshaft bearings often varies even for different engines having the same number of cylinders. For example, a crankshaft for a four-cylinder engine may have two, three, or five main bearings. A six-cylinder crankshaft may have three, four, five, or seven main bearings.

Great improvements have been made in crankshaft manufacture to

FIG. 7-17. *Two-cylinder three-bearing counterbalanced crankshaft.*

FIG. 7-18. *A statically and dynamically balanced two-cylinder crankshaft.*

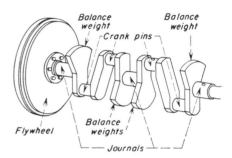

FIG. 7-19. *A statically and dynamically balanced four-cylinder three-bearing crankshaft.*

FIG. 7-20. *A four-cylinder two-bearing crankshaft.*

reduce wear. One process involves the hardening of the surface layer of metal at the journals by an electrical treatment known as induction hardening or electrohardening. Also the entire shaft may be specially heat-treated and a method of precision grinding of the journal surfaces, known as superfinishing, gives this surface a mirror finish, thus reducing friction and wear.

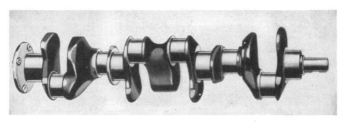

FIG. 7-21. *A statically and dynamically balanced six-cylinder crankshaft.* (Courtesy of Chevrolet Division, General Motors Corporation.)

Flywheel. Flywheels are usually made of cast iron and their primary function is to maintain uniform engine speed by carrying the crankshaft through those intervals when it is not receiving energy from a piston. The size of the flywheel varies with the number of cylinders and the type and size of engine; that is, the greater the number of cylinders, the smaller and lighter the flywheel for the same total piston displacement because of the overlapping power strokes. The flywheel usually carries the ring gear that meshes with the starter pinion for self-cranking. The rear surface or side may be finished very smooth to serve as one of the pressure surfaces for the clutch plate. Engine-timing marks are frequently stamped on the flywheel.

CRANKSHAFT AND ENGINE BALANCE—VIBRATION CONTROL

The trend toward higher operating speeds for automotive engines has introduced new problems in design. One of these is proper mechanical balance and the control of vibration. An unbalanced mechanical condition in an automotive engine not only causes annoying and wear-producing vibration, but creates excessive stresses on the bearings and other supporting parts. These strains induce faster wear and mechanism failures.

Vibration in automotive engines may be caused by any or all of the following:

1. Unbalanced centrifugal forces of rotating members, particularly the crankshaft.

2. Torsional reaction of the crankshaft.

3. Unbalanced inertia forces created by reciprocating parts, particularly the pistons and connecting rods.

4. Torque reaction resulting from effect of the explosions on the cylinders.

Static and dynamic balance. The crankshaft and flywheel are the principal engine parts having sufficient weight and rotative speed to create excessive centrifugal-force reactions. Ordinarily the flywheel is symmetrical in shape; hence, if it is uniform in structure and precision-made, it should have perfect balance at any speed. Therefore, the balance of the crankshaft alone is of major consideration.

A crankshaft should have both *static* and *dynamic* balance. For example, a single-cylinder crankshaft without counterweights is unbalanced statically because, if rotated on frictionless supports, it would stop only in one position—with the crank journal downward. If such a shaft were rotated at any appreciable speed, excessive strains and stresses would be set up within it midway between the supports as well as on the supports themselves, owing to centrifugal force created by the unbalanced crank journal. Now suppose suitable counterweights were added opposite the two crank throws (Fig. 7-15); the shaft if rotated would not come to rest in any one position each time because of static balance. Furthermore, the force reactions during rotation would be almost completely balanced and excessive bearing stresses reduced. The two- and four-cylinder crankshafts (Figs. 7-16 and 7-20, respectively) have static balance, even though they do not have counterweights; that is, the arrangement of the crank journals about the axis is such as to produce static balance.

However, neither one has *dynamic balance*, that is, balance when rotated at any appreciable speed. The centrifugal-force reactions would vary at different points along the shaft axis and thereby set up an unbalanced condition with respect to the shaft as a whole. For example, suppose the crankshaft (Fig. 7-16) is suspended in a vertical position by a strong wire attached on one end at the center point and then rotated at any speed. If there is perfect dynamic balance, it should rotate with its central or longitudinal axis remaining in a true vertical position. This shaft would not do this; the lower or free end would tend to swing outward and travel in a circular path, thus indicating a definite lack of complete balance at all points along the axis. In order to overcome this difficulty, the shaft must be equipped with counterweights (Fig. 7-18). These must be placed as nearly opposite the crank journals and crank throws as possible so that it might be said that perfect static balance exists for any section of the shaft. This explains the purpose of the arrangement of weights found on nearly all multiple-cylinder crankshafts used in automotive engines, even though it may appear that the crank journals and throws, when symmetrically arranged about the shaft axis, should produce complete balance under all conditions. Figures 7-19 and 7-21 show four- and six-cylinder crankshafts, respectively, which are statically and dynamically balanced.

Torsional vibration. Torsional vibration means vibration resulting from the twisting reaction created in the crankshaft by the explosions in the cylinders and the inertia forces in the pistons and connecting rods. This will be more clearly understood by assuming that the crankshaft is made of very strong but slightly resilient rubber instead of steel and that the flywheel on one end is sufficiently heavy to resist any instantaneous changes in speed. When an explosion occurs, the impulse reacts on the crankpin through the piston and connecting rod, and deflects or twists the shaft between that particular crank and the flywheel. When the pressure decreases, the crankpin attains maximum deflection and begins a backward swing. However, it will not stop instantly at its normal position but will swing beyond this point and continue like a pendulum. Now suppose that, before this crankpin ceases to swing, the piston receives another power impulse which reacts on the pin just as it reaches the point of maximum backswing. This will increase the deflection or magnitude of the twisting action, and if this synchronized condition were maintained for any length of time, the shaft might fail. That speed at which such a condition exists is known as the *critical speed* and creates *torsional vibration*. The maximum vibration would be created only when the next explosion occurred on the first backswing of the crankpin. Some torsional reaction may exist in any crankshaft, even at low speed; but excessive reaction and vibration usually appear in the higher speed ranges. This trouble must be avoided or controlled, not only to eliminate the vibration itself but to prevent failure of the shaft.

Torsional vibration is controlled in different ways. If any engine, such as one used in a tractor, for example, operates at a reasonably low speed or within a limited speed range, the shaft can be made of such a size that its normal operating speed does not correspond with the critical speed. Or the shaft may be made very heavy so that any harmful critical speeds are higher than the maximum operating speed.

Most multiple-cylinder automotive engines operating at relatively high speeds have their crankshafts equipped with special devices for controlling torsional vibration. These are commonly known as harmonic balancers or vibration dampers and are built into the fan-belt drive pulley. These devices (Fig. 7-22) consist essentially of two members connected with some degree of flexibility so that, at certain engine speeds, one member vibrates with respect to the other. If this vibration is out of phase with the torsional vibration of the crankshaft, it counteracts the latter and reduces it to some negligible value.

Balance of inertia forces. Complete balance of those engine parts having a reciprocating movement is extremely important in eliminating or reducing vibration. These parts include principally the piston, piston pin, and connecting rod. An inertia force is one created when an object at rest is suddenly placed in motion or when a moving object is suddenly brought to a state of rest. In other words, inertia is that property of matter by virtue of which a body tends to remain at rest or to remain in motion in a straight line. Applying this to an engine piston and con-

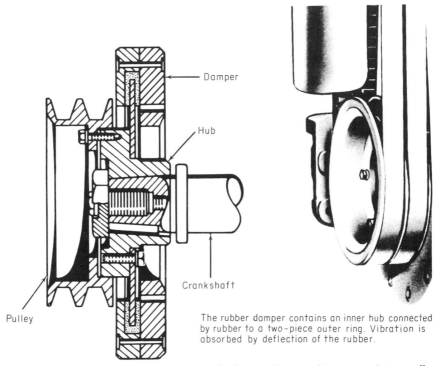

The rubber damper contains an inner hub connected by rubber to a two-piece outer ring. Vibration is absorbed by deflection of the rubber.

FIG. 7-22. *Cross-section view of a torsional vibration damper.* (Courtesy of Caterpillar Tractor Company.)

necting rod, we find that these parts come to rest and change direction of travel twice in one crank revolution. Hence there is a pronounced, continuous, and rapid change of velocity, which in turn sets up definite inertia forces. For example, if the crankshaft has a speed of 1,000 r.p.m., the piston and connecting rod come to rest, change direction of travel, and attain a definite and maximum velocity 2,000 times per minute. These changes in velocity and travel direction set up definite inertia forces which react on the cylinder and create vibration.

The effect and direction of the reaction from inertia forces is determined to a large extent by the cylinder arrangement. For a horizontal engine the forces would act in a horizontal plane, and for a vertical engine they would act vertically. If there were a definite unbalanced

condition in both cases, the vibration would be likely to be more noticeable in the horizontal engine. In a vertical engine the reaction would be
counteracted directly by the total mass or weight of the engine.

The balancing of these inertia forces in order to eliminate vibration
can be accomplished in a number of ways. The problem is more difficult in large, heavy engines with one or two large cylinders than in
light-weight, high-speed engines with several small cylinders. It is almost impossible to eliminate vibration in a large single-cylinder engine.
Counterweighting the crankshaft, as previously explained, will help to
some extent. Using counterweights and arranging the cranks and pistons
for a two-cylinder engine as shown in
Fig. 7-18 will very nearly eliminate the
vibration. Certain inertia force reactions
resulting from the connecting-rod movement are difficult to control completely.
For a two-cylinder engine, the arrangement giving the least vibration is that of
opposed cylinders with opposed cranks.
Vertical, in-line engines with three, four,
six, or eight cylinders and V-type engines
with four, eight, or twelve cylinders
give very little vibration from reciprocating forces if the cranks are properly
arranged.

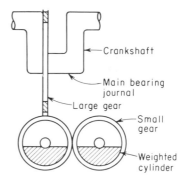

FIG. 7-23. *Lanchester-type vibration damper.*

Some four-cylinder, high-speed engines develop vibration from what
might be called secondary inertia forces. Even though the two end
pistons are equal in weight and move in an opposite direction to the
two inside pistons and all are attached to cranks in the same plane, the
inertia forces are not completely balanced, because, in any engine, the
pistons have a higher velocity during the upper half of the stroke than
during the lower half. The resulting reaction, if excessive, acts along
the vertical center line of the engine, midway between the axes of the
two inner cylinders. It may be transmitted to the front and rear supports of the engine and create undesirable vibration. Lanchester, an
English automotive engineer, developed a device for controlling this
vibration. It consists of a helical gear, attached to one of the crank arms
of the crankshaft, which meshes with another similar gear of one-half
the size located in the bottom of the crankcase and at a right angle to
the larger gear. The small gear meshes with a second one of like size
lying parallel to it. The two small gears are attached to cylinders mounted
on stationary studs and weighted heavier on one side, as shown in Fig.
7-23. These weights revolve in opposite directions and at twice crankshaft speed and are so meshed with each other that the horizontal components of their respective centrifugal forces neutralize each other, while

the vertical components are combined. Therefore, if the weights are properly proportioned, the centrifugal force created by their rotation reacts against the secondary unbalanced force created by the two pairs of pistons in their movement.

REFERENCES

Automotive Engine Bearings, *Lubrication*, May, 1953.

BARGER, E. L., W. M. CARLETON, E. G. McKIBBEN, and ROY BAINER, "Tractors and Their Power Units," John Wiley & Sons, Inc., New York, 1952.

"Engine Bearing Service Manual," 7th ed., Federal Mogul Service, Division of Federal-Mogul-Bower Bearings, Inc., Detroit, Mich., 1956.

"Engine Bearing Manual," Thompson Products, Inc., Cleveland, Ohio, 1954.

HELDT, P. M., "High-speed Combustion Engines," 16th ed., Chilton Company, Philadelphia, 1956.

How Engineers Select Metals for Oil-film Bearing Applications, *Gen. Motors Eng. J.*, Vol. 1, No. 5.

LICHTY, L. C., "Internal Combustion Engines," 6th ed., McGraw-Hill Book Company, Inc., New York, 1951.

Torsional Vibration in Diesel Engines, *Gen. Motors Eng. J.*, Vol. 1, No. 3.

PROBLEMS AND QUESTIONS

1. Describe the materials used for such parts as pistons, cylinder liners, crankshafts, and valves, and give the specific requirements of the materials for each of these parts.

2. Explain the meaning of piston clearance, and give the amount recommended for a 4½-in. plain cast-iron piston and for a similar aluminum-alloy piston.

3. Name the common types of bearing alloys, and explain the specific qualities and application of each.

4. Explain fully how crankshafts are designed to obtain proper balance under all conditions, and give the effects of a poorly balanced crankshaft.

5. Explain the meaning of inertia forces, and state how the reactions from them are controlled in high-speed engines.

6. Given two eight-cylinder engines of equal size, speed, and power but one having an in-line cylinder arrangement and the other a V-8 arrangement, which one would probably need a torsional vibration damper? Why?

8

Engine Cycles and Principles of Operation

The mechanical device or machine which converts the heat energy of some combustible material into usable power is called an engine or a motor. The basic requirement of such a machine is that it must carry out this conversion process in a continuous, efficient, practical, and reliable manner.

General types of gas and liquid-fuel engines. Three distinct types of engines have been developed for utilizing gaseous and liquid fuels. These are (1) the reciprocating or piston-type engine, (2) the gas-turbine engine, and (3) the jet engine. Although engines of all three types have been developed which operate successfully, the piston-type engine has proved to be best adapted to a wide range of applications such as automobiles, trucks, tractors, locomotives, airplanes, boats, and many others.

The gas-turbine engine and jet-engine types of power units have limited application. Attempts have been made to adapt and utilize them for automotive-vehicle power but certain difficulties and disadvantages are encountered, the chief of which are (1) a low thermal efficiency and (2) effective lubrication under high-temperature conditions. Other problems are driving accessories such as fuel, oil, and coolant pumps, and starting equipment. Recent experimental and research efforts in this area are concerned with the "free-piston" type of turbine engine and its adaptability to automotive equipment. Experimental machines have been built which operate reasonably well, but engineers are still confronted with certain serious problems and disadvantages which must be overcome before commercial production and practical use are possible. For this reason, this chapter and textbook are concerned specifically with the piston-type engine and its basic working cycles.

Cycle of operations. Any internal-combustion engine, regardless of size, number of cylinders, use, and so on, is of either one or the other of two general types. These are known as the four-stroke-cycle type and the two-stroke-cycle type, or, as more commonly stated, four-cycle and two-cycle. A cycle consists of the events taking place in each cylinder of an engine between two successive explosions in that cylinder. These events or operations, in the order in which they occur, are as follows: (1) the taking in of a combustible mixture, (2) the compression of this mixture, (3) the ignition of the compressed mixture, (4) the expansion of the burned gases producing the power, and (5) the exhaust of the products of combustion.

In the two-stroke-cycle engine, two strokes of the piston or one revolution of the crankshaft is required to complete this cycle. In the four-stroke-cycle type, four strokes of the piston or two complete revolutions of the crankshaft are needed, and the four strokes are frequently referred to as intake, compression, power, and exhaust. It must be kept in mind that, in engines of more than one cylinder, this cycle of events must be carried out in each of the cylinders; that is, one cylinder cannot perform the first event and another perform the second, and so on. Also the events can take place only in the order stated. A better understanding of these principles of operation may be obtained by referring to the following explanation and illustrations.

Two-stroke-cycle operation. Two important characteristics of two-stroke-cycle construction must be noted and kept in mind: (1) that ports or openings in the cylinder walls at some distance below the head serve as intake and exhaust valves; and (2) that the open or crank end of the engine cylinder is completely enclosed. Referring to Fig. 8-1A, the piston in its upward travel has closed the ports e and h and is compressing the charge. At the same time the crankcase volume is being increased and the fuel mixture is drawn into the crankcase through an opening d, to be compressed on the next downward stroke of the piston and forced through a connecting passage f into the combustion space when the inlet port e is uncovered. Near the end of the upward or compression stroke of the piston the spark is produced and the compressed charge is fired. The explosion and resulting expansion send the piston downward on its power stroke (Fig. 8-1B), near the end of which the two ports are uncovered as shown by Fig. 8-1C. Even though the piston is nearly at the end of its stroke, considerable pressure remains in the cylinder, thus forcing the products of combustion out through the exhaust port h. At the same time, the fresh mixture in the crankcase has been compressed on the downward stroke and passes upward through the intake port to the combustion chamber as shown. The piston has now completed two strokes, and the crankshaft has made one revolution, thus completing the cycle.

Figure 8-2 illustrates the three-port type of two-stroke-cycle engine in which the fuel mixture enters the crankcase through a third port, which is uncovered by the piston on its upward travel.

Two-stroke-cycle-engine characteristics. Two-stroke-cycle engines have the following distinguishing mechanical characteristics: (1) the crank-case is enclosed and must be as airtight as possible; (2) ports or open-

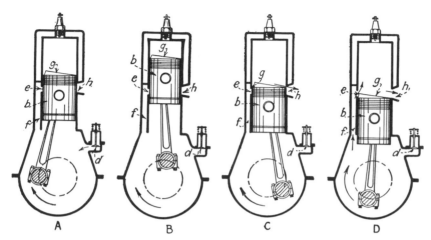

FIG. 8-1. *Two-port two-stroke-cycle engine operation.*

ings in the side of the cylinder, opened and closed by the piston slid-ing over them, take the place of valves; (3) no valve-operating mecha-nism of any kind is necessary; (4) the fuel mixture usually enters and

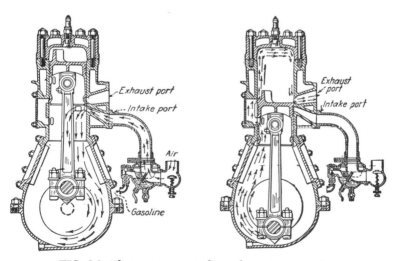

FIG. 8-2. *Three-port two-stroke-cycle engine operation.*

passes through the crankcase on its way to the cylinder; and (5) the cylinder is usually vertical.

Some of the important advantages of two-stroke-cycle engines are as follows: (1) they are lighter in weight per horsepower; (2) they are simpler in construction; (3) they have a greater frequency of working strokes or power impulses; and (4) they usually operate in either direction. Some disadvantages are as follows: (1) their fuel mixture is controlled with difficulty; (2) they are inefficient in fuel consumption; (3) they do not operate satisfactorily under fluctuating loads; (4) their speed and corresponding power are not readily controlled; and (5) their cooling and lubrication are more difficult. Two-stroke-cycle engines are usually inefficient in fuel consumption and frequently give considerable trouble in starting and during operation, largely because complete exhaust of the burned fuel residue is extremely difficult. Likewise, the problem of producing the correct fuel mixture and placing it in the cylinder is a difficult one. Unless such an engine is in perfect condition and correctly adjusted at all times, trouble will be apt to develop.

Some diesel engines utilize the two-stroke-cycle principle very successfully. Since they use fuel injection rather than carburetion, certain disadvantages and difficulties enumerated above are not encountered.

It might be assumed that a two-stroke-cycle engine of a certain bore, stroke, and speed would develop twice as much power as a four-stroke engine of the same size and speed, because it would have twice as many power strokes in a given time. Such is not the case, however, because it is impossible to get as effective a charge of fuel mixture into the cylinder.

The removal of the burned residue from the cylinder is dependent entirely upon the pressure remaining in the cylinder being somewhat greater than that existing on the outside when the exhaust port is opened. There is not a distinct exhaust stroke, as in the four-stroke-cycle engine, to push this material out; therefore its complete expulsion is unlikely, and the incoming fuel charge may be thus contaminated and its effectiveness reduced. To prevent the possible escape of a portion of the incoming fuel mixture through the exhaust port before the piston has closed the latter, a projection known as a deflector, shown by g in Fig. 8-1, is placed on the closed end of the piston at the point where it passes the intake port. As the name implies, this device deflects the charge in an upward direction toward the cylinder head.

Four-stroke-cycle operation. Figure 8-3 shows the usual four-stroke-cycle construction and operation. It will be observed, first of all, that an enclosed crankcase is unnecessary and that valves located in the cylinder head are used instead of ports. Starting with the piston at the head end of the cylinder, it moves toward the crank end, drawing in a fuel mixture through the open inlet valve. Soon after the end of this stroke, the inlet or suction valve closes and the mixture is compressed as the piston returns to the head end of the cylinder. Near the completion of this stroke a spark is produced that ignites the charge, causing an explosion which, in turn, sends the piston on the third or power stroke. Near the end of this stroke the exhaust valve is opened, and the burned residue is completely removed from the cylinder as the piston travels backward toward the cylinder head on what is known as the exhaust

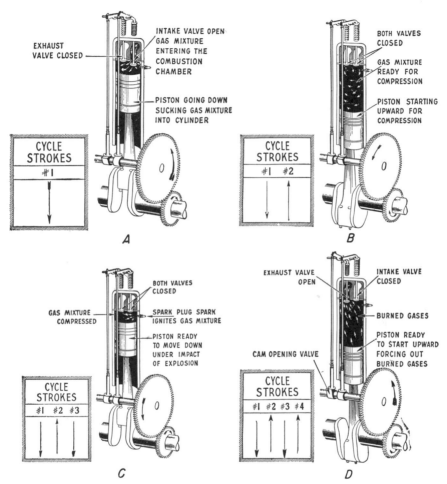

FIG. 8-3. *Four-stroke-cycle operation.* (A) *Intake stroke.* (B) *Compression stroke.* (C) *Power stroke.* (D) *Exhaust stroke.*

stroke. The piston has now passed through four complete strokes, the crankshaft has made two revolutions, and a cycle has been completed. It is thus observed that the two-stroke-cycle single-cylinder engine has a power impulse for each revolution of the crankshaft, and that the four-stroke-cycle single-cylinder engine gives one power impulse in two revolutions. This explains why heavy flywheels are necessary on one-cylinder engines. Were it not for these flywheels, such an engine when under load would have a tendency to lose speed between explosions. These fly-wheels, owing to their inertia, carry the piston through these so-called idle strokes in spite of the resistance offered by the load and thus maintain uniformity of speed. A one-cylinder two-stroke-cycle engine will not require so heavy a flywheel as the four-stroke, because it fires twice as frequently.

Multiple-cylinder operation. As previously stated, these principles of operation likewise apply to multiple-cylinder engines. That is, a four-cylinder four-stroke-cycle engine is nothing more than four single-

Crankshaft has Turned (Degrees)	Cylinder No. 1	Cylinder No. 2
180 — 360	Power	Intake
540 — 720	Exhaust	Compression
	Intake	Power
	Compression	Exhaust

FIG. 8-4. *Chart showing occurrence of events in a two-cylinder four-stroke-cycle engine with crank arrangement shown in Fig. 8-5B.*

cylinder four-stroke-cycle engines built into a single unit; or a two-cylinder two-stroke-cycle engine is nothing more than two single-cylinder two-stroke-cycle engines built into a single unit. A better understanding of the application of these principles to multiple-cylinder engines may be obtained by reference to the following illustrations and explanations.

Figure 8-5A illustrates the usual construction of a two-stroke-cycle two-cylinder engine. Note that the crankshaft consists of two opposite cranks; therefore, the pistons will move in opposite directions at all times. A cycle will be completed in each cylinder at every revolution of the crankshaft, but a power impulse or explosion will occur at every half turn, or there will be two explosions per revolution. Figure 8-5B illustrates a typical two-cylinder four-stroke-cycle engine layout. Note that the cranks on the crankshaft are arranged side by side and that the two pistons move together. By reference to the accompanying chart (Fig. 8-4), it will be noted that there will be two power impulses during two revolutions of the crankshaft or one power impulse for each revolution; that is, when piston 1 is on the power stroke, piston 2 is on intake, and so on. It is possible so to construct this engine that both pistons would be doing the same thing at the same time and, consequently, both explosions would come at the same instant, but such construction is never used in practice.

The crank and cylinder arrangement (Fig. 8-5A) also could be used for a four-stroke-cycle, two-cylinder engine, and the chart (Fig. 8-6) shows the power impulse and stroke relationship. It will be noted that the power impulses occur at unequal intervals, namely, 180 and 540 deg., but this cannot be avoided in this type of engine. It would appear that this uneven power flow would be undesirable. However, if such an engine were running at any appreciable speed—500 or more r.p.m.—there would not be any noticeable effect. The arrangement

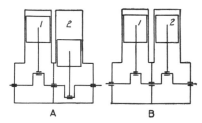

FIG. 8-5. *Crank arrangements for two-cylinder twin engines.* (A) *Opposed cranks.* (B) *Twin cranks.*

shown in Fig. 8-5B gives an equal firing interval—360 deg., according to the diagram (Fig. 8-4)—but is less preferable because of difficulty in securing mechanical balance and therefore the least possible vibration. The opposed-crank arrangement for two-cylinder twin engines seems to be preferable in spite of its unequal firing interval.

Crankshaft has Turned(Degrees)	Cylinder No. 1	Cylinder No. 2
180 360 540 720	Power	Compression
	Exhaust	Power
	Intake	Exhaust
	Compression	Intake

FIG. 8-6. *Chart showing occurrence of events in a two-cylinder four-stroke-cycle engine with opposed cranks.*

Figure 8-7 illustrates the usual four-cylinder four-stroke-cycle construction. Four-cylinder crankshafts are always arranged as shown; that is, cranks 1 and 4 are together and opposite cranks 2 and 3. Referring to the chart (Fig. 8-8) and assuming that piston 1 has just received

a power impulse so that it is on the power stroke, piston 4 must necessarily be on the intake stroke. If piston 2 is now placed on the compression stroke, piston 3 must necessarily be on the exhaust stroke. Com-

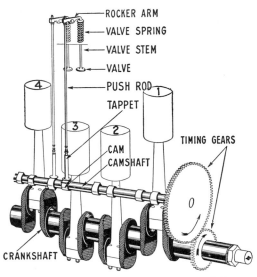

FIG. 8-7. *Typical four-cylinder four-stroke-cycle engine crankshaft and valve operation.*

pleting the chart by filling in the strokes for the four pistons in the correct
order, the *firing order* becomes 1-2-4-3.

A second firing order is likewise possible, as shown by the chart (Fig.

Crankshaft has Turned (Degrees)	Cylinder No. 1	Cylinder No. 2	Cylinder No. 3	Cylinder No. 4
180 360 540 720	Power	Compression	Exhaust	Intake
	Exhaust	Power	Intake	Compression
	Intake	Exhaust	Compression	Power
	Compression	Intake	Power	Exhaust

FIG. 8-8. *Chart showing occurrence of events in a four-cylinder four-stroke-cycle
engine having a 1-2-4-3 firing order.*

8-9); that is, again assuming that piston 1 is on the power stroke and piston 4 on the intake stroke, piston 2 could be on exhaust and piston 3 on
compression. Thus the firing order becomes 1-3-4-2. These are the only

firing orders possible, however, with such a crankshaft and crank arrangement. Both firing orders are used in four-cylinder four-stroke-cycle engines, and neither has any particular advantage over the other.

The particular firing order used is determined by the order in which the intake or exhaust valves operate and by the order in which the sparks are delivered to the cylinders. Given two four-cylinder four-stroke-cycle engines, one having a firing order of 1-2-4-3 and the other of 1-3-4-2, the

Crankshaft has Turned (Degrees)	Cylinder No.1	Cylinder No 2	Cylinder No.3	Cylinder No. 4
180 _ 360	_Power_	Exhaust	Compression	Intake
540 _ 720	Exhaust	Intake	_Power_	Compression
	Intake	Compression	Exhaust	_Power_
	Compression	_Power_	Intake	Exhaust

FIG. 8-9. *Chart showing occurrence of events in a four-cylinder four-stroke-cycle engine having a 1-3-4-2 firing order.*

FIG. 8-10. *Cutaway view of a V-type four-cylinder air-cooled engine.* (Courtesy of Wisconsin Motor Corporation.)

principal mechanical difference will be in the arrangement of the cams on the camshaft (Fig. 8-7) that operate the valves. These principles of operation likewise apply to engines having six, eight, or any number of cylinders, and the proper distribution of the explosions and the firing order are obtained by the correct crank arrangement and valve operation.

Figure 8-10 illustrates a four-cylinder V-type engine. This gives an extremely compact arrangement, but an equal power-impulse distribution cannot be obtained because the V angle is 90 deg. and at some time or

FIG. 8-11. *Crank arrangement for a six-cylinder engine.*

another two opposite cylinders must follow each other; that is, there must be a 90-deg. interval. The crankshaft for this engine has the four cranks arranged in one plane, similar to the standard four-cylinder type. The firing interval is 90-180-270-180 deg.

Six-cylinder crankshafts are constructed as shown in Fig. 8-11; that is, crank 1 is paired with crank 6, crank 2 with crank 5, and crank 3 with crank 4. The three pairs are then arranged so as to make 120 deg. with each other. With such an arrangement, three cylinders fire during each revolution of the crankshaft, and a common firing order is 1-5-3-6-2-4.

Eight-cylinder engines may have the cylinders in line or in two sets of four each, forming a 90-deg. V. An eight-in-line crankshaft has four pairs of cranks. They are usually paired, as shown by Fig. 8-12. This gives a firing order of 1-6-2-5-8-3-7-4. The crankshaft for a V-8 engine is similar to a four-cylinder crankshaft; that is, there are only four crank journals, and two connecting rods—one for each cylinder bank—are connected side by side to each crank journal.

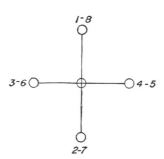

FIG. 8-12. *Crank arrangement for an eight-cylinder in-line engine.*

All cranks may be in the same plane as in a standard four-cylinder crankshaft, or they may be at 90 deg. to each other. The firing order would be determined largely by the crankshaft type. The V-8 type of cylinder arrangement (Fig. 8-13) is used extensively in automobiles and trucks because of compactness of design along with good speed and power flexibility.

Firing interval. It should now be clear that the advantage of an engine's having more than one cylinder is that it fires more frequently—

that is, there are more explosions in the same number of revolutions of the crankshaft—and consequently the power is said to be more uniform. The greater the number of cylinders, the shorter the distance moved by the crankshaft between two successive explosions in the engine.

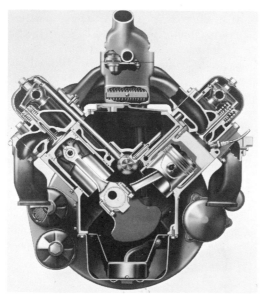

FIG. 8-13. *Cross section showing construction of a typical V-8 automotive-type engine.* (Courtesy of Reo Division, White Motor Company.)

The arc of travel of the crankshaft in degrees between successive explosions in an engine is known as the firing interval. For most multiple-cylinder engines it can be determined by the formula

$$\text{Firing interval} = \frac{360}{\text{no. cylinders}} \quad \text{for a two-stroke-cycle engine}$$

$$\text{Firing interval} = \frac{720}{\text{no. cylinders}} \quad \text{for a four-stroke-cycle engine}$$

Assuming that energy from any piston is applied to the crankshaft of the conventional four-stroke-cycle engine during 135 deg. of its rotation, it will be observed that, for a four-cylinder engine, there will be a 45-deg. no-energy interval before the next cylinder fires and releases energy to the crankshaft. However, for engines having more than four cylinders, there will be an overlapping of power impulses because the firing interval will be less than 135 deg. Obviously, this will provide more uniform power and speed, faster acceleration, and better speed flexibility and torque characteristics. A few engines, as previously explained, have an unequal firing interval. For example, most two-cylinder, four-stroke-cycle engines have opposed cranks and fire 180-540 deg., and a V-4 engine fires 90-180-270-180 deg. However, this unequal interval does not affect the power and smoothness of operation at normal running speeds.

REFERENCES

BARGER, E. L., W. M. CARLETON, E. G. McKIBBEN, and ROY BAINER, "Tractors and Their Power Units," John Wiley & Sons, Inc., New York, 1952.

Free Piston Engines, *Lubrication*, September, 1958.

HELDT, P. M., "High-speed Combustion Engines," 16th ed., Chilton Company, Philadelphia, 1956.

MOSES, BEN D., and KENNETH R. FROST, "Farm Power," John Wiley & Sons, Inc., New York, 1952.

Some Principles and Applications of the Free-piston Engine, *Gen. Motors Eng. J.*, Vol. 5, No. 3.

PROBLEMS AND QUESTIONS

1. Compare two- and four-stroke-cycle engines as to simplicity of design, efficiency, power, utility, and general adaptability to various power applications.

2. Compute the firing interval and total number of explosions per minute for a V-12, four-stroke-cycle engine having a crankshaft speed of 3,200 r.p.m.

9

Tractor-engine Types and Construction

The first gas tractors built were equipped with large slow-speed horizontal engines having only one or two cylinders. Obviously, these engines required a strong frame, large wheels, and other supporting parts. Consequently the tractors themselves were very heavy, were difficult to start and handle, and had considerable vibration. Later on, when the possibilities of lighter weight tractors were observed, designers turned their attention toward the use of a higher speed, lighter weight power plant having at least two, and possibly four, cylinders, such as those used in trucks and automobiles. The result is that the trend in the tractor industry, as in automotive design, has been toward engines having two, four, or six cylinders, with lighter weight and higher operating speeds.

Tractor-engine characteristics. Tractor power plants may be classified as two-cylinder twin horizontal engines and as four- and six-cylinder vertical engines. All tractor engines are either of the four-stroke-cycle heavy-duty carbureting type or of the diesel type. Gasoline, LP gas, distillates, and diesel fuels are the predominating fuels.

Horizontal two-cylinder engines. The horizontal, two-cylinder-type engine (Fig. 9-1) has been used by a number of leading manufacturers in the past and is still found in some makes. The advantages claimed for it are: (1) it has fewer and heavier parts with slower speed and, therefore, less wear and longer life; (2) it has greater accessibility; and (3) its belt pulley is driven direct and not through gears, because the crankshaft is placed crosswise on the frame.

A two-cylinder engine with opposed cylinders and cranks was used in some early tractors. This construction permits an equal firing interval and provides good mechanical balance but offers other serious objections such as (1) difficult manifolding and fuel-mixture distribution because of the scattered arrangement of the cylinders; (2) inaccessibility of bearings and other working parts; and (3) lack of compactness of mechanism, which is desirable from the standpoint of lubrication and adjustment.

FIG. 9-1. *Cutaway view of a two-cylinder horizontal tractor engine.*

Vertical three-cylinder engines. Figure 9-2 shows a crankshaft for a three-cylinder vertical engine. Some diesel tractors use a three-cylinder, two-stroke-cycle engine.

FIG. 9-2. *A crankshaft for a three-cylinder engine.*

Four-cylinder engines. The vertical four-cylinder type of engine, placed lengthwise of the frame, predominates in the tractor field at the present time. Some of the reasons for this are (1) good weight distribution is secured; (2) manifolding and fuel-mixture distribution are simplified; (3) uniform and positive cylinder and bearing lubrication is facilitated; (4) vibratory effects caused either by moving parts or by the explosions act in a vertical plane and are thus less noticeable and nullified by the engine and tractor weight itself; (5) valve mechanisms, ignition devices, and other parts are made more accessible; (6) the clutch and transmission parts can be assembled in such a way as to give the entire machine a balanced construction and symmetrical appearance.

Six-cylinder engines. The six-cylinder engine is being used in several makes and models of tractors. A six-cylinder engine will produce somewhat smoother power and less vibration than an engine with fewer cylinders. The cranks are always arranged as shown in Fig. 8-11, and the usual firing order is 1-5-3-6-2-4.

Features of tractor-engine design. There is now a much greater similarity in tractor-engine construction and design than in former years. Such features as valve-in-head construction, removable cylinder sleeves, and cylinders cast en bloc are used in a majority of cases. Tractor engines are classed as heavy-duty engines; that is, castings, pistons, crankshafts, bearings, valves, and practically all important parts are made heavier and larger than would be necessary in an automobile engine, in order to withstand the unusually heavy strains and continuous heavy loads to which they are subjected.

Cylinders are cast en bloc, that is, all in one casting (Fig. 7-2), for the small and medium sizes of tractors. Larger engines may have the cylinders cast in pairs.

Tractor-engine cylinders are subjected to rather rapid wear, which eventually causes excessive power losses and oil pumping. If the block is not equipped with removable cylinder liners (Fig. 9-3), the trouble can be remedied either by replacement with a new block or by reboring the old block and using oversize pistons. Most tractor engines use removable cylinder liners. The cylinder construction and sleeve removal are shown in Fig. 9-3. The usual practice is to use new factory-fitted pistons with the new liners.

Cylinder heads for tractor engines are cast separately from the block. This permits ready access to the combustion chamber for cleaning out carbon deposits and for valve servicing. With the valves located in the cylinder head, valve reconditioning and adjustment are simplified.

Tractor pistons are, in most cases, made of cast iron with three to five rings. Piston pins are made hollow and usually are of the floating type (Fig. 7-4). Piston-pin wear is usually overcome in tractors by replacement of the bronze bushings.

Crankshafts and bearings. All tractor crankshafts are one-piece drop forgings, which have been carefully machined, heat-treated, and precision finished. Two-cylinder crankshafts may have two main bearings (Fig. 7-16) or three main bearings (Fig. 7-17).

Four-cylinder crankshafts may have two or three main bearings, as shown by Figs. 7-20 and 7-19, respectively. The fewer the bearings, the larger the shaft diameter. The three-bearing crankshaft is most common. Six-cylinder crankshafts may have either three or four main bearings. Both the main and the crank journals are very accurately machined and ground to within 0.001 or 0.002 in. of the specified dimension.

Insert-type liners are used for both the main and crank journals on nearly all tractors. These may be standard tin-base babbitt inserts in the case of smaller engines or special heavy-duty bearing alloys in the case of larger engines.

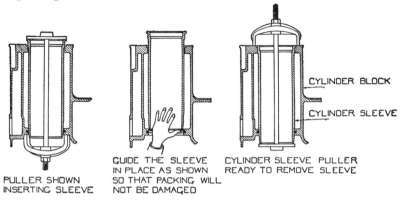

PULLER SHOWN
INSERTING SLEEVE

GUIDE THE SLEEVE
IN PLACE AS SHOWN
SO THAT PACKING WILL
NOT BE DAMAGED

CYLINDER SLEEVE PULLER
READY TO REMOVE SLEEVE

CYLINDER BLOCK

CYLINDER SLEEVE

FIG. 9-3. *Method of removing and replacing cylinder liner.*

Bore and stroke. The size of an engine is determined to a large extent by the cylinder diameter or bore, the length of stroke of the piston, and the total number of cylinders. There is no standard relationship between the cylinder bore and length of stroke but, in general, the stroke is 1.1 to 1.3 times the bore. An engine having a stroke greater than 1.3 times its bore would be considered a long-stroke engine. The trend in multiple-cylinder, high-speed engines is toward a shorter stroke compared with the bore. For example, in many automobile engines, the length of stroke is less than the cylinder bore. A stroke-to-bore ratio of 1.00 or less is particularly advantageous in very high-speed engines of six or more cylinders for the following reasons: (1) it makes possible some reduction in the amount of material needed in the engine; that is, the engine weight per horsepower can be reduced since the crank throws are shorter; (2) a shorter crank radius reduces the total moment of inertia of the crankshaft and thus reduces the probability of vibration at high speeds; (3) piston speeds and ring contact areas are less for any given crankshaft speed, which in turn means less cylinder wall and ring wear (see Table 9-1); (4) more cylinder head area is available to permit the use of larger valves, if needed. Assuming a given piston displacement, the effect of different bore-stroke ratios on the piston speed and ring contact area per stroke is shown in Table 9-1.

Table 9-1. Relationship of Bore-Stroke Ratio to Piston Speed and Ring-contact Area

Bore and stroke, in.	Piston displacement, cu. in.	Bore-stroke ratio	Piston speed at 2,000 r.p.m, ft. per min.	Top ring contact area per stroke, sq. in.
$3^{13}\!/_{16} \times 3$	34	0.79	1,000	35.9
$3\frac{1}{2} \times 3\frac{1}{2}$	34	1.00	1,167	38.5
$3\frac{3}{8} \times 3\frac{3}{4}$	34	1.11	1,250	40.0
$3^{9}\!/_{32} \times 4$	34	1.22	1,333	41.3
$3^{3}\!/_{16} \times 4\frac{1}{4}$	34	1.38	1,417	42.6

Compression ratio. The compression ratio of an engine is the ratio of the cylinder volume existing when the piston is on bottom or crank dead center and the volume remaining above the piston when it reaches top or head dead center. For example, in Fig. 9-4, if the total cylinder volume with the piston on bottom dead center is 120 cu. in. and this is reduced to 20 cu. in. when the piston reaches top dead center, the compression ratio is the relationship of 120:20 or 6:1. As previously explained in Chap. 6, the power and over-all operating efficiency of an en-

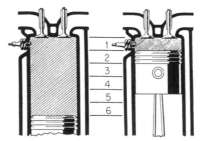

FIG. 9-4. *Sketch showing measurement of compression ratio.*

gine is dependent to a large extent upon its compression ratio; that is, in general, high compression ratios give better fuel utilization and thermal efficiency. However, as explained in Chap. 11, the fuel type and characteristics, the type of ignition system used, and other design factors determine the maximum practical compression ratio which can be used in an engine. In general, compression ratios as related to fuel type and quality are as shown in Table 9-2.

Piston displacement and engine speeds. The power output of an engine is largely determined by its piston displacement and crankshaft speed. Piston displacement is the space swept through by the piston in moving from one end of its stroke to the other and is expressed in cubic inches. For a single-cylinder engine, it is the cross-sectional area of the piston or cylinder multiplied by the length of stroke of the piston. For a multiple-cylinder engine, the total piston displacement is equal to the piston displacement of one cylinder, multiplied by the number of cylinders. For example, a $4\frac{1}{2}$- by 6-in. cylinder is one having a $4\frac{1}{2}$-in. bore

Table 9-2. Engine Compression Ratios for Different Fuels

Fuel	Compression ratio	
	Min.	Max.
Kerosene..........................	4.0 to 1	5.0 to 1
Distillate or tractor fuel............	4.7 to 1	5.2 to 1
Gasoline, regular grade.............	5.5 to 1	7.5 to 1
Gasoline, premium grade..........	7.0 to 1	9.0 to 1
Gasoline, special premium grade....	9.5 to 1	10.5 to 1
LP gas...........................	8.0 to 1	9.0 to 1
Diesel fuel.......................	13.5 to 1	18.0 to 1

or diameter and a 6-in. piston stroke. If it had but one cylinder, the piston displacement would be calculated as follows:

$$\text{Area of cylinder} = (\tfrac{1}{2}\ \text{bore})^2 \times \pi$$

$$= (2.25)^2 \times 3.1416$$

$$= 15.9 \text{ sq. in.}$$

$$\text{Piston displacement} = \text{area of cylinder} \times \text{stroke}$$

$$= 15.9 \times 6$$

$$= 95.4 \text{ cu. in.}$$

A four-cylinder engine would have 4×95.4 cu. in., or 381.6 cu. in. displacement.

Assuming that this engine has a crankshaft speed of 1,000 r.p.m., its total piston displacement per minute would be $2 \times 1,000 \times 381.6$, or 763,200 cu. in. If its power rating were 50 hp., then the piston displacement per minute per horsepower would be 15,264 cu. in. A study of tractor-engine tests shows that the piston displacement per minute per horsepower ranges from 13,500 to 17,000 cu. in., depending upon the operating efficiency. Hence the total piston displacement per minute of an engine is a reasonably good indicator of its maximum power output.

REFERENCES

BARGER, E. L., W. M. CARLETON, E. G. McKIBBEN, and ROY BAINER, "Tractors and Their Power Units," John Wiley & Sons, Inc., New York, 1952.

HELDT, P. M., "High-speed Internal Combustion Engines," 16th ed., Chilton Company, Philadelphia, 1956.

MOSES, BEN D., and KENNETH R. FROST, "Farm Power," John Wiley & Sons, Inc., New York, 1952.

PROBLEMS AND QUESTIONS

1. Discuss the trend in tractor-engine design, and give the principal design characteristics of such an engine.

2. What are the advantages of removable cylinder liners and why are they particularly desirable in a tractor engine?

3. To what extent and why is the compression ratio selected for an engine affected by the kind or type of fuel to be used?

4. An engine has a 3¾-in. bore and 3⅜-in. stroke. Compute the bore-stroke ratio, the piston displacement, and the top-ring contact area per stroke.

5. Tractor A has a two-cylinder engine with 5¾- by 8-in. cylinders and develops 48.6 hp. at 1,000 r.p.m. Tractor B has a four-cylinder engine with 4½- by 5½-in. cylinders and develops 51.8 hp. at 1,400 r.p.m. Compare the two engines with respect to total piston displacement and piston displacement per minute per horsepower.

10

Valves and Valve Operation

As stated in the preceding discussion, a single-cylinder engine has at least two ports or two valves, depending upon whether it is of the two-or the four-stroke-cycle type, respectively. The intake port or valve allows the fuel mixture to enter the combustion chamber on the intake stroke. The exhaust port or valve allows the products of combustion to escape following the explosion and expansion. As previously mentioned, some two-stroke-cycle engines have three ports, the extra port serving as a passage for the fuel from the fuel tank and carburetor to the crankcase.

Since the ports in a two-stroke-cycle engine are nothing more than openings in the cylinder wall that are opened and closed by the piston in its movement, no special valve-operating mechanism is required and the problem of valve timing is not present. The following information, therefore, applies to the four-stroke type of engine entirely.

Valve construction. Gas-engine valves are of the poppet or mushroom type (Fig. 10-1). The valve itself consists of a flat head with a beveled edge called the face, and the

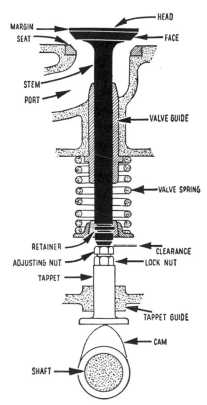

FIG. 10-1. *L-head valve construction and operation.*

stem. The valve opening in the cylinder block or head has a similar beveled edge called the seat. A strong spring, held in place by a retainer and key or wedge, holds the valve face tightly against the seat and thus prevents leakage on the compression and power strokes. The usual face and seat angle is 45 deg. However, a 30-deg. angle is frequently used for intake valves.

Valves are subject to considerable strain and wear owing to the high temperature to which they are exposed and the speed at which they must operate. Obviously the exhaust valve becomes much hotter than the intake because it is exposed to an almost continuous flame. In fact, it probably attains a dull red heat under load conditions. In order to resist breakage, corrosion, warping, and rapid wear, exhaust valves are made of special alloy steels containing relatively high percentages of chromium, nickel, and silicon as well as smaller amounts of other metals. Inlet valves operate much cooler and therefore are less subject to burning, corrosion, and wear. The composition of some typical steel alloys for valves is shown in Table 10-1. The stem of the valve need not be as hard as the head but must be hard enough to resist rapid wear. Sometimes the end is hardened to reduce tappet or rocker-arm wear.

Table 10-1. Steel Alloys for Values

Element	Intake, per cent	Exhaust, per cent
Carbon.........	0.45– 0.80	0.20 - 0.70
Chromium......	0.50–20.00	15.00–21.00
Manganese.....	0.40– 0.90	0.60– 9.00
Nickel.........	0.55– 1.30	1.90–11.50
Silicon.........	0.30– 3.30	0.15– 3.00

The valve stem operates in a sleeve or guide. In a few cases, the guide is merely a hole bored in the block or head, but in most automotive engines the guide is removable. It may be either one-piece or split and is usually made of cast iron. The valve stem should work freely in the guide, but the clearance should be limited in order to prevent leakage and to permit the valve to seat properly.

Sodium-cooled valves. Airplane engines and other types of heavy-duty engines have large valves which may reach excessive temperatures under certain conditions. Valve-temperature control and reduction are often obtained by the use of sodium. The valve stem and head are hollow and the space is partly filled with metallic sodium (see Fig. 10-2). This material has a high heat conductivity characteristic and melts at about

207°F. The rapid reciprocating movement of the valve results in a rapid movement of the liquid sodium from the head of the stem and back again, which, in turn, provides a faster transfer of the heat away from the valve head. The operating temperature of sodium-filled valves is estimated to be from 200 to 400°F. lower than that of solid valves operating under like conditions.

Valve rotators. Effective and positive valve operation is extremely important in obtaining efficient engine performance. The valve must have

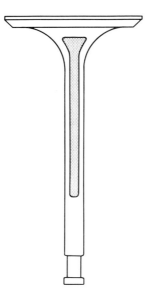

complete freedom of action and remain free of any deposits on the face, seat, and stem. Exhaust valves, particularly, are subject to certain troubles arising from the high temperatures and the resulting deposits of combustion products. The normal operation of a simple poppet valve involves only reciprocating movement of the stem and head. It is quite evident that if the valve can be given some slight rotative movement with respect to its seat, more uniform wear, longer life, and cooler operation will be attained. The first successful valve rotators were developed about 1945 and are now used extensively in tractor, diesel, truck, and other heavy-duty engines. In general, rotators are used only on exhaust valves but a few engines use them on the intake valves.

FIG. 10-2. *Sodium-cooled valve.*

Two principal types of mechanisms have been developed to provide valve rotation. The first is the release-type rotator (Fig. 10-3). The mechanism is composed of a special valve-spring retainer A, a cup B, and a pair of half-round keys or locks C. A special key groove in the valve stem D is required with this type of rotator. By means of the clearance E between the valve-spring tip and rotator cap, the cap, keys, retainer, and valve spring are lifted by the rocker arm or cam follower before the valve is moved. This arrangement momentarily releases the valve from its spring load and thus allows it to turn as it is lifted off its seat. Turning or rotation is induced by forces arising from vibrations of the valve train.

The other type of rotator in general use is a positive type known as the *Rotocap* (Fig. 10-4) which turns the valve by the positive action of the mechanism. The Rotocap replaces the standard valve-spring retainer in most instances, although it is sometimes placed between the valve spring and its seat in the cylinder head or block. In the valve-closed position, the spring washer A rests lightly under the steel balls B which are held at the top of their inclined races by small coil springs D. As the valve opens, the Rotocap is compressed, thereby flattening the washer and forcing the balls down the inclined races. As the balls roll down the races, they cause the spring washer and retainer cap C to turn a slight amount with respect to each other, thus rotating the valve.

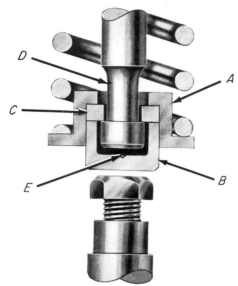

FIG. 10-3. *Release-type valve rotator.* (Courtesy of Ethyl Corporation.)

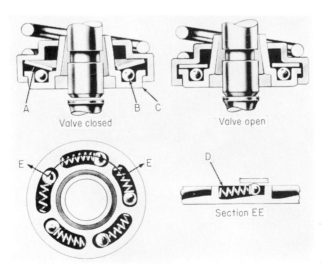

FIG. 10-4. *Positive-type valve rotator.* (Courtesy of Ethyl Corporation.)

Valve springs. The basic function of the valve spring is to close the valve after it has been opened and to hold it tightly closed against its

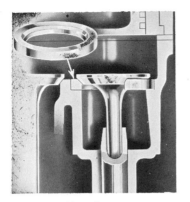

seat. Furthermore, modern, high-speed engines require that each valve complete its open-and-close cycle in a fraction of a second. For example, each valve in a single-cylinder engine having a crankshaft speed of 1,000 r.p.m. must operate 500 times per minute or 8 times per second. This means that the spring must be of such design and strength that it will be positive in action and does not weaken during prolonged use. Also it should not be affected by increase in temperature. Valve springs are made of a special alloy steel wire having the desired qualities to give good valve performance, depending upon the engine type, design, and speed.

FIG. 10-5. *Valve seat insert.*

Valve-seat inserts. Normally the valve seat is a part of the cylinder block or head, the material being cast iron. Obviously, if a hard-steel valve is constantly hitting against a cast-iron seat under high-temperature conditions, there will be rapid wear, burning, and corrosion of the

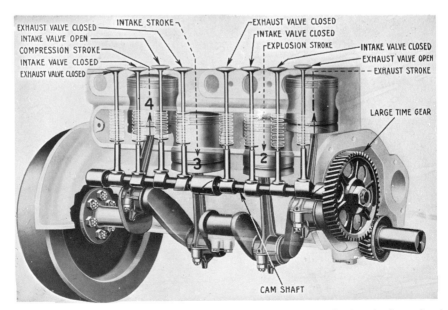

FIG. 10-6. *Valve arrangement and operation for a typical multiple-cylinder L-head engine.*

seat. Hence most engines are now equipped with seat inserts (Fig. 10-5), particularly for the exhaust valves. They are made of a special wear-resistant steel alloy and are pressed into place as shown. These inserts wear very little but can be replaced if necessary.

Valve location and arrangement. The two common valve arrangements are (1) the L-head (Fig. 10-6) and (2) the valve-in-head (Fig.

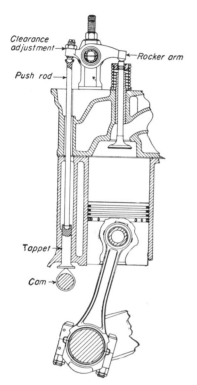

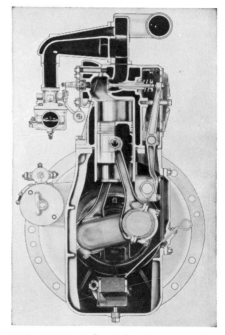

FIG. 10-7. *Valve-in-head construction and operation.*

FIG. 10-8. *Valve-in-head construction with long rocker arm and horizontal valve.*

10-7). A third arrangement (Fig. 10-8) consists of horizontal valves in the head operated by a long rocker arm directly from the camshaft. The valve-in-head arrangement is found in many types of engines and is used almost entirely in farm-type and other heavy-duty multiple-cylinder engines. Nearly all tractor engines are of this type. Some advantages given are: (1) the valves are removable with the cylinder head and, therefore, are accessible and easily serviced and replaced; (2) in case of a damaged valve seat, it is necessary to purchase only the cylinder head, while in other types it might be necessary to replace the complete cylinder or cylinder block; (3) uniform and effective cooling of the valves is greatly facilitated. The principal disadvantages are (1) a more complicated valve-operating mechanism; (2) more places to wear, hence more frequent adjustment and more noise.

The L-head arrangement is used quite extensively in automobile engines and some small power units. The valve-operating mechanism is simple because the cam and tappet act directly against the valve stem. However, the valve mechanism is somewhat inaccessible, and the intake and exhaust manifolds must usually be removed to permit adjustment of the valve clearance. Since the valves and openings are on the side of the block, the combustion space in the head is shallower and spread out with a part of the space to one side of the piston and over the valves.

Valve operation—automatic intake valves. Both the intake and exhaust valves on most types of engines are operated mechanically, but on some small, single-cylinder engines the intake valve is said to operate automatically. When thus operated, it is equipped with a very light spring. On the suction stroke of the piston, the valve is drawn open by the suction or decreased pressure in the cylinder, and the fuel charge is drawn in through the open valve. Near the end of the stroke, as the suction decreases, the light spring causes the valve to return to its seat. This method of intake-valve operation is very simple, but unless the valve is in perfect condition it may not seat properly, creating loss of compression. It is also noisy and not well adapted to high-speed engines, for the reason that there is no control of the time of opening and closing of the valve. Therefore the engine may not receive a full charge of fuel mixture.

Mechanically operated valves. In many single-cylinder engines and in all multiple-cylinder types, the intake as well as the exhaust valves are operated mechanically. For an L-head engine (Figs. 10-1 and 10-6), the mechanism consists of (1) a small gear on the crankshaft; (2) a half-time or cam gear; (3) a cam or, in the case of multiple-cylinder engines, a camshaft with a number of cams; (4) a tappet or short push rod. As the cam gear rotates the cam, the latter moves the tappet, and it in turn pushes the valve open. In addition to the parts enumerated above, the valve-in-head arrangement (Fig. 10-7) includes a push rod and rocker arm.

Camshafts and driving mechanisms. It has already been stated that, in any four-stroke-cycle engine, there are four strokes of the piston per cycle, the first stroke of the cycle being known as the intake stroke and the last stroke as the exhaust stroke. Therefore, the intake valve must open and close on the intake stroke, and the exhaust valve must open and close on the exhaust stroke; that is, each valve must operate one time per cycle. Consequently, the cam gear and cams that open and close these valves must make one revolution per cycle. The cam gear, however, is driven by a gear on the crankshaft that makes two revolutions per cycle. Therefore, the speed of the cam gear will be one-half that of the crankshaft, and it will have twice the number of teeth found on the crankshaft gear. Likewise, in multiple-cylinder engines having more than two valves, the speed of the cam gear will be one-half the speed of the crankshaft, because, as previously explained, all cylinders complete a cycle during the same two revolutions of the crankshaft. Therefore, all valves must open and close once during any two revolutions, and the camshaft, in order to open and close all these valves one time, must make one revolution to two of the crankshaft.

FIG. 10-9. *Silent chain camshaft drive.*

Camshafts are driven either by gears (Fig. 10-6) or by the tooth-type silent chain (Fig. 10-9). Freedom from noise is most important, and, for this reason, the chain drive is preferable in very high-speed automotive engines. Gears are predominant in the slower-speed heavy-duty engines such as tractor engines and similar power units. Quiet operation in gear drives is obtained by the use of nonmetallic materials such as bakelite instead of iron for the larger camshaft gear and also by the use of helical teeth.

Hydraulic valve lifters or adjusters. The hydraulic-type valve lifter or lash adjuster has been designed and adopted by some automotive-type engine manufacturers to eliminate certain objectionable factors involved in valve clearance and its adjustment. Basically, the hydraulic valve lifter gives better engine performance by keeping the valve operating parts in full contact with each other at all times, as well as eliminating periodic clearance adjustment. Specific advantages are (1) elimination of tappet clearance noise, (2) elimination of periodic valve clearance adjustments, (3) automatic compensation for expansion and contraction of the valve mechanism and motor block due to temperature changes and normal wear, (4) longer valve life owing to elimination of pounding, and (5) better engine performance because of precise control of valve timing.

Figure 10-10 shows one type of hydraulic valve lifter which operates as follows: The lifter body-guide cavity is connected by small drilled holes to the engine lubricating system. Referring to position 1, the oil enters the lifter body through the body-feed holes and flows into the

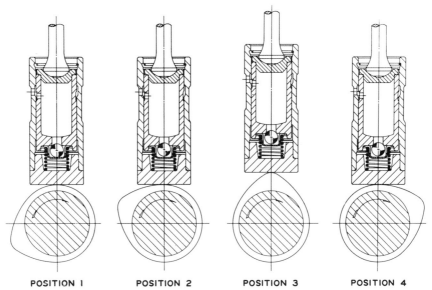

POSITION 1   POSITION 2   POSITION 3   POSITION 4

FIG. 10-10. *Hydraulic-type valve lifter.* (Courtesy of Diesel Equipment Division, General Motors Corporation.)

inside of the plunger through the holes in its side. The oil continues to flow through the hole in the bottom of the plunger, around the ball, and down through holes in the ball retainer, completely filling the ball retainer cavity. As the lifter is raised, position 2, the oil below the plunger tries to escape past the ball check. This rush of oil around the ball check forces the ball check to seat on the plunger, which, in turn, seals the hole at the bottom of the plunger. The lifter then follows the cam as a relatively solid unit. As the lifter rises on the cam and the full valve assembly load is applied, a predetermined and closely held clearance between the plunger and the body permits a controlled amount of oil to escape from below and past the plunger. This condition—the relative movement of the plunger with respect to the body after the ball check is seated—is termed leakdown. As the lifter plunger reaches the cam nose, position 3, the plunger has leaked down a very minute distance relative to the body as compared with its location in position 2. As the lifter reaches the closing ramp, position 4, the plunger is lower in relation to the body than in position 2, where the ball had just seated. As the lifter continues to ride down the ramp, the ball check opens if the valve gear has remained the same or contracted. The spring under the plunger compensates by taking up the clearance and the cycle is repeated. However, if the valve gear has expanded more than the relative amount of movement of the plunger in the body during leakdown, then the ball check will not unseat until enough cycles have taken place to account for the expansion of the valve gear. Therefore, when the engine structure and valve gear expand and contract with changes in engine temperatures and other differentials, the lifter automatically adjusts its own length to compensate for these changes. When temperature changes require shortening of the lifter length, the engine valve spring forces the plunger down because of the leakdown characteristics, thus constantly correcting for this condition. When lengthening of the lifter length is required, the lifter spring raises the plunger, causing oil to flow into the spring chamber.

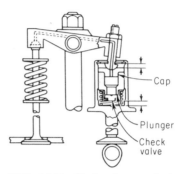

FIG. 10-11. *Hydraulic-type lash adjuster.*

Figure 10-11 shows a second type of hydraulic valve lifter which is located in the valve train next to the rocker arm. Its general construction and operation are essentially the same as Fig. 10-10; however, the oil is fed to it from the rocker arm through a drilled hole in the valve adjusting screw and a mating hole in the plunger cap into the supply chamber of the adjuster.

Hydraulic valve lifters give little trouble and seldom require attention. After an engine has been standing for some time, a certain amount of valve-lifter noise will occur when the engine is first started. This is due to leakdown on those lifters which were holding valves open against spring pressure when the engine stopped. Oil pressure will refill these lifters after a few seconds of engine operation and the noise will disappear. Cleanliness and the use of a high-quality engine oil of correct viscosity are most important in an engine equipped with hydraulic valve lifters.

Valve timing. The timing of any valve is specified with respect to the instant it begins to open and the instant it closes in relation to the crankshaft rotation and the piston position; that is, if a valve starts to open and then closes at the specified time with respect to the crankshaft and piston position for that cylinder, it is said to be correctly timed. These opening and closing points are determined by (1) the timing of the crankshaft and camshaft gears, (2) the shape of the cam, and (3) the tappet or rocker-arm clearance. A study of some typical cam shapes (Figs. 10-1 and 10-7) shows that the valve action is a gradual one; that is, the valve is pushed open gradually rather than abruptly, reaches its maximum lift and remains so only for an instant, and then closes gradually.

It would be assumed, ordinarily, that a valve would start to open at the beginning of its stroke and be completely closed at the end. Such, however, is not necessarily the case. It has been found that most engines operate efficiently only when the valves open and close at certain points

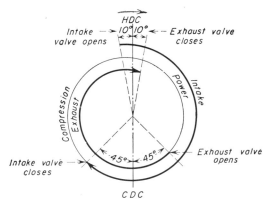

FIG. 10-12. *Diagram showing usual timing of valves.*

in the cycle and remain open a certain length of time. Therefore, the timing of the valves in any engine is very important.

Figure 10-12, commonly known as a valve-timing spiral or diagram, illustrates the timing of the average engine. The vertical line might be called the dead-center line with crank dead center (C.D.C.) at the bottom and head dead center (H.D.C.) at the top. The crankshaft and piston may be said to be on dead center when the centers of the piston pin, crankshaft, and crankpin all fall in this line. The spiral represents the travel of the crankpin or connecting-rod journal. Starting at H.D.C., the crank rotates in the direction of the arrow toward C.D.C., moving the piston through the intake or suction stroke, followed by compression from C.D.C. to H.D.C., expansion from H.D.C. to C.D.C., and exhaust from C.D.C. to H.D.C., thus completing the cycle.

Referring to the figure, it is noted that the intake valve should begin to open when the crankshaft lacks about 10 deg. of reaching H.D.C., and that it remains open throughout the stroke and does not close until the crankshaft has reached a point about 45 deg. after C.D.C. The exhaust valve begins to open before the piston reaches the end of the power stroke, that is, when the crankshaft is making an angle of about

45 deg. before C.D.C. with the piston on the power stroke. It remains open through the exhaust stroke and closes when the crankshaft has rotated about 10 deg. after the piston has reached H.D.C. The figures given are not correct for all engines but are very near the average.

Range of operation and cam shape. The number of degrees through which the crank rotates, from the point where the valve starts to open to the point where it is just completely closed, is known as the range of operation of that valve. The average range of operation for both valves, according to the figure, is 235 deg.

The range of operation is determined by the cam shape and the valve clearance (Figs. 10-1 and 10-7). Too much valve clearance decreases

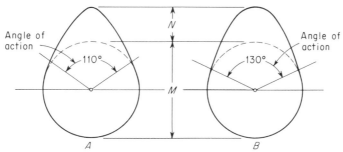

FIG. 10-13. *Valve cam profiles.*

the range of operation, and too little clearance increases it. Figure 10-13 shows some typical cam shapes and their effect on the timing of the valve. The camshaft diameter is *M* and *N* is the cam lobe height or valve lift. Both cam *A* and cam *B* have the same lift, but *B* has a greater angle of action and would give a range of operation of 260 deg. Likewise, cam *B* has a longer "dwell" interval which would be desirable for the intake valve on a very high-speed engine in order to permit a maximum charge of fuel mixture to enter the cylinder. The cam shape varies with respect to the intake and exhaust valves on any engine and, particularly, with respect to different types of engines, depending upon engine size and speed and other factors.

Even though the range of operation is correct, the valve may open too early and therefore close too early by the same amount, or it may open too late and therefore close too late by the same amount. This is due to the fact that the cam gear is out of time; that is, the cam is not coming around at the correct time to open and close the valve at the proper time with respect to the travel of the piston. To time the valve, the cam gear must be removed and rotated the correct amount in the the right direction and remeshed with the gear on the crankshaft. This shifting of the gear will not change the range of operation of the valve.

Most manufacturers place marks on their engines (Fig. 10-14) by which the correct valve and ignition timing of the engine may be determined and checked. However, the system of marking used is not standard; that is, every manufacturer has a somewhat different system. Consequently, the instruction book supplied with an engine should be studied carefully so that the method used will be well understood.

Effects of incorrect intake-valve timing. As previously discussed, the intake valve starts opening at the beginning of the intake stroke and remains open until the crankshaft has rotated considerably past crank dead center. At first thought, it would seem more reasonable to close the intake valve at the end of the intake stroke, but experience has

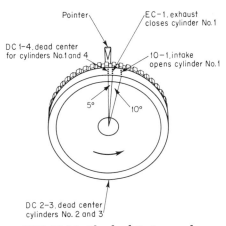

FIG. 10-14. *Flywheel timing marks.*

proved that allowing this valve to remain open, after the piston has started back on the compression stroke, enables the engine to generate more power and operate more efficiently. The explanation is that the charge rushing into the cylinder has not completely filled the space when the piston reaches the end of the intake stroke, but if the valve is allowed to remain open somewhat longer, the fuel mixture will continue to pour in because of its inertia; thus a more complete charge will enter the cylinder and greater power will be generated. There is some variation in the closing of this valve in different types of engines, but in general the point is determined by the speed of the engine; that is, a high-speed engine would have the intake closing possibly as much as 45 to 60 deg. after C.D.C.

Effects of incorrect exhaust-valve timing. In practically all types of engines, regardless of size, number of cylinders, speed, or other factors, the exhaust valve starts opening before the end of the power stroke of the piston, that is, when the crankshaft lacks about 45 deg. of having completed the stroke. Experience has proved that this early opening gives more satisfactory results in that the engine generates more power, runs cooler, and uses less fuel than when the valve is opened later, or at a point near the end of the stroke. It would seem that, in opening the exhaust valve before the completion of the expansion stroke, this power would be lost or wasted. But what actually happens is that this unspent pressure is utilized to better advantage to force the exhaust gases out, thus producing better cleaning of the cylinder.

Overheating of the engine is one of the most pronounced effects of too late exhaust-valve opening. This overheating develops because the hot gases are allowed to remain in the cylinder longer and to follow the piston through the entire stroke, thus coming in contact with a greater cylinder area. The closing of the exhaust valve occurs shortly after the completion of the exhaust stroke. If the valve were closed before or even at the end of the stroke, a small amount of burned residue might remain in the cylinder.

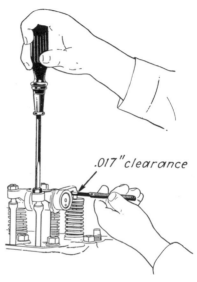

FIG. 10-15. *Valve-in-head clearance adjustment.*

Multiple-cylinder valve timing— valve clearance. The correct timing of the valves in any internal-combustion engine is very important. It is essential to proper operation of the engine if efficient fuel consumption, maximum power, and smooth running are desired. In the design of an engine, the manufacturer determines accurately the correct timing for his engine and sees that the valves open and close so as to give the best possible results. In many engines, certain teeth on the cam gear and crankshaft are marked or center-punched so that, when either is removed and replaced (if the marks are placed together), the valves will be in time. Marking of the timing gears in multiple-cylinder engines is important and almost universally practiced.

The timing of the valves in multiple-cylinder engines is a comparatively simple matter, consisting in (1) meshing the timing or cam gears so that the marked teeth are together, and (2) providing the correct valve clearance or lash. Valve clearance is defined as the space allowed between the end of the valve stem and the rocker arm (Fig. 10-15), or, in the case of the L-head type, between the valve stem and the tappet (Fig. 10-1).

The valve-in-head construction requires more mechanism than the L-head construction. Therefore, slightly more wear is possible, and frequent adjustment is usually necessary. Figure 10-14 shows the usual mechanism involved and the method of adjustment. Figure 10-1 shows the L-head arrangement and the usual provisions for adjusting valve clearance.

A certain amount of valve clearance is necessary to allow for the expansion of the valve stem and engine parts when they get hot and thus permit the valves to seat properly. At the same time, too much clearance affects the timing of the valves and the smooth operation of the engine and also produces noise. In some cases the adjustment is made when the engine is cold, while in others the engine should be warmed up or at its normal running temperature. In many cases, the exhaust valve is given more clearance than the intake because its operating temperature is much higher. This clearance varies as follows, depending upon the size and type of engine: intake valve, 0.006 to 0.012 in. for auto engines and 0.010 to 0.020 in. for tractor engines; exhaust valve, 0.010 to 0.020 in. for auto engines and 0.012 to 0.030 in. for tractor engines.

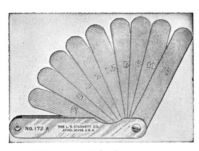

FIG. 10-16. *Thickness gauge.*

The importance of correct valve-clearance adjustment cannot be over-stressed, because if it is neglected, more or less faulty operation may result. The following rules for adjusting valve clearance apply to either the L-head or the valve-in-head type and should be observed carefully:

1. Read the instruction book supplied with the tractor and see whether the manufacturer advises making the adjustment when the engine is hot or when cold.

2. When making the adjustment, always be sure that the push rod and tappet are resting on the low part of the cam.

3. Some manufacturers mark the flywheel as shown by Fig. 10-14. If this is done, check the valve adjustment and timing by referring to these flywheel marks. The instruction book will explain just how to do this.

4. Valve clearance should always be adjusted whenever the valves are ground or reconditioned. In valve-in-head engines always readjust the clearance whenever the cylinder head bolts are tightened.

5. For accurate adjustment, use a standard thickness gauge (Fig. 10-16).

6. Always see that the lock nuts are tight.

REFERENCES

BARGER, E. L., W. M. CARLETON, E. G. McKIBBEN, and ROY BAINER, "Tractors and Their Power Units," John Wiley & Sons, Inc., New York, 1952.

HELDT, P. M., "High-speed Combustion Engines," 16th ed., Chilton Company, Philadelphia, 1956.

Hydraulic Valve Lifters in Passenger Car Engines, *Lubrication*, May, 1954.

LICHTY, L. C., "Internal Combustion Engines," 6th ed., McGraw-Hill Book Company, Inc., New York, 1951.

MOSES, BEN D., and KENNETH R. FROST, "Farm Power," John Wiley & Sons, Inc., New York, 1952.

The Design, Development, and Manufacture of Hydraulic Valve Lifters, *Gen. Motors Eng. J.*, Vol. 1, No. 6.

PROBLEMS AND QUESTIONS

1. Discuss the design of valves and the materials used for them.

2. Compare the common valve locations as to construction, operation, and adaptability to various types of engines.

3. Make a suitable valve-timing diagram for the intake and exhaust valves of an engine, if their operating ranges are 215 and 235 deg., respectively.

4. Make a diagram of the valve timing to be recommended for a high-speed, six-cylinder engine.

5. Give the probable recommended clearance for the valves for a 50-hp., four-cylinder tractor engine.

11

Fuels and Combustion

One disadvantage of the internal-combustion engine is that the fuels required for its successful operation must be of a specific nature and, therefore, are somewhat limited with respect to source and supply. Under certain conditions these fuels may be difficult to secure, and their use becomes economically prohibitive. Some of the essential characteristics of such fuels are:

1. They must have a reasonably high energy value.

2. They must vaporize at least partially at comparatively low temperatures.

3. The fuel vapors must ignite and burn readily when mixed in the proper proportions with oxygen.

4. Such fuels and their combustion products should not be unduly harmful or dangerous to human health or life.

5. They must be of such a nature that they can be handled and transported with comparative ease and safety.

CLASSIFICATION AND COMPOSITION OF FUELS

Gaseous fuels. Fuels for internal-combustion engines may be classified in two ways: (1) as either gaseous or liquid, according to the physical state before going into the engine cylinder; and (2) as artificial or natural, according to whether the fuel is obtained from natural sources or is a manufactured product.

The common gaseous fuels derived from nature are (1) natural gas, and (2) propane and butane or LP (liquefied-petroleum) gases. Natural gas is used directly as it comes from the well, without being subjected to any complex refining or purifying action. It is colorless and odorless and consists largely of methane (CH_4) and other simple hydrocarbon gases and small amounts of carbon dioxide and nitrogen. It is distributed under pressure through pipe lines and used largely as a fuel for cooking, heating, lighting, and refrigeration, and for industrial purposes.

Natural gas is a very satisfactory fuel for internal-combustion engines, but its use must be confined to stationary power units, which can be permanently connected to a supply line. The only special equipment needed is a suitable pressure regulator or control and a mixing device similar to a carburetor.

In the manufacture of iron and steel, certain so-called by-product gases are produced such as blast-furnace gas, coke-oven gas, and producer gas. These artificial gaseous fuels are limited in use to the production of power in or near these plants and are not available for general use.

In some countries in which petroleum fuels are expensive and difficult to obtain, equipment has been devised for use on automobiles, trucks, and tractors which generates a gaseous fuel from coal, wood, charcoal, sawdust, or similar materials. This gas is called *producer gas* and consists of a mixture of carbon monoxide, hydrogen, methane, nitrogen, and carbon dioxide. The equipment is quite complex and bulky and includes devices to clean and cool the gas and separate out tarry and other undesirable matter, as well as the mixer for supplying the engine with the correct quantity of air and gas mixture.

Butane and propane or a mixture of the two is used to a considerable extent as engine fuels. Referring to Table 11-1, both are simple hydrocarbons of the paraffin series and become gases at normal atmos-

Table 11-1. Characteristics of Paraffin Hydrocarbons

Formula	Name	Weight per gallon, lb.	Gravity		Boiling temp., °F.	Self-ignition temp., °F.	Heating values, B.t.u. per lb.	
			A.P.I.	Specific			High	Low
CH_4	Methane	...	....	....	−258	1346	23,850	21,597
C_2H_6	Ethane	3.11	247.0	0.374	−128	1050	22,400	20,597
C_3H_8	Propane	4.23	147.0	0.508	−44	995	21,650	20,015
C_4H_{10}	Butane	4.86	110.8	0.584	31	961	21,300	19,795
C_5H_{12}	Pentane	5.25	92.8	0.631	97	933	21,100	19,597
C_6H_{14}	Hexane	5.53	81.6	0.664	155	909	20,900	19,432
C_7H_{16}	Heptane	5.73	74.2	0.688	209	893	20,850	19,408
C_8H_{18}	Octane	5.89	68.6	0.707	258	880	20,750	19,329
C_9H_{20}	Nonane	6.01	64.5	0.722	303	871	20,700	19,292
$C_{10}H_{22}$	Decane	6.11	61.3	0.734	345	866	20,600	19,205
$C_{15}H_{32}$	Pentadecane	6.41	52.3	0.770	518	....	20,450	19,091
$C_{18}H_{38}$	Octadecane	6.49	49.9	0.780	603	....	20,400	19,047

pheric pressure and temperature. For this reason they are stored and transported under pressure in liquid form in heavy tanks. This explains why they are called *liquefied-petroleum gases.* Usually they are more or less by-products of the petroleum-refining process. They may be recovered (1) from the dry gas and gasoline as it is removed from crude oil, (2) from recycling plants from the wet gas drawn from natural-gas

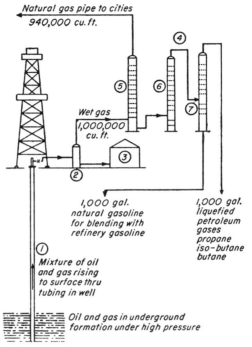

FIG. 11-1. *Natural-gas well with storage and distribution equipment.* (Handbook of Butane-Propane Gases.)

wells, or (3) from the normal processing of crude oil into commercial gasoline and distillates (see Figs. 11-1 and 11-3).

Liquid fuels. The most common liquid fuels are gasoline, kerosene, distillate, and diesel fuel. Liquid fuels have the advantage over gaseous materials of being more concentrated and readily portable. They are obtained almost entirely from petroleum, a product of nature. The only artificial liquid fuel of any consequence that might be used for internal-combustion engines is alcohol. It has never been used extensively, however, and will be discussed later. Gasoline and kerosene are lighter fuels obtained from petroleum. Distillates and diesel fuels are heavier products resulting from the distillation and refining of crude oil.

Origin of petroleum. Crude oil is obtained from natural deposits existing usually at depths varying from several hundred to thousands of feet below the surface of the earth. For this reason petroleum and its products are said to be of mineral origin or derived from nature. The first crude oil of any consequence was discovered in Pennsylvania in 1859 and came from a well having a depth of about 70 ft. This state continued to be the only producer for a number of years, but eventually oil was discovered in Ohio, Indiana, and Illinois, and later in California, Texas, Oklahoma, Kansas, Louisiana, Mississippi, and other states and in Canada, Mexico, South America, and other foreign countries.

There is considerable variation in the character of crude oil obtained in these different regions, but they are generally placed in one or the other of three classes, namely, asphalt-base crudes, paraffin-base crudes, and mixed-base crudes. An asphalt-base crude is usually a heavy dark liquid and, when distilled, produces an end product of a black, tarry nature. Paraffin-base crudes are lighter in weight and color and upon distillation produce a residue that is light in color and resembles paraffin. The ordinary paraffin wax is obtained from such crudes. Some crude oils have been found which contain both asphaltic and paraffin materials and are therefore known as mixed-base crudes.

Crude oils, as obtained from these various regions, differ considerably from the standpoint of the final products of distillation and vary greatly in the amount of the lighter products of distillation that they yield, such as gasoline and kerosene. The so-called light crudes, that is, those which are comparatively thin and lighter in weight per unit volume, produce a higher percentage of gasoline and kerosene and a lower percentage of lubricating oil and heavy products, whereas the heavier crude oils contain less gasoline and kerosene and produce a greater quantity of lubricating oil and heavy products. It was thought originally that the gasoline and lubricants from certain crude oils were superior to those obtained from others, but with the modern refining processes the products produced from these different crudes do not vary greatly in character or quality.

Chemical and physical characteristics of petroleum products. A brief and elementary consideration of the chemical and physical characteristics of these petroleum products is important and will assist in explaining their action as fuels and lubricants. Crude oil and the products obtained from it are known as *hydrocarbons;* that is, they are products made up almost entirely of carbon and hydrogen, having such general chemical formulas as C_nH_{2n}, C_nH_{2n+2}, etc. A simple hydrocarbon, therefore, would be CH_2; another, CH_4; a third, C_2H_6; and so on. A careful analysis of crude oils and the common fuels obtained from them indicates that they contain about 84 per cent carbon and 15 per cent hydrogen by weight, with the remaining 1 per cent made up of nitrogen, oxygen, and sulfur. Table 11-1 shows some typical simple petroleum products and their physical characteristics. It will be noted that as the molecular structure becomes more complex the material changes from a gas to a light liquid and then to a heavy liquid at ordinary temperatures. For example, butane (C_4H_{10}) is a gas at 32°F., while hexane (C_6H_{14}) and octadecane ($C_{18}H_{38}$) are normally liquids and become gases at temperatures of 155 and 603°F. respectively. Most liquid fuels including gasoline and distillates are thus made up of a mixture of these somewhat less complex hydrocarbons, while heavier products such as diesel fuels, fuel oils, lubricants, and greases are composed of the heavier hydrocarbons having a very complex molecular structure. Table 11-2 gives the principal charac-

Table 11-2. Characteristics of Liquid Fuels

Fuel	A.P.I.[1] test, deg.	Specific gravity	Weight per gallon, lb.	Initial boiling point, °F.	End point, °F.	Heating value, B.t.u.[2] per lb.	
						Low	High
Gasoline	65–56	0.720–0.755	5.99–6.28	85–105	300–435	19,000	21,000
Kerosene	45–40	0.802–0.825	6.68–6.87	340–360	500–550	18,000	20,000
Distillates (tractor fuel)	47–35	0.793–0.850	6.60–7.08	200–350	460–550	18,000	20,000
Diesel tractor fuel	40–30	0.825–0.876	6.87–7.30	325–460	600–725	18,000	20,000
Crude oil	57–10	0.751–1.000	6.25–8.30	....	....	18,000	20,000
Denatured alcohol	45–40	0.802–0.825	6.68–6.87	150	....	10,000	13,000
Propane	147	0.509	4.24	−44	....	20,015	21,600
Butane	111	0.584	4.86	32	....	19,795	21,300

[1] American Petroleum Institute.
[2] British thermal unit.

teristics of the common liquid fuels. It should be noted that there is very little difference in the heating value of crude oil and its products, even though there is a marked variation in the weight of a given volume of each. As shown, alcohol has about the same gravity as kerosene but a much lower heating value.

Heating value of fuels. The heating value or the amount of heat energy contained in any fuel is measured by means of the heat unit known as the *British thermal unit* (B.t.u.). This unit is the quantity of heat required to raise the temperature of 1 lb. of water 1°F. The heating values of the common liquid fuels are given in Table 11-2.

Petroleum refining. The production of crude oil and its conversion into hundreds of commercial products by the various distillation and refining processes have become one of the greatest industries of the age. As a result of economic and other factors, changes and improvements in refining methods are being constantly introduced. The manufacture of the numerous crude-oil products has developed into a highly complex industry, and it is difficult to convey to the average layman, by any simple or limited explanation, just how the various products are made. A study of a typical flow chart (Fig. 11-2) shows that the first stage in

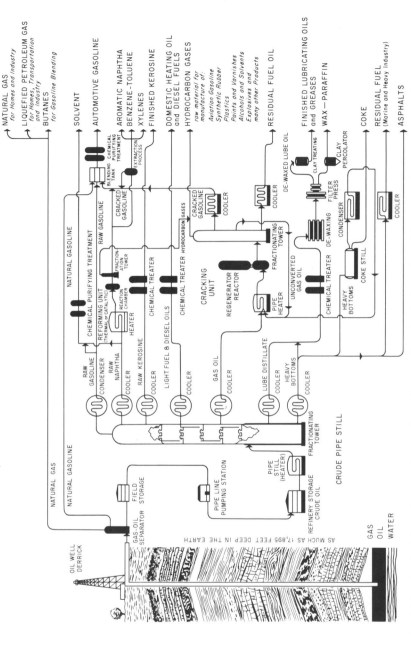

FIG. 11-2. *Typical flow chart tracing crude oil from well to finished product.* (Courtesy of American Petroleum Institute.)

149

the refining process involves the breakdown of the crude, by straight distillation, into about seven groups, the lightest of which is entirely gaseous in nature, the heaviest being a semisolid or solid such as asphalt and coke. The second stage consists in converting the fractions into their respective end products by means of distillation, chemical action, and special treatment. It will be noted that gasoline is obtained from the raw product in two ways: (1) by direct distillation, and (2) by a special

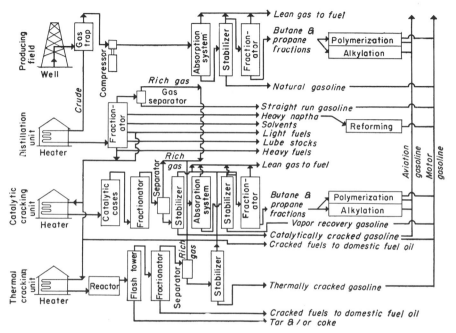

FIG. 11-3. *Refinery processes for manufacturing fuels.* (Courtesy of Society of Automotive Engineers.)

process called *cracking*, which converts a part of the heavy "gas oil" fraction into fuel. The refining process for manufacturing fuels is shown by Fig. 11-3. Lubricants for various purposes are obtained from the lubricating-oil "cut," which is heavier than that of gas oil.

GASOLINE

Gasoline manufacture. Gasoline originally was a product obtained only by the distillation of the crude oil. It was formerly somewhat lighter and more volatile than the average gasoline now found on the market. As indicated in Fig. 11-2, it can be produced in three distinct ways and classified as natural, raw, and cracked, depending upon the manner of production. So-called raw or straight-run gasoline is produced by the ordinary distillation of crude oil. The crude is heated to a given temperature for a certain length of time, and the resulting product that distills over is gathered in a condenser. This distillation product is not ready for use, however, but is known by the refiner as crude benzene or crude naphtha. Before being placed on the market, it must be subjected to a refining process, which consists in heating it with chemicals and redistilling it to separate out any heavy materials that may have passed over during the first distillation and to remove any impurities.

Cracked gasoline is manufactured from heavier distillation fractions, particularly gas oil. As the term implies, the process consists in breaking up the so-called heavy molecules into the lighter ones that make up gasoline. The process consists essentially in placing these heavier distillation products in receptacles and heating them under pressure. This results in certain lighter products that pass off, are condensed and further treated and refined, and eventually resemble straight-run gasoline.

Natural gasoline is manufactured from the gas that issues from oil wells or is obtained in the distillation of the crude oil. The process consists in compressing and liquefying the gases and then distilling these liquids under pressure, thus producing a very light and volatile product. This gasoline makes up only a very small percentage of the total amount manufactured. Ordinarily it is not used in its original condition, owing to its great volatility, but it is mixed with heavier, lower quality gasoline to form what is known as a *blended* product. Much of the gasoline now found on the market is known as blended gasoline and consists in many cases of all three types—natural, raw, and cracked—as mixed together in the refining process.

Grades of gasoline. Gasoline for automotive vehicles and stationary power units is available in four grades: (1) white or fourth-grade, (2) regular, (3) premium, and (4) super-premium. White gasoline may be very little different from the others except that it contains no antiknock material and therefore is undesirable for use in high-compression engines. It may also have a slightly higher distillation range and lower A.P.I. gravity but, otherwise, is a satisfactory fuel. Regular-grade gasoline contains some tetraethyl lead and therefore has better antiknock qualities than white gasoline. It will give satisfactory results in nearly all high-compression auto, tractor, and truck engines under most conditions. Premium-grade gasolines have the best antiknock characteristic and are usually somewhat higher quality fuels from the standpoint of distillation range and performance under all conditions. They contain more tetraethyl lead than second-grade gasoline and should be used in engines having unusually high compression ratios. Also they provide better starting and operation under low-temperature conditions.

Impurities in gasoline. Wilson [1] gives the following information concerning gasoline impurities:

[1] *Bull. Univ. Wisconsin Eng. Expt. Sta. Ser. 78.*

The two chief impurities in gasoline that may cause trouble are sulphur and gum. While small traces of sulphur seldom cause noticeable damage, and even a large amount may not result in serious difficulties in warm weather or under conditions where there is no moisture present, where appreciable condensation occurs so that sulphuric acid is formed, a small amount of sulphur may raise havoc. In exceptional cases such as with the present mufflers in which the number of baffle plates has been increased in an effort to eliminate exhaust noises, gasoline of only 0.015 per cent sulphur has resulted in serious corrosion of the muffler in a single winter.

The gum-forming tendencies of certain gasolines have become of increasing interest in late years because of the increased popularity of the cracked gasolines and especially those which have been vapor phase cracked. The objection to gum in gasoline is that it tends to build up objectionable deposits. When the gasoline is sprayed from the carburetor, any dissolved gum present may be deposited on the heated portions of the intake manifold and on the inlet valves. Imperfect engine operation and loss of power may result from either a partial clogging of the manifold or delayed seating of the inlet valves. In severe cases, engine failure may be caused by complete sticking of an inlet valve. No other deleterious effects on the engine have been noted. Only a fraction of the dissolved gum in the gasoline is deposited in the intake system, the percentage of the total depending on the design and operating conditions of the engine. The undeposited gum is carried into the combustion chamber and burned with the charge. Carbon deposits seem to bear no relation to the quantity of gum in the fuel. Gum has been defined as a residue that is left by the evaporation of gasoline, while the residue which separates from the liquid has been called resin. Resin is especially apt to form in the presence of copper. Gum exists in gasoline in a dissolved state and may be formed during storage and remain in solution until the gasoline is used, at which time it causes trouble. Gum formed during storage is referred to as "potential gum." Hence, a cracked gasoline may be free from gum immediately after refining and yet contain an appreciable quantity of dissolved gum when it is used. Certain tests are used which are intended to indicate "potential gum," the gum which may be expected to form later. The results of such tests are intended to indicate the proportional amount of gum that may give trouble after a rather extended period of storage. Some gum tests will show an exceedingly high gum value for straight-run gasoline, and yet it is ordinarily considered as nil for such gasoline. The terms "actual gum," "preformed gum," and "residual gum" are generally considered identical in meaning, and they refer to the gum which is already present as dissolved gum in gasoline.

The exact nature of the compounds in gasoline that deposit as resin or gum is not known. In some cases, it has been found that the same compounds cause the yellow color or strong varnishlike odor in some cracked gasolines. Cracked gasolines from heavy crudes and fuel oils have a more pronounced color which increases with time. However, insofar as the operation of a motor car is concerned, it has never been established that either colors or odors are important factors, except as possible indices of the qualities already discussed. Contrary to popular belief, gasolines may be yellow without containing gum, or may be colorless and yet contain large quantities of gum.

The problem of predicting how long a gasoline may be stored without excessive gum formation is difficult, for not only is the gum stability a function of the particular gasoline under consideration, but it is also dependent upon conditions of storage. The process of refining has the greatest single effect upon the stability as regards gum formation. Cracked gasolines from the same gas oil, but made by different processes, vary widely in this respect. The rate of gumming is increased by aeration, by rise in temperature, by the action of light, and by the presence of deleterious substances.

HEAVY FUEL—SPECIAL FUELS

Kerosene. Kerosene is a heavier product of the distillation of crude oil than gasoline. Its initial boiling point is about 350°F., the end point is 550°F., and it is normally water-white or pale straw in color. It is produced and sold primarily as a fuel for domestic cooking, heating, and lighting. It has been used to some extent as an engine and tractor fuel, but because of its excessive detonation characteristic, it has been supplanted by distillates and special tractor fuels having a better octane rating and costing less per gallon.

Distillates. Distillates are crude-oil products greatly resembling kerosene but usually having a different color and odor. Owing to differences in crude oils, in the refining processes, and in trade demands, distillates produced by different refiners vary greatly in gravity, distillation range, and other qualities. However, the better grades of distillates are usually cracked and partly refined products made from selected crudes in order to secure high antiknock qualities and freedom from gum. Certain low-grade distillates are usually straight-run products with higher boiling and end points than the No. 1 grade.

Special tractor fuel. To meet the demand for a satisfactory low-cost fuel of the nature of distillate, some refiners supply a special distillate-type fuel of controlled uniformity for tractor use. These fuels are prepared from special crudes and treated and refined in such a manner that they have a reasonably low initial boiling point and end point, a high antiknock characteristic, and a low gum and sulfur content.

Diesel tractor fuel. Fuels for compression-ignition engines resemble a low-grade distillate, particularly with respect to gravity and distillation range. However, they are largely straight-run rather than cracked products.

In general, large, slow-speed, stationary diesel engines can utilize a rather wide variety of heavy fuels, whereas the smaller, multiple-cylinder, high-speed diesel engines require fuels having certain specific qualities. Diesel fuels are obtainable in two grades, namely, No. 1 (light) and No. 2 (heavy). The No. 2 grade gives the most satisfactory performance under most conditions. The use of No. 1 fuel is usually restricted to very low-temperature conditions where a lower-viscosity fuel is required. In general, all diesel fuels should meet the following specifications:

1. A.P.I. gravity...................... 30–40°
2. Initial boiling point.................. 325–350°F.
3. End point........................... 650–725°F.
4. Viscosity at 100°F. (Say. Univ.)......... 30–40 sec.
5. Sulfur.............................. 0.5 per cent (max.)
6. Carbon residue...................... 0.25 per cent (max.)
7. Moisture and sediment................ 0.05 per cent (max.)
8. Flash point......................... 150°F. (min.)
9. Cetane number...................... 45 (min.)

Two important qualifications of diesel fuels, particularly those used in high-speed engines, are (1) freedom from solid matter, sediment, and moisture; and (2) viscosity. An absolutely clean fuel is highly essential to the satisfactory operation of the injection mechanism, including the injection pumps and nozzles. Even slight traces of fine sediment or moisture may cause trouble.

A fuel having a certain viscosity range is likewise necessary to permit the injection mechanism to handle it properly and, at the same time, to provide some lubrication. A fuel having free-flowing characteristics at all temperatures at which the engine may be operated is also important.

Cetane rating of diesel fuels. The marked increase in the application of high-compression ignition to high-speed engines of the automotive type has disclosed the necessity of utilizing, in these engines, fuels having certain specific physical and chemical qualities that will provide the necessary combustion characteristics when injection occurs.

For the purpose of comparing and designating the ignition qualities of such fuels, the so-called cetane rating method has been developed. The cetane rating of a diesel fuel is its designated ignition quality as determined by comparing it with a standard reference fuel consisting of a given blend of cetane ($C_{16}H_{34}$) and alpha-methylnaphthalene ($C_{11}H_{10}$). For example, a 40 cetane fuel is one having the same ignition qualities as a blend containing 40 per cent cetane and 60 per cent alpha-methylnaphthalene. The actual rating of a given fuel must be determined by means of a standard test engine and standard conditions.

Alcohol and alcohol-gasoline blends. Two kinds of alcohol might be used as gas-engine fuel, namely, methyl alcohol (CH_4O), and ethyl or grain alcohol (C_2H_6O). Neither of these is available, however, in its pure form, but a third, which is known as *denatured alcohol,* is manufactured in considerable quantities and would make a satisfactory fuel under certain conditions. Denatured alcohol consists largely of grain alcohol with some wood or methyl alcohol mixed with it, together with pyridine, which gives it a distinct odor and color. Perhaps the principal reason that alcohol is not used as a fuel at the present time is that it offers no advantages over hydrocarbon fuels, and the cost of manufacture is much greater. Other possible objections are that (1) it has only about one-half the heating value of other fuels, hence a greater quantity is required to generate the same amount of power for the same period of time; (2) it does not vaporize so readily as gasoline; (3) it requires a higher compression pressure for the best results.

Anhydrous or absolute ethyl alcohol will mix with gasoline in all proportions. Commercial alcohol (alcohol of 95 per cent purity) will not mix with gasoline unless it constitutes at least 50 per cent of the mixture. It can be made to blend with gasoline in any proportion by adding blending agents, such as propyl, butyl, and amyl alcohols, benzol, or acetone.

When added to gasoline, alcohol will raise the octane rating of the fuel. Its use with higher compression ratios shows a corresponding improvement in efficiency. A mixture containing 10 per cent absolute alcohol and 90 per cent gasoline has an octane value between that of ordinary gasoline and that of the standard ethyl gasoline.

Alcohol has a distinct advantage in that it burns with an absence of smoke and without disagreeable odors. It produces no carbon in the engine cylinders and may even be regarded as a carbon remover. It should be run with considerable excess of air to avoid the formation of corrosive products such as aldehyde or acetic acids.

Reported results of engine tests of alcohol-gasoline blends vary because of differences in test conditions. However, they do indicate that the variation in power over a straight gasoline will be likely to be less than 5 per cent, and it is generally conceded that any increase in power does not offset the increased cost of the fuel.

Gravity method of testing fuels. Formerly it was the practice to express the comparative quality of fuels, especially gasolines, in terms of gravity; that is, the owner or operator of an automotive vehicle such as an automobile or a tractor was led to believe that a so-called high-test gasoline was a higher quality product and, therefore, more desirable than a low-test gasoline. As the demand for gasoline increased it became necessary for the oil refiner to meet the situation by converting more of the heavier fractions of crude oil into gasoline. Thus the commercial gasoline now being produced is a slightly heavier product than formerly and possibly somewhat less volatile. However, this apparent lowering of the quality of the fuel has had very little effect upon satisfactory engine operation, because the engine manufacturers have promptly taken steps to adapt their products to these fuels. In fact, the present-day automotive engines operate more smoothly and with less trouble on these lower gravity fuels than did those of a few years ago on fuels that were considered as more desirable in quality.

The gravity of a fuel or an oil may be expressed as *specific gravity* or as A.P.I. (American Petroleum Institute) gravity, formerly known as Baumé gravity. The latter scale is preferred in the United States in connection with petroleum products. The *specific gravity* of a liquid is the ratio of its weight to the weight of an equal volume of water at 60°F. The relationship of the A.P.I. gravity scale to specific gravity is expressed by the following formula:

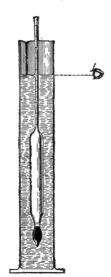

$$\text{Degrees A.P.I.} = \frac{141.5}{\text{sp. gr. } 60°/60°\text{F.}} - 131.5$$

The device used for testing the gravity of a liquid is known as a *hydrometer*. Usually two hydrometers are necessary, one for liquids lighter than water, and another for liquids heavier than water. Figure 11-4 illustrates how the hydrometer is placed in the liquid and read.

Table 11-2 gives the A.P.I. gravities of the more common liquid fuels. The values vary from about 65° for a high-test, very volatile gasoline to 30° for diesel fuel. It is thus observed that the lighter the fuel and the lower its specific gravity, the higher the A.P.I. gravity value in degrees. The A.P.I. gravity of pure water is 10°.

FIG. 11-4. *Use of hydrometer in determining gravity of fuels.*

Distillation test of liquid fuels. A more reliable and widely used method of determining the value of liquid fuels is known as the ASTM distillation test. In making such a test a given quantity (100 cc.) of the fuel is placed in a flask (Fig. 11-5), heated, and its so-called initial boiling point noted from the thermometer inserted in the top of the flask. Then, as the heating is continued, a certain amount vaporizes, passes off, and is condensed. The temperatures at which certain percentages of the fuel pass off are noted, and finally the end point is observed, that is, the temperature at which the last drop evaporates. The usual practice is to plot a curve of the distillation values for a given sample and compare it with that of a similar fuel of recommended or standard requirements and specifications. Figure 11-6 shows distillation curves for the more common liquid fuels.

The most significant information indicated by a fuel-distillation curve in relating volatility characteristics of gasoline to engine performance is obtained from the temperatures at which 10, 50, and 90 per cent of the fuel is evaporated. The initial boiling point is the temperature at which the first drop of liquid leaves the condenser. The lower the initial point, the greater is the "front-end" volatility of the gasoline, and, in general, the higher the vapor pressure. Although the initial point is of some importance in cold engine starting, it is difficult to measure accurately. The 10 per cent point can be measured more accurately and therefore is more

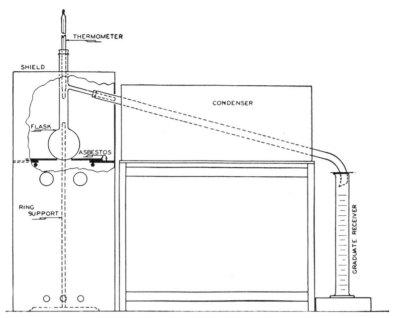

FIG. 11-5. *Apparatus for making distillation tests of gasoline and other liquid fuels.*

useful. For this reason the initial boiling point is of less importance as a specification for gasoline.

The "10 per cent point," as it is commonly called, is of primary importance as a specification related to engine starting. The lower this temperature, the better the starting characteristics of the gasoline, other factors being equal. The 10 per cent point is also used to indicate the relative vapor-locking tendencies of fuels having equal vapor pressures.

The "50 per cent point" is important as an index of the engine warm-up characteristics of gasoline; that is, the lower the 50 per cent point temperature, the faster the warm-up. The presence of high-boiling components in the gasoline is likely to cause poor mixture distribution in the intake manifold and therefore may affect engine performance during acceleration. Also the presence of a large portion of such materials may lead to crankcase dilution. This results from the failure of the fuel to evaporate and burn. The unburned portions may enter the crankcase past the piston rings and dilute the oil. The 90 per cent temperature provides a good indication of the fuel performance in this respect, and it has become an important part of gasoline specifications. The end point has little significance and is not usually included in gasoline specifications. The 90 per cent point is used in preference to the end point because the latter is difficult to determine accurately.

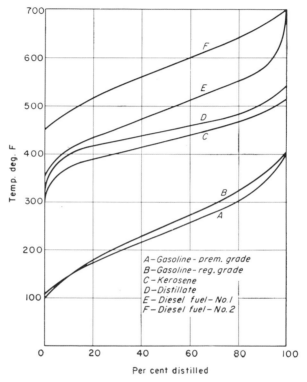

FIG. 11-6. *Distillation-test curves of common fuels.*

Detonation—preignition—knock rating. The tendency of designers of automotive and tractor-type engines to resort to higher compression pressures, in order to obtain more power and speed and increase efficiency, has resulted in pronounced fuel-knocking effects in many of these engines. This knocking, properly termed *detonation,* causes an unpleasant, sharp, clicking sound that is most noticeable when the motor is operating at low speed with wide-open throttle. Detonation is often confused with preignition, but there is a distinction. Preignition occurs when the charge is fired too far ahead of the compression-dead-center position of the piston, owing either to excessive spark advance or to premature, spontaneous ignition resulting from excessive heat in the cylinder. The resulting noise is that of the pistons and bearings as the piston completes its stroke against abnormally high pressure. Ordinarily, retarding the spark will eliminate this type of knock.

Detonation occurs during the process of combustion of the mixture within the cylinder after ignition has taken place. It is often referred to as "knock," "pink," or "ping." According to Wilson,[1]

While there is still much to be learned concerning just what takes place in a combustion chamber during the one-hundredth of a second period of combustion, the theory of detonation has been quite definitely established in the last few years. It is known that a combustible mixture of fuel and air, when ignited by a spark, will burn in a progressive manner, and an average value for the rate of spread of the flame has been determined as approximately 70 feet per second. It takes time for the flame to spread to the charge occupying the most distant portion of the combustion chamber. In the meantime things are happening to this unburned portion of combustible mixture. It is being compressed by the burned charge, which is rapidly increasing in volume as heat is liberated by the combustion process. This compression raises the temperature of the unburned charge. Moreover, this "last-to-burn" portion is being heated by radiation of heat from the flame itself and from any hot spots in its immediate vicinity. Once the detonating temperature (1400 to 1500°F.) is reached, the "last-to-burn" portion goes off with a bang before the orderly progression of the flame front ever reaches it. This sets up violent pressure waves within the combustion chamber. The force of these waves creates hammerlike blows against the interior walls and surfaces of the combustion chamber.

The problem of control of detonation is handled in a number of ways, as follows:

1. Using specially designed cylinder heads and pistons to so shape the combustion space that the last-to-burn portion of the charge will be spread out into a thin sheet and its temperature held down more effectively.

2. Providing more effective water circulation and cooling around the cylinder head and exhaust valves.

3. Using cylinder head and piston materials—particularly aluminum alloys—that provide more rapid heat dissipation.

4. Using a properly designed spark plug and locating it in the "hot region" and preferably near the exhaust valve.

5. Eliminating or reducing carbon deposits. Carbon is an excellent heat insulator and thereby induces detonation by creating ineffective cooling of the combustion space.

6. Maintaining the correct mixture of fuel and air and the proper spark setting and valve adjustment.

7. Using specially treated or so-called "doped" or antiknock fuels.

8. Adding water as in the case of tractors using heavy fuels having excessive detonating characteristics.

[1] *Bull. Univ. Wisconsin Eng. Expt. Sta. Ser.* 78.

Antiknock fuels. Wilson [1] states:

The nature of the fuel has an important effect upon the tendency to detonate, and there are two factors which determine the extent of this tendency. They are the temperature at which the air-fuel mixture will autoignite, and the rate at which pressure builds up during combustion. The antiknock value of gasoline is dependent upon several factors. These include the source of the crude oil and the method of cracking and distilling. The gasoline produced from naphthenic base crudes such as those from California and Gulf Coast fields have higher natural antiknock qualities than those from the Pennsylvania fields. The cracking process can be controlled to produce gasoline of very high antiknock properties.

Certain chemicals may be added to gasoline to reduce its tendency to detonate. The effect of these so-called "dopes" upon combustion is to raise the autoignition temperature and also to slow down the combustion process. This affords time for the piston movement to provide some increase in volume for the hot gases. There are many substances which will successfully slow down combustion but which are unsatisfactory for one reason or another.

Tetraethyllead compound is the most popular gasoline knock suppressor in use today. Gasoline treated with this compound is marketed under the trade name Ethyl. Ethylene dibromide is added to prevent the formation of lead oxide, which would otherwise deposit on spark plugs, valve seats, and valve stems. The red aniline dye serves only for identification. The amount of tetraethyllead added to gasoline varies from about 1.4 to 2.7 cc. per gal., depending upon the desired octane requirement. Although it is very effective in slowing the combustion process and preventing detonation, the addition of ethyl increases the price of the fuel which is only partly offset by the increased fuel economy resulting from the use of higher compression ratios.

Antiknock (octane) rating. Since fuel detonation has become such an important factor in fuel selection and its relation to proper engine performance, a means of designating the antiknock quality of certain fuels and particularly the different grades of gasoline seemed desirable. Such a rating system was developed by automotive and petroleum engineers. It is based upon the fact that certain pure hydrocarbons have a very high antiknock quality while others are very poor in this respect. For example, isooctane (C_8H_{18}) has excellent antiknock qualities and is given a rating of 100. Normal heptane (C_7H_{16}), on the other hand, would knock excessively even under low-compression conditions and was assigned a value of zero. Therefore the antiknock value of a fuel is determined by comparing it with a mixture of isooctane and heptane, and the fuel is given an octane rating value based upon the percentage by volume of iso-

[1] *Bull. Univ. Wisconsin Eng. Expt. Sta. Ser. 78.*

octane in an isooctane-heptane mixture; that is, a fuel having the same knock characteristic as a 70-30 per cent isooctane-heptane mixture is called a 70 octane fuel.

Numerous attempts have been made to find some physical or chemical property of motor fuels that would predict the knocking tendency that

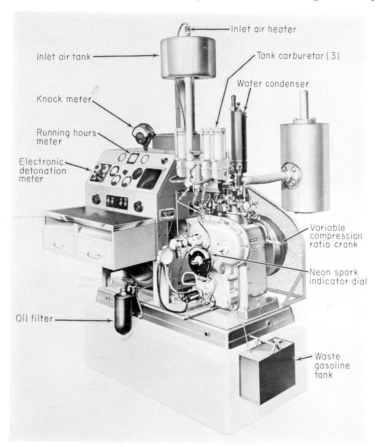

FIG. 11-7. *Waukesha ASTM-CFR octane-rating test engine.* (Courtesy of Waukesha Motor Company.)

the fuel would have when used in a motor. These attempts have been only partially successful, and hence standard methods of determining the octane ratings of fuels have been developed. These methods involve the use of a standard test engine (Fig. 11-7) specifically designed and equipped for testing the knock rating of fuels. The first engine was introduced in 1932 and was known as the *CFR* (*Cooperative Fuel Research*) *engine*. This method was later approved by the American Society for Testing Materials and is now known as the *ASTM* (*CFR*) *motor method*. About 1939, as a result of changes in automotive engine design and fuel characteristics, it was decided that the motor method was no longer fully adequate and reliable as an index of the road performance of fuels. Hence certain changes were made in the original CFR test engine and test specifications, particularly with respect to engine speed, spark timing, and inlet air temperature. The outcome was a modified knock test

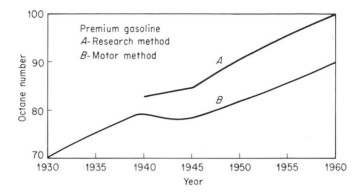

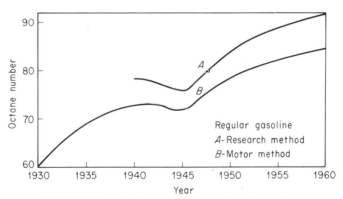

FIG. 11-8. *Trends in antiknock quality of gasoline.*

method known as the *CFR research method,* which was adopted as a tentative standard by the ASTM in 1948. In both the motor method and the research method, the octane number of a fuel is determined by comparing its knocking tendency with those for blends of the reference fuels of known octane number under standard operating conditions. This is done by varying the compression ratio for the sample to obtain the standard knock intensity as defined by a guide curve and as measured by a bouncing pin and knock meter. When the knock meter reading for the sample is bracketed between those for two reference blends differing by not more than two octane numbers, the rating of the sample is calculated by interpolation.

In general, there is a difference in the octane value for a given fuel when tested by each method. With few exceptions, the research method gives higher readings than the motor method. Figure 11-8 shows the trends in the antiknock quality of regular and premium-grade gasoline over a 30-year period.

Use of water with heavy fuels. When kerosene, distillate, or similar heavy fuels are used in tractor engines, better vaporization and, consequently, more power and greater efficiency often result if a comparatively high compression pressure—75 to 90 lb. per sq. in.—is maintained. However, pronounced detonation occurs, particularly at heavy loads for the reason, principally, that such heavy-fuel mixtures ignite at a lower temperature than a gasoline-and-air mixture, as shown by Table 11-3. It

Table 11-3. Autoignition Temperatures for Liquid Fuels When Vaporized and Mixed with Air [1]

Fuel	Temperature, °F.
Coal-tar oil	1076
Benzol	968
Ethyl alcohol	950
Gasoline	779
Kerosene	716
Gas oil	662

[1] *Purdue Univ. Eng. Expt. Sta. Bull. 27.*

has been found that this knock can be eliminated and smooth action produced by permitting a certain amount of water vapor to enter the fuel mixture. This is done by equipping the carburetor with a water-jet nozzle and needle valve, similar to the fuel nozzle and valve. This valve is opened and the water turned on only when the knock develops; that is, the engine may operate smoothly on kerosene and, therefore, requires no water at certain loads. When the knock does develop, usually at heavy loads, the water valve should be opened just enough to eliminate the noise and no farther. The action of the water has never been clearly determined, but the following theories seem most plausible:

1. It produces a slower burning mixture, that is, one that may be ignited at the usual time, but which burns slower than the same mixture without water vapor. Therefore, the explosion occurs later, or when the piston has reached the end of the stroke.

2. It reduces the temperature in the combustion space, thereby retarding or preventing the preignition of the mixture.

3. It results in some sort of chemical action whereby compounds are formed that do not ignite so readily at the existing temperature.

Vapor lock. Vapor lock, gas lock, or air lock is the partial or complete interruption of the fuel flow in the fuel-feed system as a result of vapor-ization of the fuel and the formation of vapor or gas bubbles at some point. It may be due to the use of a fuel having a too high percentage of light or volatile material or to the location of the fuel tank, lines, pump, and so on, with respect to the hotter parts of the engine. Vapor lock often occurs with engines operated at high altitudes as a result of the lower boiling point.

Difficulties from vapor lock show themselves most commonly in fail-ure of the engine to idle after a fast, hot run or in traffic; sometimes in intermittent or uneven acceleration after idling; and sometimes by ir-regular operation during a sustained high-speed run. Complete stoppage of the engine rarely occurs, but when it does, the cause may be traced either to vapor lock in the line leading to the carburetor or to boiling in the filter bowl.

Combustion of hydrocarbon fuels. The term *combustion* is applied to the process by which a fuel unites chemically with oxygen, producing what is known as an oxide and often generating heat of considerable intensity, and sometimes light. It may be a very slow or a very rapid action. For example, the rusting of a piece of iron is a comparatively slow process, resulting in the union of the iron with oxygen, forming what is known as red iron oxide or rust. In a common wood or coal stove there is a more rapid union of oxygen with the carbon of the wood or coal, resulting in a high temperature and a heating effect.

In the internal-combustion engine, rapid combustion takes place; that is, the fuel, when mixed with the proper amount of oxygen and ignited, burns instantaneously, resulting in the production of gaseous oxides—largely carbon monoxide and dioxide—and water. These gases, being con-fined in a very small space, produce high pressure and consequently exert great force on the piston of the engine and thus generate power.

Oxygen, therefore, is necessary for combustion in all cases, and the chemical action taking place during the combustion of the fuel mixture in a gas engine may be represented by the following chemical equation:

$$CH_4 + 2O_2 = CO_2 + 2H_2O$$

or, for a pure liquid fuel such as octane (C_8H_{18}),

$$C_8H_{18} + 12.5O_2 = 8CO_2 + 9H_2O$$

The oxygen, in all cases, is obtained from the atmosphere; that is, a certain amount of air is mixed with the fuel before ignition takes place. Although air is only about 23 per cent oxygen, the other 77 per cent is largely nitrogen, which does not have any effect upon combustion.

Correct fuel mixtures. Knowing the chemical composition of a fuel, the atomic weight of the principal elements involved, namely, carbon, hydrogen, and oxygen, and the percentage of oxygen in the atmosphere, we can readily calculate the amount of air necessary to produce perfect combustion in the gas-engine cylinder.

If pure octane is used as a fuel and the atomic weights are 12 for carbon, 1 for hydrogen, and 16 for oxygen, such a calculation would be as follows:

$$C_8H_{18} + 12.5O_2 = 8CO_2 + 9H_2O \tag{1}$$

or $$(96 + 18) + 12.5(32) = 8(12 + 32) + 9(2 + 16) \tag{2}$$

or $$114 \quad + \quad 400 \quad = \quad 352 \quad + \quad 162 \tag{3}$$

From Eq. (3) it is observed that 114 lb. of fuel requires 400 lb. of oxygen. Therefore, if air is 23 per cent oxygen, a total of 1,739 lb. of air is needed to supply this oxygen and the fuel-air ratio is 1,739 ÷ 114, or 15.3. In general, a fuel-air mixture of 1 to 15 by weight is considered as correct for complete and normal combustion.

A fuel mixture containing less than the required amount of air is known as a rich mixture; that is, there is not enough oxygen present to combine with all the carbon in the fuel and produce complete combustion. Hence free carbon is liberated, creating a black smoke at the exhaust. The usual indications of a too rich mixture are (1) black smoke at the exhaust, (2) lack of power, and (3) overheating of the engine.

A mixture containing more than the required amount of air is known as a lean mixture, and is best indicated by what is known as backfiring through the intake passage and carburetor. Such a mixture is very slow burning and produces (1) uneven firing, (2) lack of power, and (3) overheating. Table 11-4 shows the effect of various air-fuel mixtures on the color of the exhaust flame.

Table 11-4. Colors of Exhaust Flame

Air-fuel ratio	Color of exhaust flame	Condition of mixture
8.5 to 1	Bright yellowish-orange–black smoke	Very rich
9.5 to 1	Bright yellow	Rich
9.7 to 1	Bluish-white with faint yellow tinge	Rich
10 to 1	Light blue with trace of yellow	Rich
11.3 to 1	Light blue	Slightly rich
13.6 to 1	Intense light blue	Approaching ideal
15 to 1	Light blue of maximum intensity	Ideal
17.3 to 1	Whitish-blue of less intensity	Lean

Effects of fuel mixtures on efficiency and power. The effects of fuel mixture on engine performance are discussed by Wilson [1] as follows:

The mixture ratio can vary over a wide range without causing the engine to stop. However, for good performance and economy of operation the ratio should not differ much from 13 to 15 lb. of air per pound of gasoline, and this

[1] *Bull. Univ. Wisconsin Eng. Expt. Sta. Ser. 78.*

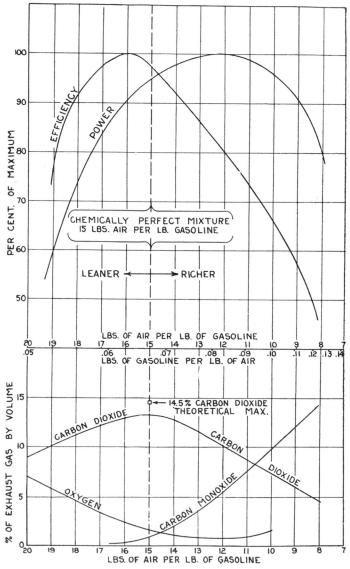

FIG. 11-9. *Curves showing the effect of air-fuel ratio upon power, economy, and exhaust-gas analysis.*

ratio should be maintained for all speeds and all loads except full load. Figure 11-9 shows the effect of varying the air-fuel ratio by changing the carburetor adjustments or the size of the gasoline jets. The point of maximum efficiency (16 lb. of air per pound of gasoline) occurs for a carburetor adjustment leaner than that required for maximum power (12 lb. of air per pound of gasoline). Hence, the proper adjustment is somewhere in between these two limits. Maximum power may be obtained only at the expense of supplying an excess amount of gasoline per horsepower delivered. An adjustment of the carburetor for about 14¾ lb. of air per pound of gasoline would mean about 96 per cent maximum efficiency. Maximum efficiency may be anywhere between 17 and 24 per cent of the heat applied in the fuel, depending upon the design and condition of the engine.

As the throttle approaches the wide-open position, some increase in the richness of the mixture is desirable in order to permit the development of maximum horsepower. This can be accomplished only at the expense of economy, for the use of a rich mixture of 12 lb. of air to 1 lb. of gasoline results in a decrease in efficiency to 80 per cent of the maximum.

In addition to the lack of economy resulting from the use of overrich mixtures, there is the still more serious effect of the resulting deadly carbon monoxide, which is the poisonous element in the exhaust gas. It is colorless, almost odorless, and has no irritating effect upon the lungs. The presence of only 1 part in 5,000 parts of air taken into the lungs for a period of 5 or 6 hr. will cause severe headache, while 1 part in 500 for a period of 1 hr. is sufficient to cause death. It acts largely by poisoning the brain cells through the displacement of oxygen in the blood. Figure 11-9 shows that the amount of carbon monoxide is practically negligible for air-fuel ratios of 16:1 or greater. For rich mixtures there is not enough oxygen present for complete combustion. Carbon dioxide measurements are being used as a good indication of the completeness of combustion, for the carbon of the fuel must be burned to carbon dioxide in order to liberate the maximum amount of energy.

Proper carburetor adjustment is usually the only means by which a correct fuel mixture may be obtained. Some of the factors affecting it are (1) the load on the engine, (2) the speed of the engine, (3) the size and type of the engine, (4) the type of cooling system used, and (5) the kind of fuel used.

REFERENCES

Alcohol-Water Injection for High Compression Tractor and Automobile Engines, *Agr. Eng.*, Vol. 31, No. 2.

ASTM Standards on Petroleum Products, issued annually by the American Society for Testing Materials, Philadelphia.

BARGER, E. L., W. M. CARLETON, E. G. McKIBBEN, and ROY BAINER, "Tractors and Their Power Units," John Wiley & Sons, Inc., New York, 1952.

Forum on Tractor Fuels, *ASTM Spec. Tech. Publ.* 82.

HELDT, P. M., "High-speed Combustion Engines," 16th ed., Chilton Company, Philadelphia, 1956.

LICHTY, L. C., "Internal Combustion Engines," 6th ed., McGraw-Hill Book Company, Inc., New York, 1951.

MOSES, BEN D., and KENNETH R. FROST, "Farm Power," John Wiley & Sons, Inc., New York, 1952.

OBERT, EDWARD F., "Internal Combustion Engines," 2d ed., International Textbook Company, Scranton, Pa., 1950.

Oil and Gasoline Information for Motorists, *Bull. Univ. Wisconsin Eng. Expt. Sta. Ser. 78.*

POPOVICH, M., and CARL HERING, "Fuels and Lubricants," John Wiley & Sons, Inc., New York, 1959.

Significance of ASTM Tests for Petroleum Products, *ASTM Spec. Tech. Publ. 7-B.*

SMITH, MARION L., and KARL W. STINSON: "Fuels and Combustion," McGraw-Hill Book Company, Inc., New York, 1952.

Symposium on Diesel Fuels, *ASTM Spec. Tech. Publ. 167.*

Tractor Fuels, *Kansas State Coll. Eng. Expt. Sta. Bull. 37.*

WORTHINGTON, W. H., The Economic Evaluation of Farm Tractor Fuels, *Agr. Eng.*, Vol. 32, No. 9.

PROBLEMS AND QUESTIONS

1. Explain the refining process followed in producing gasoline.

2. Discuss the chemical composition, gravity, vaporizing characteristics, and heating value of the most common engine fuels.

3. Distinguish between kerosene and distillate as to their physical characteristics and use as engine fuels.

4. Discuss alcohol as an engine fuel.

5. Prepare typical distillation curves for regular-grade gasoline, kerosene, distillate, and diesel fuel.

6. Explain with reasons what points in a fuel distillation curve are most indicative of the fuel quality and value.

7. Explain how fuels are tested and rated for antiknock quality.

8. Explain the combustion process as it takes place with a simple gaseous fuel and the relationship of this process to correct fuel-mixture control.

9. Sketch curves showing the relationship of air-fuel ratio to engine power, efficiency, and exhaust-gas composition.

10. Assuming that air contains 22.7 per cent oxygen, compute the number of pounds of air required for the perfect combustion of a gallon of butane.

11. Compare the cost per 1,000 B.t.u. of good-quality gasoline, diesel fuel, and a "half-and-half" butane-propane mixture, assuming the cost per gallon for each fuel is 15 cents.

12

Fuel Supply and Carburetion

The fuel-supply and carburetion system for an ordinary-compression carbureting-type engine consists essentially of (1) a fuel-supply container or tank, (2) a carburetor, (3) the necessary connecting lines, pump, filter, etc., and (4) the intake manifold to conduct the mixture from the carburetor to the cylinder. The usual systems are:

1. The suction system, as used on some single-cylinder engines (Fig. 12-2).

2. Gravity feed with float-type carburetor and elevated fuel tank, as used on both single- and multiple-cylinder stationary and automotive-type engines (Fig. 12-3).

3. The force-feed system with float-type carburetor, as used on both single- and multiple-cylinder stationary and automotive-type engines (Fig. 12-4).

Principles of carburetion. The functions of a carburetor are (1) to assist in properly vaporizing the fuel, (2) to mix the vaporized fuel in the correct proportions with air, and (3) to supply the engine with the proper quantity of this mixture depending upon the load, speed, temperature, and other conditions present. All carburetors, regardless of the type, size, speed, number of cylinders, and other engine characteristics, operate on the same basic principles, as illustrated in Fig. 12-1. The carburetor is attached to the cylinder block by the intake manifold and, in turn, is connected to the combustion chamber by the intake valve (see Fig. 12-2). On the intake stroke this valve opens and the piston movement creates a low pressure in the cylinder. This results in a suction action at the air entrance to the carburetor and a high-velocity air flow past the fuel-jet nozzle in which a certain fuel level is maintained. Thus a reduced pressure is created at the nozzle and atomized fuel enters the airstream at this point and forms a combustible mixture. The air passage in the carburetor is reduced in cross section at the nozzle in order to increase the air velocity at this point and thereby create a greater reduction in the nozzle pressure than would exist otherwise. This restriction in the carburetor air passage is called the venturi and is common to all types of carburetors.

The following conditions are of fundamental consideration in the proper functioning of any carburetor:

1. A constant and specific fuel level must be maintained in the nozzle.

2. There must be at least partial if not complete vaporization of the liquid fuel, regardless of surrounding temperatures.

3. The correct mixture of vaporized fuel and air must be maintained at all times, regardless of engine load, speed, temperature, atmospheric pressure, and other operating conditions.

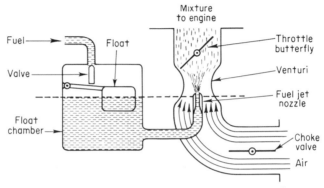

FIG. 12-1. *Operation of a simple jet-nozzle type of carburetor.*

Mixture proportioning by a simple carburetor. The problem of maintaining an optimum fuel mixture and supplying the correct amount of this mixture to each cylinder of an engine regardless of speed and speed range, power output, temperature, atmospheric pressure, and other operating conditions is a complex one and explains why the carburetors used on most automotive-type engines are relatively complex. For example, suppose that an engine is equipped with a simple carburetor, as shown in Fig. 12-1, and is operating at a comparatively low speed and light load, but with the proper fuel mixture. Obviously, the throttle butterfly will be nearly closed. Now suppose that the throttle is suddenly opened with the idea of increasing the engine speed or power output. The increased throttle opening itself permits a greater suction at the nozzle, causing more fuel to be taken up by the airstream. Likewise, the velocity of the air through the carburetor increases so that it would seem likely that the correct air-fuel proportion would be maintained. However, such is not the case. Experience as well as theory has proved that the quantity of air drawn in does not increase at a rate great enough to maintain the correct air-fuel mixture, and the mixture becomes too rich. Now suppose that with the engine running at this increased speed, the fuel flow from the nozzle is readjusted and reduced so that the mixture is again correct. If the engine were again slowed down by closing the throttle, the mixture would be too lean, because the decreased suction would not permit the required amount of fuel in proportion to the air to be drawn from the nozzle. The explanation of this change and variation in the fuel mixture with changes in engine speed and load is based upon certain fundamental laws pertaining to the flow of air and liquids and the differences in their densities and other physical characteristics.

FUEL-SUPPLY AND CARBURETION SYSTEMS

The suction system. The fuel is placed in a tank that is located below the carburetor, with a fuel line connecting the two (Fig. 12-2). On

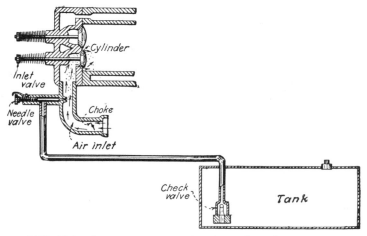

FIG. 12-2. *The suction system of fuel supply and carburetion.*

the suction stroke of the piston, owing to the vacuum produced in the cylinder, fuel is drawn through the fuel line to the carburetor. At the same time, air is drawn through the air passage. The fuel mixture thus formed passes into the combustion space of the cylinder and is ignited. The correct mixture is obtained by the proper adjustment of the fuel needle valve, which controls the amount of fuel passing through the jet nozzle. With this system, as well as with all others, it is necessary to maintain a certain fuel level in the nozzle of the carburetor. This is done by placing some kind of check valve in the fuel line, which prevents the fuel from running back into the tank at the end of the suction stroke, so that, at the beginning of the next intake stroke, fuel is available at the nozzle and is immediately drawn from it.

Gravity system. The second, or gravity, system, as illustrated in Fig. 12-3, consists of (1) the tank, placed above the carburetor; (2) the fuel line; (3) a filter; and (4) the carburetor, fed by gravity. The quantity of fuel that is allowed to flow into the carburetor is controlled by a hollow metal float. This float is attached to a float valve in such a way as to allow the fuel to enter the carburetor at the same rate at which it is being consumed by the engine. This system likewise maintains an absolutely uniform level of fuel in the carburetor, regardless of the quantity in the tank, and therefore is adapted to gasoline and other liquid-fuel-burning engines.

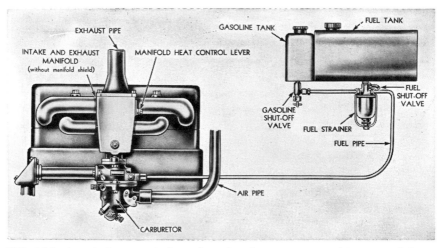

FIG. 12-3. *A typical tractor fuel-supply and carburetion system.* (Courtesy of International Harvester Company.)

Force-feed system. All automobile engines and some stationary power units have the fuel tank located at a level below that of the carburetor. This permits placing the tank where it is convenient for filling yet out of the way. However, a special type of pump is needed to lift the fuel from the tank to the float-type carburetor. This system is shown by Fig. 12-4.

The operation of the pump (Fig. 12-5) is as follows: Movement of the rocker arm *D*, which is pivoted at *E*, by a cam on the camshaft, pulls the diaphragm *A* downward against the pressure of spring *C* and creates a vacuum in pump chamber *M*. Fuel from the tank enters the sediment bowl *K* through strainer *L* and passes through the check valve *N* into pump chamber *M*. On the return stroke, spring pressure pushes the diaphragm upward, forcing fuel from the chamber *N* through outlet valve *O* into vapor dome *P* and out to the carburetor. When the carburetor bowl is filled, the float in the float chamber will close the float valve, thus creating a pressure in pump chamber *M*. This pressure will hold diaphragm *A* downward against the spring pressure, and it will remain in this position until the carburetor requires further fuel and the float valve opens. The rocker arm *D* is in two pieces and is split at *R*. Therefore the movement of the rocker arm is absorbed by this "break" at R when fuel is not required. Spring S is merely for the purpose of keeping the rocker arm in constant contact with the actuating cam. Figure 12-6 shows another more compact type of pump.

Carburetor types and construction. The suction type of carburetor, illustrated in Fig. 12-2, is the simplest possible device that can be used.

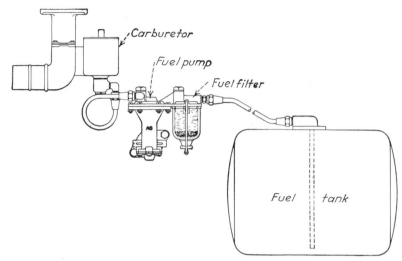

FIG. 12-4. *Float-type carburetor with pump feed.*

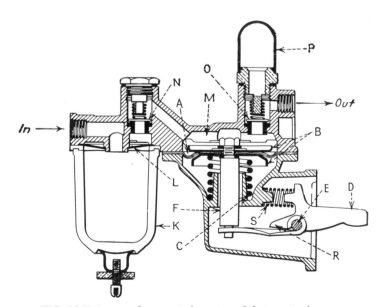

FIG. 12-5. *Sectional view of the automobile-type fuel pump.*

It consists essentially of a cast-iron body, the jet nozzle, a fuel needle valve, and the choke. Its use is confined almost entirely to small, single-cylinder stationary engines burning gasoline.

The narrow part of the air passage around the nozzle of a carburetor (Fig. 12-7), usually called the *venturi,* is for the purpose of creating a

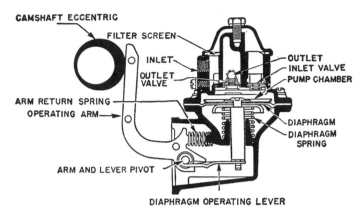

FIG. 12-6. *Late type of fuel pump and filter.*

greater air velocity and, therefore, a stronger sucking effect at this point. The purpose of the choke is to shut off the air so that a greater amount of fuel may be drawn in, when the engine is being started, because the slow piston movement provides only limited suction. Ordinarily, the

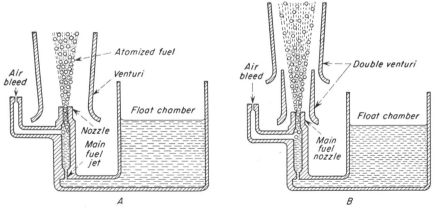

FIG. 12-7. *Air-bleed principle with* (A) *single venturi and* (B) *double venturi.*

choke should be used for starting only and not for adjusting the mixture during operation. The needle valve is the only means of adjusting and controlling the mixture in the suction system.

The float-type carburetor (Fig. 12-8) is a rather complex device and is usually made up of the following essential parts: (1) choke, (2) float and float valve, (3) venturi, (4) main jet, (5) main-jet nozzle, (6) main-jet needle valve, (7) idling jet, (8) idling-jet-adjustment needle valve, (9) air bleed, and (10) throttle butterfly. The float, together with the float valve, controls the fuel entering the float or fuel chamber of the carburetor from the tank and thus maintains a constant fuel level in this chamber and at the jet nozzle. The float is made of light-gauge copper or brass and is hollow.

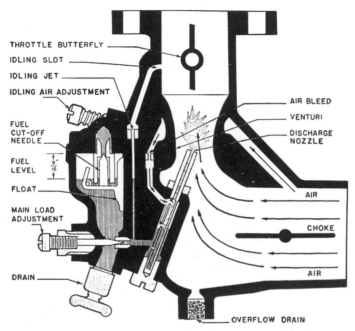

FIG. 12-8. *Updraft tractor carburetor with single venturi and both load and idling mixture adjustments.*

The main jet is a small opening or passage of exact size through which fuel passes from the float chamber to the main-jet nozzle. The fuel flow through the main jet may be controlled by means of a needle valve or it may be what is known as a *fixed jet*. The small, stationary, single- and multiple-cylinder engines and all automobile and truck engines are usually equipped with a fixed-jet carburetor (Fig. 12-9). Medium- and large-size tractor engines, and particularly those burning a heavy fuel, use carburetors with an adjustable main jet (Figs. 12-12 and 12-13). Some automobile-engine carburetors are equipped with a special type of main-jet control, such as a metering pin that controls and varies the fuel flow from the main jet according to the throttle position and engine speed. Such a carburetor is shown in Fig. 12-16.

The idling jet, as the name implies, supplies fuel at idling or low engine speeds only. It usually consists of a special fuel passage that leads to an opening into the airstream at the edge of the throttle butterfly. The opening is on the manifold side of the butterfly; hence when the latter is practically closed, the manifold suction pulls the necessary idling fuel from this orifice. As the throttle opens for increased speed, the suction on the idling orifice decreases and reacts directly on the main-jet nozzle. All carburetors are equipped with a needle valve for maintaining the correct idling mixture adjustment. In most cases this valve controls the air flow rather than the fuel, although there are a few exceptions.

The term *air bleed* refers to certain types of carburetors that control the fuel flow from the main jet and the resultant fuel mixture by permitting a fine stream of air to mix with the fuel in the nozzle. This device is shown in Figs. 12-7 and 12-8. The air bubbles break up the fuel into smaller particles before it leaves the nozzle and thereby aid in producing better atomization and mixture control.

The throttle butterfly is for the purpose of controlling the quantity of mixture allowed to enter the cylinders. It therefore controls the engine speed and power. With a low speed or a light load, less fuel mixture would be required, and the throttle would be only partly open. For a high speed or a heavy load, the throttle would be wide open in order to permit the cylinders to receive a full charge. The opening and closing of this device, according to the engine speed and power output required, are effected by a foot lever, as in automobiles, or by means of a hand lever and mechanical governor, as in farm tractors.

All float types of carburetors are equipped with some sort of compensating device or arrangement or are so constructed that the mixture adjusts itself instantly to any changes in engine speed or load and thus remains properly proportioned. Several different methods are employed by carburetor manufacturers to bring about this action. The more important of these are explained in the descriptions of a number of well-known makes of carburetors.

Downdraft vs. updraft carburetors. A downdraft carburetor is one that is mounted above the intake manifold and engine so that the air enters the upper part of the carburetor and the mixture flows downward into the manifold. An updraft carburetor is mounted below or beside the engine block and the mixture flows upward into the engine. Downdraft carburetors are used almost exclusively on automobile and truck engines and for some stationary power units, particularly V-type engines, for the reason that installation is easier and the device is more accessible and less exposed to dust, oil, and moisture. Another advantage of the downdraft carburetor is that any excess fuel caused by "flooding" or overchoking will run directly into the engine and thus eliminate a fire hazard. Updraft carburetors are used exclusively on tractors and many stationary power units because of more suitable installation adaptability and accessibility. There is no difference in the operating economy or efficiency of these two types of carburetors, provided they are properly designed and adapted to the engine in other respects.

FLOAT-TYPE CARBURETORS

Zenith Model 61. The Zenith Model 61 carburetor (Fig. 12-9) is a single-venturi plain-jet updraft carburetor with a fixed main jet. It is used on some small tractors and stationary engines. Figure 12-10 shows the operation of the device under low-speed or idling conditions. The fuel for idling is supplied through the main jet to a well directly below the main discharge jet. The fuel travels from this well through the idle

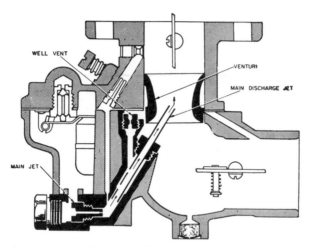

FIG. 12-9. *Updraft tractor carburetor with single venturi showing fixed jet and operation under load conditions.*

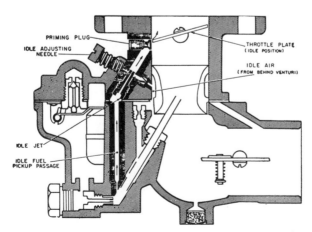

FIG. 12-10. *Updraft tractor carburetor showing operation under idling conditions.*

fuel passage to the idle jet. The air for the idle mixture originates behind the venturi. The position of the idle adjusting needle in this passage
controls the suction on the idle jet and hence the idle mixture. Figure 12-9 shows the operation under high-speed and load conditions. The
main jet controls the fuel delivery during the part-throttle range from
about one-fourth to full throttle opening. To maintain a proper mixture
ratio, a small amount of air is admitted through the well vent into the
discharge jet through the air-bleed holes at a point below the level of
the fuel in the metering well.

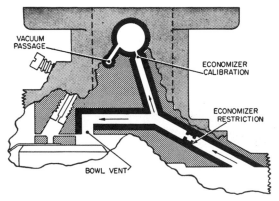

FIG. 12-11. *Economizer system for Zenith Model 61 carburetor.*

Figure 12-11 shows the economizer system used on the Zenith Model
61 carburetor. It consists of (1) a "milled" slot in the throttle shaft,
which acts as a valve to open or close the system; (2) a vacuum passage
from the throttle bore to the slot in the throttle shaft; and (3) a vacuum
passage from the slot in the throttle shaft to the fuel bowl. The purpose
of the economizer is to provide economical fuel mixtures for part-throttle
operation while still permitting the richer ratios that are needed for full-
load operation. The economizer system performs its function by establishing a "back suction" on the fuel in the fuel bowl during most of
the part-throttle range of operation. This "back suction" is created by
manifold vacuum through the channels connecting the throttle bore with
the fuel bowl. This retards the flow of fuel through the metering systems
and thus permits the carburetor to operate on leaner part-throttle mixture ratios. The rotation of the throttle shaft controls the economizer
system. During part-throttle operation from about one-quarter to three-
quarters throttle, the passages are open and the pressure in the fuel bowl
is lowered. This retards the flow through the main jet and a leaner mixture is supplied. On full-throttle opening the passages are closed and the
main jet flows to full capacity to supply the richer mixture required.

International Model D-10. The International Model D-10 carburetor (Fig. 12-12) is a plain-tube, single-venturi, updraft carburetor with an adjustable main jet as well as idling jet.

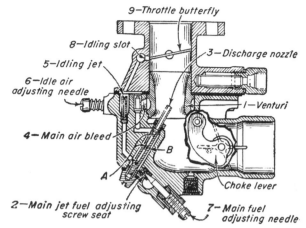

FIG. 12-12. *Sectional view of International Model D-10 carburetor.* (Courtesy of International Harvester Company.)

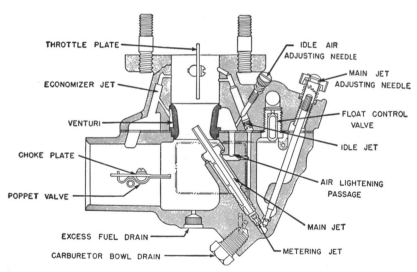

FIG. 12-13. *Sectional view of Marvel-Schebler Model TSX carburetor.*

Marvel-Schebler Model TSX. The Marvel-Schebler Model TSX carburetor (Fig. 12-13) is used on a number of tractors and stationary engines. It is a plain-tube, single-venturi, updraft carburetor with adjustable main and idling jets.

Deere Duplex Model DLTX-75. The Deere duplex carburetor (Fig. 12-14) is a two-barrel device; that is, it has a separate barrel for each cylinder. There is a single body and fuel chamber, but there are two choke valves, two main jet nozzles, two venturis, two idling adjusting

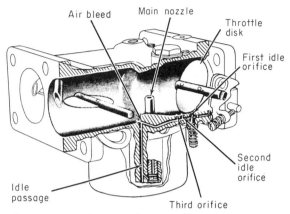

FIG. 12-14. *Duplex tractor carburetor showing idling-mixture circuit.* (Courtesy of Deere and Company.)

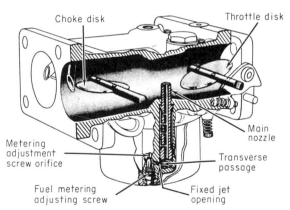

FIG. 12-15. *Duplex tractor carburetor showing load-mixture circuit.* (Courtesy of Deere and Company.)

needles, and two throttle butterflies. This duplex feature permits more precision control of the fuel mixture for maximum power and economy. Figures 12-14 and 12-15 show the idling and load circuits. Under load conditions, the main supply of fuel enters the main nozzle through a fixed jet. Usually enough fuel flows through this jet to give normal engine operation. However, an auxiliary orifice provides an additional supply of fuel to the nozzle if it is needed. This fuel supply is controlled by a metering adjusting screw.

Automotive-engine carburetors. The Carter Model W-1 and Zenith Model 228 carburetors (Figs. 12-16 and 12-17) are representative of the construction and operation of carburetors used for automobile and truck engines. Both are downdraft types. The Carter W-1 has two special features for maintaining a correct fuel mixture for variable speeds and loads. The first is the triple-venturi arrangement with the main-jet nozzle feeding fuel into the airstream of the smallest venturi. The second feature is the three-step metering rod that controls the fuel flow from the chamber

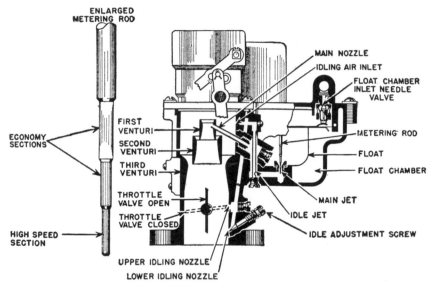

FIG. 12-16. *Downdraft automotive-type carburetor showing triple venturi and metering rod.*

to the main-jet nozzle according to speed and load conditions. Figure 12-16 shows the metering rod in detail. It is connected to the throttle-butterfly control linkage in such a way that it is lifted as the butterfly is opened. As it rises in the calibrated orifice, its diameter decreases and thereby an increased fuel flow occurs. This metering rod is precision-made to an exact size, and two or more sizes are available. For example, if a rod of greater "step" diameter is used, the fuel flow through the main jet will be decreased and the mixture made leaner.

The Zenith Model 228 downdraft carburetor utilizes a vacuum-controlled jet valve to supplement the main jet in supplying the correct amount of fuel to the mixture at high speeds and heavy loads. Referring to Fig. 12-17, the main jet controls the fuel mixture at one-quarter to three-quarter throttle opening. Precise mixture control is obtained by means of the well vent or high-speed bleeder which feeds air into the main discharge jet through small holes at a point below the fuel level.

As the throttle approaches a full-open, maximum-speed position, a second vacuum-controlled power jet (Fig. 12-18) comes into action and supplies some additional fuel to the main discharge jet. The vacuum piston assembly is connected to the intake manifold through a passage in the carburetor body which connects to a similar passage in the mani-

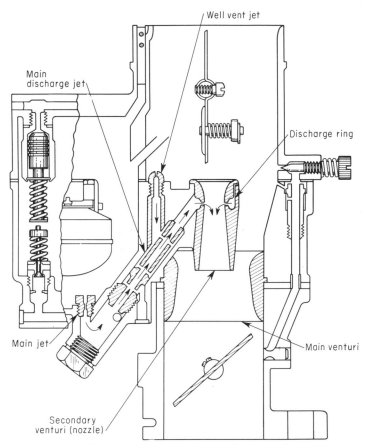

FIG. 12-17. *Downdraft carburetor showing medium-speed mixture control.*

fold. Normally, with a partly closed throttle, the vacuum effect holds the piston assembly in a raised position. However, as the throttle opening increases, the vacuum decreases and the spring pressure forces the piston assembly downward, opening the power-jet valve and feeding additional fuel to the main discharge jet. The entire system functions automatically depending upon the throttle butterfly position as determined by the engine load and speed.

Multiple-barrel carburetors. Very high-speed engines having six or more cylinders such as are used for automobiles, trucks, and airplanes are usually equipped with multiple-barrel carburetors. Such carburetors have a single-body fuel chamber, float, air opening, and choke valve but have multiple idling and high-speed or load circuits and throttle butterflies. For example, if a six-cylinder engine is equipped with a two-barrel carburetor, one set of jets provides the mixture for only three cylinders.

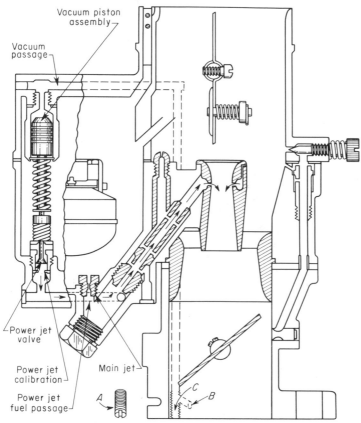

FIG. 12-18. *Downdraft carburetor showing high-speed mixture control.*

If an eight-cylinder engine is equipped with a four-barrel carburetor, one set of jets provides the mixture for only two cylinders. The advantage lies in the fact that in such high-speed, multiple-cylinder engines, there is a limit to the rate at which the mixture can be formed and transferred to each cylinder in proper sequence. In other words, a plain single-barrel carburetor would be unable to supply a maximum fuel-mixture charge to each cylinder at very high speeds, and the volumetric efficiency and power output would be below normal. The principal disadvantage of these carburetors is their extreme complexity and the difficulty often encountered in obtaining proper adjustment. In other words, there is a

separate idling- and speed-mixture adjustment for each barrel, and care
and skill are required in correlating these adjustments so that all cylinders
receive a correct fuel mixture.

Automatic choke. All carburetors are equipped with a choke valve for
the purpose of reducing the air flow and increasing the suction at the
fuel jets in order to permit the cylinders to receive an effective charge
of fuel mixture to ensure instant starting, particularly when the engine
is cold. For stationary power units and tractors the choke is usually

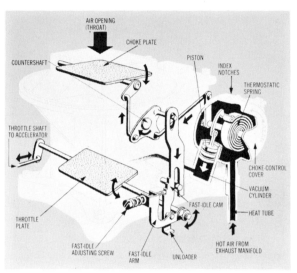

FIG. 12-19. *Construction and operation of an automatic choke mechanism.* (Courtesy
of *Popular Science Monthly.*)

manually operated, but carburetors for automobile and truck engines
are equipped with automatic chokes (Fig. 12-19). Their operation involves the use of manifold vacuum and a thermostatic coil spring. The
spring is tightly enclosed and connected to the engine-exhaust manifold
by a small tube. When the engine is cold, the spring holds the choke
closed against the pull of the vacuum piston and gives the desired starting mixture. When the engine starts, heated air gradually warms the
spring, causing it to uncoil and open the choke. Likewise, when the
engine is running, the manifold vacuum also acts on the piston, which,
in turn, assists in holding the choke valve open. A simple adjustment
on the thermostatic spring housing permits adjusting the tension so as
to give correct choke control under any operating conditions.

Accelerating devices. Automobile-engine carburetors are equipped
with a special device to provide positive and instant fuel-mixture flow
when the throttle butterfly is opened quickly to obtain quick acceleration. Without such a device there would be a lag in engine-speed pickup

and a delayed acceleration. The device usually consists of a small plunger pump that is linked to the throttle-butterfly mechanism. When the latter is opened quickly, the pump plunger forces an extra charge of fuel through a jet into the airstream. Figure 12-20 shows the operation of this device.

Superchargers. A supercharger is a device that forces more fuel mixture into the cylinders than would be drawn in under normal atmos-

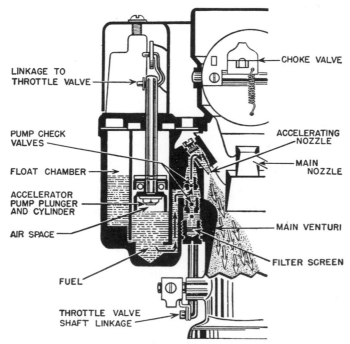

FIG. 12-20. *Downdraft carburetor showing accelerating pump and nozzle.*

pheric conditions, thus making possible a greater power output with the same piston displacement. Its use is particularly important on piston-type airplane engines operating at high altitudes in order to maintain the engine power as the atmospheric pressure decreases. Superchargers are also used on racing engines in order to increase their power and speed without increasing the engine size and weight.

A supercharger is a gear-driven rotary-type air pump which is usually inserted between the carburetor and the engine manifold. Obviously, the entire fuel supply and induction system must be specially designed so that all units work together efficiently. Figure 12-21 shows the two most common types of blowers. Figure 12-22 shows the general construction and operation of the turbocharger used on one make of diesel engine. This device differs from most superchargers in that the required power is derived from an exhaust-driven turbine and not directly from the engine itself. This is a definite advantage because most superchargers operate at relatively high speeds and therefore absorb an appreciable part of the generated engine power.

Carburetion of distillate, kerosene, and special tractor fuels. As previously discussed, distillate and kerosene are not so volatile as gasoline, and a higher engine operating temperature is essential for their successful use. The principal requirements for an engine to use these fuels satisfactorily are:

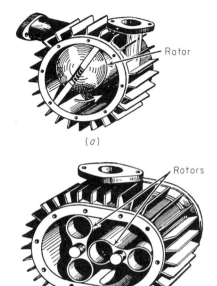

(a)

(b)

FIG. 12-21. *Supercharger blower types.* (a) *Vane.* (b) *Roots blower.*

1. The engine must operate at a uniform speed and under a medium to a heavy load.

2. Provision must be made for starting on gasoline with some convenient means of changing over when the engine is warmed up. For this reason the use of such fuels is impractical if frequent starting and stopping are necessary.

3. Provision must be made for maintaining a higher intake manifold temperature than is normally required for gasoline.

4. The cooling-system temperature must be relatively high and closely controlled according to weather and load conditions by means of a thermostat valve and a radiator curtain or shutters.

5. A relatively low compression ratio—1:4.5 or 1:5—must be used to eliminate detonation.

6. A careful and precise adjustment of the fuel mixture is essential.

Heavy-fuel carburetors are constructed and operate in practically the same way as gasoline carburetors. In fact, any engine that burns distillate successfully will also burn gasoline readily. However, owing to the lower compression ratio, maximum fuel economy will not be obtained. Figure 12-12 shows a carburetor adapted to handling distillate-type fuels.

Distillate-burning tractor engines are usually equipped with a heated manifold and a heat-control valve (Fig. 12-23) whereby the temperature can be varied according to the kind of fuel used, weather, and other conditions.

Carburetion of LP gas. Mention has previously been made of the use of commercial butane and propane as fuel for stationary engines,

tractors, and trucks. These LP gases have certain advantages over gasoline and liquid fuels which make their use desirable and economical,
provided there is a plentiful supply at a reasonable cost per gallon.

LP fuels for commercial use are often referred to as "butane" or "propane" and usually are a mixture of both. The mixture may vary from a

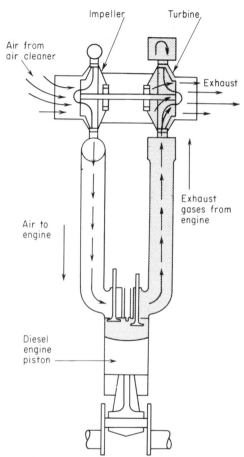

FIG. 12-22. *Exhaust-gas–driven supercharger for diesel engine.* (Courtesy of Caterpillar Tractor Company.)

nearly 100 per cent propane mixture for winter use to a 70-30 per cent
butane-propane mixture for summer use. Some propane is desirable for
the reason that it has a lower boiling temperature than butane and
thereby ensures vaporization at extremely low temperatures.

A study of the physical characteristics of LP gases, Table 12-1, shows
that they differ considerably from liquid fuels; hence their storage and

carburetion must be handled in a different manner. First of all, the boiling temperature of LP fuels is very low and below the freezing temperature of water. This means that such fuels have a high vapor pressure at ordinary temperatures. Hence, they must be stored in a heavy, leakproof tank capable of withstanding considerable pressure. Furthermore, special equipment is needed to convert the liquid fuel to a gas, reduce the pressure, and feed it to the engine in the proper manner.

Figure 12-24 shows the make-up of a complete LP-gas fuel-supply and carburetion system, and Fig. 12-25 shows the pressure-reducing, vaporizing, and carbureting devices as they actually appear. Referring to Fig. 12-24, the liquid fuel passes through a filter to the high-pressure regulator. This device reduces the pressure to about 8 lb. per sq. in., and partial expansion and vaporization begin. The fuel then enters the vaporizer coils, which are surrounded by heated water from the engine cooling system, and further expansion and vaporization occur. The

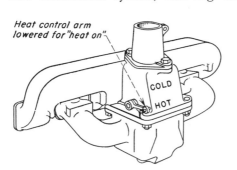

FIG. 12-23. *Manifold with adjustable heat control.*

vapor then passes through the low-pressure regulator, which reduces its pressure slightly below atmospheric. This regulator also controls the gas supply to the carburetor and cuts it off when the engine demand has ceased. The carburetor serves as a mixer to mix the vapor and air in the correct ratio and to supply the proper quantity of this mixture to the engine at all loads and speeds.

A second system (Fig. 12-26), which is used to a limited extent, depends upon the gas vapor itself to flow directly from the tank through

Table 12-1. Characteristics of Commercial Butane and Propane

Characteristic	Propane	Butane
Formula.	C_3H_8	C_4H_{10}
Specific gravity of liquid at 60°F.	0.509	0.584
Init. boiling point at normal atmospheric pressure.	−44°F.	32°F.
Weight per gal. of liquid at 60°F.	4.24	4.86
Vapor pressure at 60°F., lb. per sq. in.	92	12
Vapor pressure at 100°F., lb. per sq. in.	172	37
B.t.u. per lb.	21,600	21,300
B.t.u. per gal.	91,500	103,500
Approximate octane rating.	110	90

pressure regulators to the carburetor. A heat exchanger or special vaporizer is not used, and a fuel with a very low boiling point such as propane gives best results, particularly in cold weather. Usually the original gasoline carburetor is used with this system, and it is possible to operate the engine on gasoline at any time if necessary.

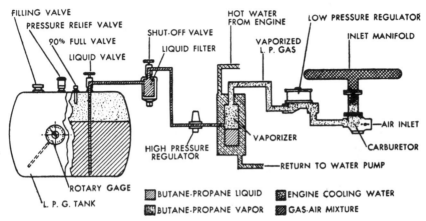

FIG. 12-24. *Basic parts and operation of an LP gas fuel-supply and carburetion system particularly adapted to butane.* (Courtesy of Ensign Carburetor Company.)

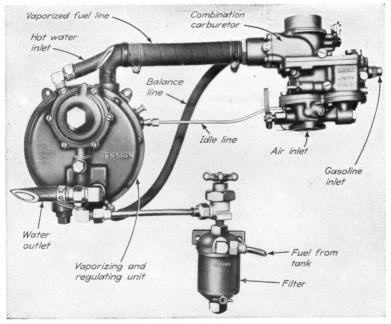

FIG. 12-25. *Butane-vaporizing, pressure-control, and carburetion equipment for tractor engine.* (Courtesy of Ensign Carburetor Company.)

Advantages and disadvantages of LP gases. The principal advantage of any LP gas as an engine fuel is the reduction in engine wear and upkeep expense. Since it is a dry gas, it mixes readily with air and burns cleanly and completely without leaving residue of any kind. This means less carbon deposits, limited piston ring and cylinder wear, and no crankcase dilution.

A second advantage of this fuel is its high antiknock characteristic. LP gases have an octane rating of about 100. Hence they can be used

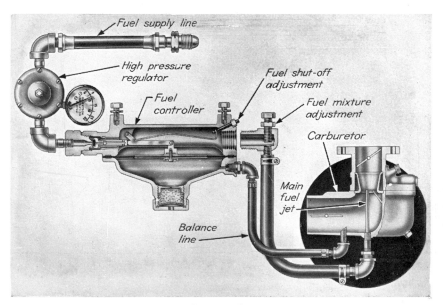

FIG. 12-26. *Propane pressure-control and carburetion equipment for tractor engine.* (Courtesy of Garretson Carburetion System.)

in any high-compression, spark-ignition engine requiring a high-octane gasoline. In fact, to obtain the highest possible thermal efficiency with LP gases a compression ratio of about 8.5:1 is recommended. For optimum results it is also recommended that (1) a cold intake manifold be used in order to improve the volumetric efficiency; (2) the spark be carefully timed; and (3) cold spark plugs be used.

In comparing the cost of LP gases and gasoline as engine fuels, consideration must be given to their comparative weights per gallon and their heating values as well as to their actual prices per gallon. Referring to Table 12-1, propane and butane have heat energy values of 91,500 and 103,500 B.t.u. per gal., respectively. The heat value of regular-grade gasoline is 124,000 B.t.u. per gal. Assuming that an engine will have the same thermal efficiency when burning either LP gas or gasoline, it is obvious that gasoline will give a greater horsepower-hour output per gallon and that the cost per gallon of LP gas must be somewhat less than the cost of gasoline to offset this lower power output. On the other hand, as previously explained, if a higher compression ratio is used with the LP gas, the thermal efficiency may be increased sufficiently to partly offset the effect of this difference in heat value. The curves (Fig. 5-18) show the fuel consumption and other comparative performance characteristics when an engine is operated on LP gas, gasoline, diesel fuel, and tractor fuel.

Handling and storage of LP gas. Since butane and propane vaporize readily at subnormal temperatures, and since the vapor is heavier than air and settles near the floor or ground area, extreme caution must be observed in handling them. Furthermore, the high pressure existing in the storage tanks and equipment increases the possibility of leaks. Open flames, electric arcs, engine exhausts, and the like should be avoided around the storage tanks. Engines should always be stopped when butane is being transferred from one tank to another. A grounding wire or other method of carrying off static electricity should be used on tanks and hoses to prevent sparks. Hose, fittings, and safety devices should be the type recommended for butane service.

REFERENCES

BARGER, E. L., W. M. CARLETON, E. G. McKIBBEN, and ROY BAINER, "Tractors and Their Power Units," John Wiley & Sons, Inc., New York, 1952.

Butane-Propane Gases (handbook), Jenkins Publications, Inc., Los Angeles, Calif.

FISHER, CHAS. H., "Carburetion," 3d ed., Chapman & Hall, Ltd., London, 1951.

HELDT, P. M., "High-speed Combustion Engines," 16th ed., Chilton Company, Philadelphia, 1956.

LICHTY, L. C., "Internal Combustion Engines," 6th ed., McGraw-Hill Book Company, Inc., New York, 1951.

L-P Gas as a Fuel for Farm Power Units, *Agr. Eng.,* Vol. 31, No. 5.

LPG-Engine Fuel and Lubricant Requirements, *Lubrication,* November, 1956.

MOSES, BEN D., and KENNETH R. FROST, "Farm Power," John Wiley & Sons, Inc., New York, 1952.

OBERT, EDWARD F., "Internal Combustion Engines," 2d ed., International Textbook Company, Scranton, Pa., 1950.

PROBLEMS AND QUESTIONS

1. Compare tractor- and automobile-engine fuel-supply systems as to make-up, fuel transfer, and carburetion.

2. Explain why all carburetors are equipped with a separate or special jet and adjustment to supply the fuel and to control the mixture for idling or low engine speeds.

3. Explain why a carburetor with a simple single jet would not give satisfactory results at all loads and speeds on any variable-speed engine.

4. Explain the meaning of mixture compensation, and list as many distinct methods of inducing compensation as shown in the carburetors described.

5. Give a suitable procedure that could be followed in adjusting a tractor carburetor having both idling- and load-mixture adjustments.

6. What effect, if any, does altitude have on the fuel mixture and engine power? How can the situation be adjusted?

7. Under what conditions are multiple-barrel carburetors and superchargers desirable for internal-combustion engines?

8. If gasoline costs 17 cents and weighs 6.15 lb. per gal. and has a B.t.u. value of 20,000 per lb., and if LP gas costs 12 cents and weighs 4.25 lb. per gal. and has a B.t.u. value of 21,600 per lb., which is the most economical fuel to use, assuming the same thermal efficiency in each case?

9. If, in Prob. 8, the engine developed 30 hp. and used 0.60 lb. of fuel per hp.-hr. in each case, which fuel would be cheaper and what would the saving be per 10-hr. day?

13

Air Cleaners

Early tractors were not equipped with any means or device for supplying clean air to the carburetor, mainly because the machines were so large that the air intake was high enough to be out of the zone of dust-laden air. Then, too, little thought was given to the harmful effects of even a very small quantity of fine dust. With the introduction of the smaller, lightweight tractors, it was soon discovered that, under most field conditions, enough dust and fine grit found its way into the cylinders through the carburetor to cause rather rapid wear. In fact, in some sections under certain conditions, enough damage could be done in even a day or two of operation to practically ruin the tractor.

The first idea of the manufacturers of small tractors was to attach a vertical tube to the carburetor air intake, extending it above the tractor far enough to obtain air that was comparatively free from the dust and grit stirred up by the machine itself. It was soon found that this arrangement, though simple, failed to do the work. Some device was needed that would prevent the finest dust as well as the more harmful coarse gritty material from getting into the engine. Then, too, these periscopes soon worked loose and fell off or were removed by the owner in order to permit the tractor's being run under a shed. When once removed, they were seldom replaced, and the resulting trouble was blamed upon the tractor and its maker.

The subject of air cleaners for tractors and trucks, and even for automobiles, has been given a great deal of study by research engineers and manufacturers. A number of reports of experimental work and experience with air cleaners have been published. These are listed at the end of the chapter, and the reader is referred to them for more complete information on the subject.

METHODS OF SUPPLYING CLEAN AIR AND TYPES OF CLEANERS

Partial or complete elimination of engine troubles caused by foreign material entering the carburetor can be secured in the following ways:

1. By a periscope or long metal tube extending above the dust level.

2. By some form of air cleaner or filter.

3. By a combined air cleaner and elevated intake opening.

Any type of air cleaner to give maximum satisfaction must fulfill the following requirements:

1. It must have high cleaning efficiency at all engine speeds and under all operating conditions.

2. It should offer very little restriction to the air flow, since that would reduce the power and fuel economy, nor should it interfere otherwise with the satisfactory operation of the engine.

3. It should require very little or only infrequent attention.

4. It should be compact, rigid, not too heavy, and rattleproof.

Early types of air cleaners. The first tractor air cleaners were of the dry-filter type, consisting essentially of a sheet-metal closed container with an air opening in the side or bottom and an outlet in the top connected to the carburetor air intake. A filtering element, consisting of one or more layers of felt, eider-down cloth, wool, or similar fibrous material, was placed in the bottom of the cleaner and collected the dust as the air passed through. This type of filter soon proved unsatisfactory for several reasons. If it was dense or heavy enough to catch most of the dust, it offered too great restriction to the air flow. Also, it soon became clogged and required frequent cleaning or renewal, and it frequently got out of place as a result of backfiring.

A second simple type (Fig. 13-1) was known as an inertia cleaner. Its operation was based upon the principle that if a liquid or a solid mixture of materials of varying specific gravity is whirled violently, the heavier particles or portions will be thrown to the outside. Therefore, if the dust-laden air, on its way to the carburetor, is first made to whirl violently, the dust, grit, and other solid particles, being heavier, will be thrown to the outside and deposited or carried away, leaving the clean air to enter the carburetor at a small, central opening.

The inertia cleaner cannot be considered as efficient and effective by itself, but it is used on some tractors as a precleaner to remove the coarser material in the air before it enters the regular cleaner, as shown by Fig. 13-4. The dust and trash are caught in the glass jar, which must be removed and emptied periodically.

Another type of air cleaner, which was used quite extensively on tractors at one time, was the water-bath cleaner. As the name implies, the air on its way to the carburetor was drawn through water, which took up any dust and foreign material. Deflector or baffle plates in the upper part of the cleaner body prevented water being taken into the engine.

Water air cleaners proved unsatisfactory for the following reasons: (1) they do not necessarily remove all the dust and dirt; (2) they require too frequent cleaning and replacement of the water, because a certain amount is taken up by the air and goes into the engine; (3) there is considerable air-flow restriction and variation with the change in water level; (4) the metal parts corrode and leak or break; and (5) there is danger of freezing in cold weather.

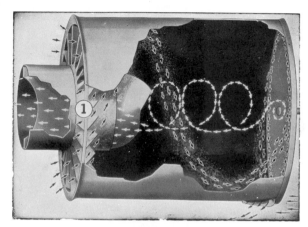

FIG. 13-1. *Dry inertia-type air cleaner.*

Dry-type air filters. Figure 13-2 shows a dry-type air filter as used on some diesel tractors. Air enters at the top, as indicated, where a coarse-mesh screen catches any coarse trash and then flows downward through the center tube to the primary or cyclone cleaner section. This section contains a number of small tubes, each of which consists of an enclosed spiral fin and a smaller center tube. As the dirt-laden air passes downward through these tubes, it is given a whirling action which separates out much of the coarser material which drops into the bottom pan. The partly clean air then passes up through the smaller inner cyclone tubes to the outside of the replaceable element made of resin-impregnated cellulose material. This secondary filter removes the remaining smaller dust particles. Servicing consists in emptying the dust collector cup periodically as necessary and occasional checking of the filter element and possible need of replacement.

Oil-type air filters. Air filters using oil as the dust-collecting medium are used extensively for both stationary and automotive engines of all types. The simplest cleaner using oil (Fig. 13-3) consists of a loose mass of oil-saturated metal shavings through which the air must pass on its way to the carburetor, the dust particles adhering to the oily shavings. This cleaner was used chiefly on some automobile engines and was not reliable and effective under extremely dusty conditions. It was serviced by merely washing the filter element and then applying a coat of fresh oil.

The most dependable and effective oil-type cleaner is known as the *oil-bath type* (Figs. 13-4 and 13-5). The air enters a central tube, passes

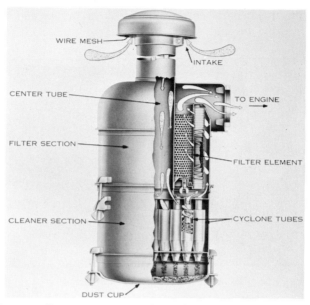

FIG. 13-2. *Dry-type filter using inertia and dry filter element.* (Courtesy of Caterpillar Tractor Company.)

downward at high velocity against the surface of the oil held in a removable cup, makes a sharp 180-deg. turn, and then passes upward through the oil-saturated filtering screens or fibrous material and on to

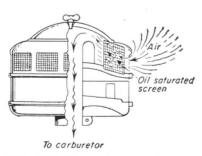

FIG. 13-3. *Plain oil-saturated metal-fiber-type air cleaner.*

the carburetor. The oil mist created by the high-velocity air flow keeps the lower portion of the filter element well saturated with oil at all times. Hence, as long as the proper oil level in the cup is maintained, all dust and dirt particles will be caught by the element. Eventually the dirt is washed from the element and collects in the bottom of the oil cup.

Figure 13-5 shows an oil-bath air cleaner as used on auto and truck engines. Its principle of operation is the same, but it has a different shape, requires less oil, and is constructed so as to eliminate any carburetor suction noise.

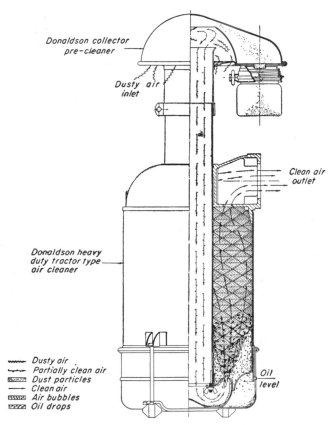

Donaldson collector
pre-cleaner

Dusty air
inlet

Clean air
outlet

Donaldson heavy
duty tractor type
air cleaner

Dusty air
Partially clean air
Dust particles
Clean air
Air bubbles
Oil drops

Oil
level

FIG. 13-4. *Oil-bath tractor air cleaner with collector precleaner.* (Courtesy of Donaldson Company, Inc.)

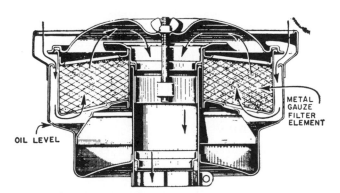

METAL
GAUZE
FILTER
ELEMENT

OIL LEVEL

FIG. 13-5. *Oil-bath air cleaner for automobile and truck engines.*

Most air cleaners used on tractors and farm power units are equipped with a precleaner to catch coarse dirt particles such as chaff, straw, and leaves. The precleaner may be merely a removable cap with coarse screen wire or a centrifugal device with a jar in which the trash is caught.

Breather cleaners. Any engine, such as a tractor motor, with an enclosed crankcase must have a breather opening and cap to permit the unequal pressure in the crankcase, caused by the pumping effect of the pistons, to be balanced by the outside atmospheric pressure. The air drawn in by this action obviously carries considerable dust and dirt with it, which, when taken up by the lubricating oil, eventually causes considerable wear. This trouble is prevented by using a special breather cap containing filtering material such as steel wool, or by connecting the breather opening to the carburetor air cleaner.

Care and servicing of air cleaners. Modern air cleaners are designed to perform efficiently under all conditions, provided they are given regular attention and servicing. Steps and precautions recommended are as follows: (1) keep oil exactly at indicated level at all times; (2) use the kind and viscosity of oil recommended by the manufacturer; (3) remove oil cup and clean out dirt and residue at regular intervals according to instructions; (4) check condition of filtering screens or material frequently and wash with kerosene if necessary; (5) push a rag through the air-inlet tube occasionally to remove dust deposits; (6) check all connections between cleaner and carburetor for leaks, and tighten joints or replace hose if necessary; (7) keep precleaner open and free of trash accumulation at all times.

REFERENCES

Air Cleaners for Motor Vehicles, *Univ. Calif. Agr. Expt. Sta. Bull.* 499.

BARGER, E. L., W. M. CARLETON, E. G. McKIBBEN, and ROY BAINER, "Tractors and Their Power Units," John Wiley & Sons, Inc., New York, 1952.

Dust and the Tractor Engine, *Univ. Calif. Agr. Expt. Sta. Bull.* 362.

MOSES, BEN D., and KENNETH R. FROST, "Farm Power," John Wiley & Sons, Inc., New York, 1952.

The Physical Characteristics of Road and of Field Dust, *S.A.E. Journal*, Vol. 16, p. 243.

PROBLEMS AND QUESTIONS

1. What would be the effect of (a) low oil level in the oil reservoir of an air cleaner, (b) high oil level in the oil reservoir, (c) using very thin oil, and (d) using very heavy oil?

2. Why is it desirable to keep the precleaner free of trash accumulation?

3. What factors are involved which determine the over-all size and filtering capacity of an air cleaner?

14

Cooling and Cooling Systems

As explained in preceding chapters, an internal-combustion engine converts only a limited portion of the total heat energy of the fuel into useful power. The unavoidable losses include (1) friction and mechanical losses, (2) cooling system losses, (3) exhaust heat losses, and (4) losses due to radiation. An analysis of the conversion and disposition of the heat energy received by an engine is known as its heat balance. This is well illustrated by Fig. 14-1, which shows the power output and heat losses for a four-stroke-cycle, spark-ignition engine under different

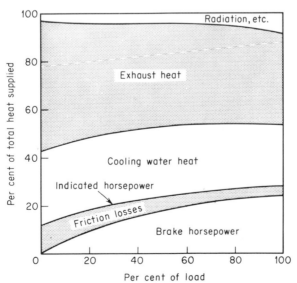

FIG. 14-1. *Typical heat-balance curves for a four-stroke-cycle gas engine.* (Reprinted with permission from H. E. Degler, "Internal Combustion Engines," John Wiley & Sons, Inc., New York, 1938, p. 351.)

load conditions. In general, if such an engine has a thermal efficiency of 25 per cent, the losses are approximately as follows: friction 5 per cent, cooling system 25 per cent, exhaust gases 37 per cent, and radiation and other losses 8 per cent.

It is thus evident that the cylinder, cylinder head, piston, piston rings, valves, and other parts must absorb and transmit a considerable quantity of heat; therefore special provisions must be made to dissipate this heat at a reasonable rate and, at the same time, maintain an efficient engine operating temperature. Such provisions or equipment constitute the engine cooling system.

If an engine were not equipped with some means of cooling, at least three troubles would arise as follows:

1. The piston and cylinder would expand to such an extent that the piston would seize in the cylinder, injuring the latter and stopping the engine.

2. The lubricating qualities of the oil supplied to the cylinder and piston walls would be destroyed by the high temperatures existing.

3. Preignition of the fuel mixture would take place, resulting in knocking and loss of power.

All internal-combustion engines must operate at a certain temperature to produce the best results, and they seldom give the greatest efficiency unless the temperature around the cylinder is between 160 and 200°F. Therefore, a cooling system that permits an excessive absorption of heat, resulting in a low operating temperature, is undesirable and indicates improper design.

The following is a classification of the common methods and systems of engine cooling:

1. Air
2. Liquid
   a. Open jacket or hopper
   b. Thermosiphon
   c. Forced circulation
3. Combination of air and liquid

Air cooling. Cooling by air alone is not used extensively but is satisfactory for certain types of engines and under certain conditions. The cooling effect is produced usually by means of fins or projections on the walls of the cylinder, as shown in Fig. 8-10. These fins may be placed transversely or longitudinally with respect to the cylinder, depending upon the use of the engine and the direction of the air flow past the cylinder. Such an arrangement of fins increases the radiating surface, and therefore the heat escapes faster than it would otherwise. Figure 8-10 illustrates an engine that has the cylinder and crankcase enclosed in a sheet-metal housing and the flywheel equipped with blades so that it will create a suction of air down through the cylinder, thus producing a greater cooling effect.

Air-cooled engines are usually of small bore and stroke; that is, they have small cylinders. Multiple-cylinder air-cooled engines have the cylinders cast individually rather than in pairs or in one block, so that the maximum cooling effect will be obtained. Common examples of air-cooled engines are airplane and motorcycle engines and the power units used for lawn mowers, garden tractors, and other small machines. An air-cooled engine has the following advantages:

1. It is light in weight.
2. It is simpler in construction.
3. It is more convenient and less troublesome.
4. There is no danger of freezing in cold weather.

The principal disadvantages of air cooling are that it is difficult to maintain proper cooling under all conditions, and that it is almost impossible to fully control the cylinder temperature. Air-cooled engines usually run a little hotter than water-cooled engines and require the use of heavier lubricating oil.

Cooling by liquid. Cooling systems using liquids, usually water, are employed for all types of engines from the simple stationary farm engine to the most complicated multiple-cylinder high-speed types.

Water might be termed the universal cooling liquid for tractors, as well as for trucks and automobiles. It has certain important advantages, among which are the following:

1. It is plentiful and readily available nearly everywhere.
2. It absorbs heat well.
3. It circulates freely at all temperatures between the freezing and boiling points.
4. It is neither dangerous, harmful, nor disagreeable to use or handle.

The principal disadvantages of water for cooling are:

1. It has a high freezing point.
2. It may cause excessive corrosion of the radiator and certain metal parts of the engine. Clean, pure water such as rain water gives the best results.
3. It may cause troublesome deposits in the cylinder jackets.
4. Evaporation and boiling require frequent replenishing.

LIQUID COOLING SYSTEMS

Open-jacket or hopper cooling. The simplest system of liquid cooling, known as the open-jacket or hopper system (Fig. 14-2), consists of a hollow space around the cylinder and cylinder head, known as the water jacket, and a cast-iron reservoir, usually cast with the cylinder and opening directly into this jacket. Such an arrangement is simple and convenient but is not adapted to portable engines because the cooling is dependent upon the heat taken up by the water as it evaporates and escapes from the hopper in the form of steam; therefore, if an automobile or tractor engine, for example, were equipped with this system, the water would naturally be thrown and splashed about. Another disadvantage is that more liquid is required. Consequently, the weight of the engine is greater. It is used only on a few stationary single-cylinder engines.

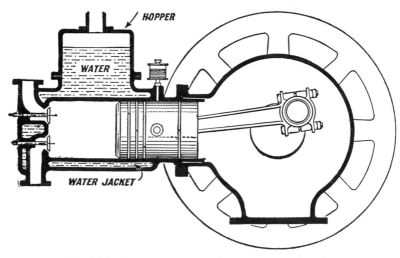

FIG. 14-2. *The open-jacket or hopper system of cooling.*

Thermosiphon system. The thermosiphon system of liquid cooling (Fig. 14-3) includes, in addition to the water jacket about the cylinder, a separate reservoir connected at the top and bottom by a pipe leading to the upper and lower parts of the cylinder, respectively. In tractors, this reservoir is replaced by what is known as the radiator, this being nothing more than a tank made up of many fine passages through which the water flows and in which it cools more rapidly than if held in one solid mass. The operation is based upon the fact that, when water or any other liquid is heated, it expands and its weight per unit volume decreases; that is, the temperature of the water in the cylinder jacket increases as the engine warms up, and therefore the liquid expands and decreases in specific gravity and rises, being pushed out by the heavier cold water coming in from the reservoir through the lower pipe. A slow but continuous circulation is thus started and continues as long as the engine runs, the water passing upward through the upper pipe into the tank and reentering the cylinder from the tank by means of the lower connection. Since the circulation is somewhat slow or sluggish, large radiator connections and a slightly greater amount of liquid are necessary.

Forced-circulation system. The forced-circulation system resembles the thermosiphon system with the exception that some sort of a pump is placed in the lower pipe leading to the cylinder, as shown by Fig. 14-4. This pump, usually of the centrifugal type, forces the water through the cylinder jacket and around to the reservoir, causing a more rapid circulation than that produced by the thermosiphon system. The advantage, therefore, of this system is that, since the water is circulated more

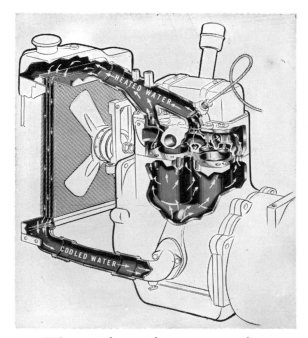

FIG. 14-3. *Thermosiphon system of cooling.*

rapidly, it is cooled faster, and less liquid is required to produce the same cooling effect. Another advantage is that, since the circulation is dependent upon the speed of the pump and therefore upon the speed of the engine, a more uniform temperature is apt to be maintained at all engine speeds and loads.

Combined air and liquid cooling. The combination air and liquid cooling system (Fig. 14-4) is used almost exclusively in automobiles, tractors, and trucks. The pump and fan are mounted on the same shaft and driven by a V belt from the crankshaft. The fan draws cool air through the radiator, cooling the liquid rapidly, and also sends a blast of air past the cylinders, driving the heat away from the engine.

Radiator construction. Water-cooled tractor engines are equipped with the conventional radiator (Fig. 14-5), consisting of the core, an upper and a lower reservoir, and the side members or frame pieces. Since tractors are subjected to considerable jarring and vibration, and surplus weight is of little consequence, the reservoirs and frame parts are made of cast iron rather than sheet metal.

There are two general types of radiator cores, the tubular type with fins (Fig. 14-6) and the cellular or honeycomb type (Fig. 14-7). The

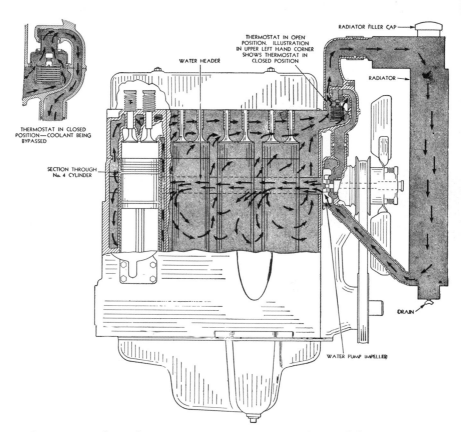

FIG. 14-4. *Forced-circulation system of tractor engine cooling with bypass thermostat.* (Courtesy of International Harvester Company.)

former seems to predominate, probably because of the lower manufacturing cost. The tubes are either round (Fig. 14-6) or flat (Fig. 14-8). Horizontal, thin, metal fins fastened to the tubes increase the rate of heat radiation.

Circulating pumps—fans and fan drives. Engines equipped with the forced-circulation system of cooling use a centrifugal-type pump (Fig. 14-9) to produce this circulation. Such a pump consists of a cast-iron body, the rotating member or impeller with its curved blades, the drive shaft, and the necessary bearings, packing, and oil seals. The pump assembly is usually located on the cylinder head or block behind the radiator. Bearings are of the ball or roller antifriction type and are usually grease-packed and well sealed from water contact. The pump receives the water from the lower radiator connection and forces it through the motor block and out the upper connection.

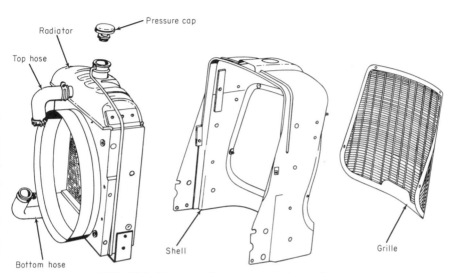

FIG. 14-5. *Tractor radiator construction and parts.*

Fans have four blades and are mounted on the pump shaft. The V-belt drive has some means of tightening or adjusting the belt tension.

Pressure cooling. Some cooling systems operate under pressure by using a special type of radiator cap (Fig. 14-10) which fits very tightly and prevents leakage under low pressures. The overflow opening is also cut off by this cap. The cap is equipped with a spring-controlled valve which permits the escape of the liquid or steam if the pressure becomes too high. Another valve opens to relieve any vacuum effect caused by the cooling of the water or condensing of the

FIG. 14-6. *Tubular radiator construction.*

vapor. The pressure system permits operating the engine at a higher temperature without boiling the water and losing it by evaporation. An increase in pressure of 1 lb. per sq. in. will raise the boiling temperature of the water about 3°F.

Engine-heat control. Since tractors are operated under a great variety of weather and load conditions, designers provide some means of control by which a uniform engine operating temperature may be maintained regardless of the varying factors mentioned. The best operating

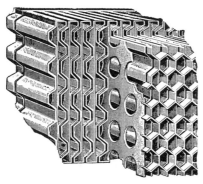

FIG. 14-7. *Cellular-type radiator construction.*

FIG. 14-8. *Flat-tube type of radiator construction.*

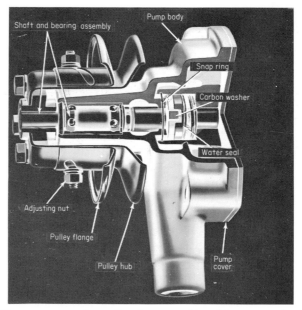

FIG. 14-9. *Water-pump and cooling-fan assembly.* (Courtesy of Allis-Chalmers Manufacturing Company.)

temperature is between 170 and 200°F. If the cooling liquid can be maintained within this temperature range at light as well as heavy loads, or in cold as well as warm weather, better engine performance will be secured.

The usual method of heat control is to restrict or vary the circulation of the coolant through the radiator according to operating conditions such as engine load and atmospheric temperature. Referring to Fig. 14-11, a thermostatic valve in the upper radiator connection opens and

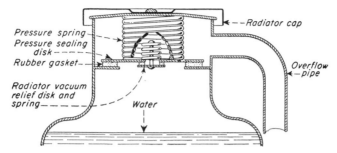

FIG. 14-10. *Radiator cap with valves for pressure cooling system.*

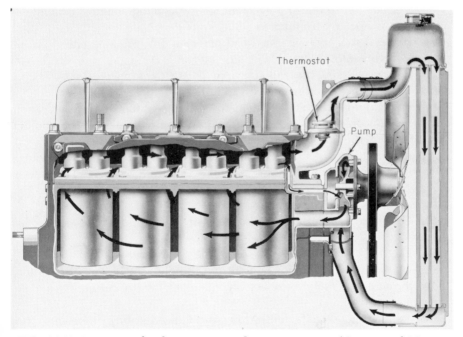

FIG. 14-11. *Heat-control valve in upper radiator connection.* (Courtesy of Massey-Ferguson, Inc.)

closes according to the coolant temperature. The valve is actuated by a copper bellows containing a liquid which expands when heated and contracts when cooled. The expansion of the liquid causes the bellows to expand and thereby move the valve attached to it to the open position, thus permitting circulation through the radiator. Likewise, a decrease in temperature contracts the liquid and the bellows moves the valve in the opposite direction to a closed position which restricts or stops the coolant flow through the radiator. The bellows action is sufficiently sensitive to maintain the coolant temperature within a range of 10 deg. Although some engines use a direct cutoff type of thermostat, most are equipped with the bypass type (Fig. 14-4) which prevents circulation through the radiator when the engine is cold but permits limited circulation around the cylinders. Thus the engine warms up faster and, eventually, the thermostat opens and permits circulation through the radiator.

Another heat-control device consists of adjustable metal shutters on the front of the radiator. They can be manually adjusted according to the air temperature and engine operating conditions.

Antifreezing cooling mixtures. In certain sections, where freezing temperatures exist for several days or even months at a time, it is often advantageous to replace the water in a cooling system with some solution that will not freeze readily. Freezing of the cooling solution usually results in one or more troubles as follows:

1. It may crack the cylinder head or block and produce either an internal or an external leak.

2. It may weaken the radiator and connections or create a leak in these parts, which is often difficult to repair.

3. Freezing at a certain point in the cooling system during operation of the engine may interfere with the proper circulation of the cooling liquid and permit the engine to run too hot.

A number of liquid materials, used either alone or mixed with water, can be utilized to prevent these troubles. Only a very few, however, meet the usual requirements of a satisfactory antifreeze solution, which are as follows:

1. The ingredients used should be easily obtainable in operating localities.

2. The possibility of freezing should be negligible.

3. The solution should not be injurious to either the engine or the radiator through corrosion or electrolytic action, or to rubber-hose connections.

4. It should not lose its nonfreezing and noncongealing properties after continued use.

5. The possibility of fire hazard should be a minimum.

6. The boiling point of the solution should not differ materially from that of water.

7. The viscosity should be as constant as possible through the entire temperature range involved, and the solution should remain perfectly fluid and not tend to stop up any small openings in the system.

8. The specific heat and heat conductivity of the solution should be high in order to dissipate the heat as rapidly as possible.

There are no substances satisfying all the requirements of an ideal antifreeze. However, the major requirements have been met satisfactorily by properly treated solutions of the simple alcohols (methyl, ethyl, and isopropyl) and of the ethylene and propylene glycols. Various other substances that have been tried, such as inorganic salts, sugar, honey, glycerine, and petroleum coolants, lack certain desirable qualities and are unsatisfactory.

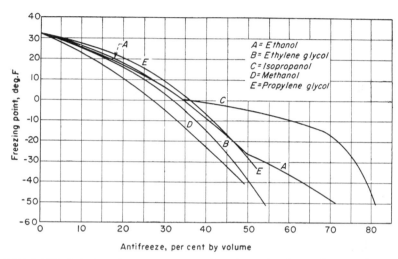

FIG. 14-12. *Relation of concentration to freezing point for antifreeze solutions.*

Alcohol antifreezes. The alcohols commonly used as bases for antifreezes are methyl (wood) alcohol, ethyl (grain) alcohol, and isopropyl alcohol. The technical names of these compounds are methanol, ethanol, and isopropanol, respectively. The boiling points of alcohol antifreezes are below that of water, the difference increasing with the concentration of alcohol, or the protection, as shown in Fig. 14-12.

Antifreeze solutions of alcohols, when properly inhibited, do not attack radiator hose and should protect the cooling system from corrosion for at least one winter's use in properly maintained vehicles. Such solutions, when installed in reasonably clean cooling systems, are generally free from sediment, rust, or discoloration when drained in the spring.

Glycol antifreezes. Ethylene glycol has long been on the market as an automotive antifreeze compound. More recently, propylene glycol has been marketed for this purpose. The boiling points of glycol solutions are above that of water and increase with the concentration of the glycol, or the protection, as shown in Fig. 14-12. Because the glycols boil at higher temperatures than water, they are termed *high-boiling or permanent antifreezes.*

Although glycol antifreeze solutions will operate at higher engine temperatures without boiling, liquid may be lost through the overflow pipe, when such solutions boil violently, in the same manner that alcohol solution or water would be lost. Any evaporation of glycol solution is practically all water, whereas evaporation of alcohol antifreeze solutions results in loss of alcohol, the antifreeze base. In actual service, however, the loss by evaporation of either ethylene glycol or alcohol has been found to be negligible as compared to the overflow loss of liquid from violent boiling.

Antifreeze solutions composed of ethylene glycol, when properly inhibited, should protect the cooling system from corrosion for a winter's driving season, in properly maintained vehicles. As in the case of alcohol antifreezes, the inhibitors may be weakened and depleted by hard or extended driving or through lack of proper vehicle maintenance. The service life of inhibitors is shortened by such conditions as high driving mileage, high engine speeds and heavy loads, air leaks into the solution (around the water-pump drive shaft, for example), combustion gas leakage into the coolant through a loose cylinder-head joint, rust deposits in the system, localized hot spots in the engine, and added contamination such as that from radiator cleaners that have not been thoroughly flushed out after use.

Salt-base antifreezes. The low cost of salt antifreezes, such as calcium, magnesium, or sodium chlorides, and their effectiveness in lowering the freezing point of water have made these compounds appear attractive as automotive antifreezes. Numerous tests made of various salt antifreeze solutions show that they have been found to be too corrosive for automotive use.

Petroleum coolants. Petroleum coolants are quite like kerosene in properties and do not mix with water. It is necessary to drain the entire cooling system completely and to refill with the antifreeze compound, regardless of the protection needed. The amount of petroleum coolant needed will therefore be several times that of the water-soluble antifreeze compounds. Properly refined petroleum coolants do not freeze at temperatures as low as $-40°F$. Suitably refined petroleum is not corrosive to the cooling-system metals.

Petroleum coolants attack ordinary radiator hose made of natural or reclaimed rubber, and also hose made from some kinds of synthetic rubber. However, the better grades of ordinary hose, having several layers of fabric, in some cases are reported to have been used for a full season with petroleum coolant without failure. Some other types of synthetic rubber are not seriously affected by petroleum products. The availability of oil-resistant synthetic hose would obviate the above objections to the use of petroleum coolants.

At engine operating temperatures, all petroleum coolants that have been tested are inflammable. Should a source of ignition, such as a static spark from the fan belt, be present, a leak may result in a fire. If the engine is operating under load, such as climbing a moderate grade at 40 m.p.h., the exhaust manifold will serve as a source of ignition.

Petroleum coolants have less heat capacity than other types; hence the engine itself runs hotter. Although this may not be a drawback in extremely cold weather or under light driving conditions, it is disadvantageous in mild weather.

REFERENCES

Automotive Antifreezes, *Natl. Bur. Standards* (*U.S.*) *Circ.* 474.

BARGER, E. L., W. M. CARLETON, E. G. McKIBBEN, and ROY BAINER, "Tractors and Their Power Units," John Wiley & Sons, Inc., New York, 1952.

HELDT, P. M., "High-speed Combustion Engines," 16th ed., Chilton Company, Philadelphia, 1956.

LICHTY, L. C., "Internal Combustion Engines," 6th ed., McGraw-Hill Book Company, Inc., New York, 1951.

Major Cooling Problems Encountered in Today's Automobiles, *Gen. Motors Eng. J.*, Vol. 1, No. 4.

MOSES, BEN D., and KENNETH R. FROST, "Farm Power," John Wiley & Sons, Inc., New York, 1952.

Solving the Thermal and Structural Problems in Radiator Design for Automotive Cooling Systems, *Gen. Motors Eng. J.*, Vol. 2, No. 4.

PROBLEMS AND QUESTIONS

1. Name the specific heat losses encountered in an internal-combustion engine, and explain just how they vary with respect to the power output of the engine.

2. What are the objections to overcooling an engine?

3. In designing an engine, what are the principal factors to be considered in the selection of the best type of cooling system to use?

4. What is meant by pressure cooling, and what are its advantages?

5. Explain the operation of a typical thermostat as used in cooling systems, and describe the two methods of installing it and controlling the liquid flow.

6. Name the different types of antifreeze materials, and discuss their relative merits and undesirable characteristics.

15

Governing and Governing Systems

Nearly every stationary farm machine, such as a thresher, ensilage cutter, feed mill, and so on, must operate at a certain uniform speed. The power-supplying device must, therefore, maintain this speed whether the machine is running empty or at its maximum capacity. In other words, it must instantly adjust its power output to the power required, at the same time maintaining uniform speed. For this reason, the stationary engine or farm tractor, when used for belt work particularly, must be equipped with a governor, a mechanical device that instantly adjusts the power output to the power requirements of the driven machine in such a way as to maintain practically a uniform speed.

Suppose a wood saw is being operated by a stationary engine. The load on the latter fluctuates constantly; that is, when the saw is cutting, the load is a maximum, and when the stick is shifted for the next cut, the load becomes a minimum. If the power output of the engine remained at the maximum required by the saw when cutting, the engine would run away or race under lighter loads, and wear rapidly or fly to pieces. A governor on the engine would vary its power output to meet the power required by the saw and thus keep the speed of the latter practically constant.

On the other hand, it is desirable and necessary to vary the engine speed in such machines as automobiles, trucks, and airplanes in order to obtain different traveling speeds. When such a machine is in use, the operator of course must be present to guide it; therefore, the manual control of the speed involves no great difficulty. The speed of a tractor engine operating a stationary belt-driven machine might be held fairly constant by the manual operation of a convenient hand lever, but the use of a governor would eliminate the need of the extra man and soon pay for itself.

Systems of governing. Two types of governing systems, the hit-and-miss system and the throttle system, are used for gas engines. However, the former is adapted only to slow-speed, single-cylinder engines and is little used, as it has no advantages over the latter system.

The fundamental principle involved in the hit-and-miss system is to keep all explosions alike and at the maximum intensity, but to vary the number per time interval depending upon the power output required.

Example. A single-cylinder four-stroke-cycle engine running at 500 r.p.m. and developing its maximum power would produce a maximum

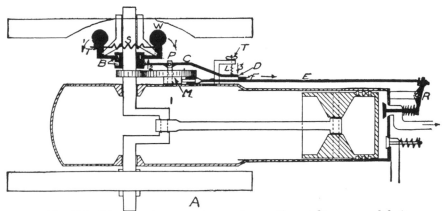

FIG. 15-1. *Hit-and-miss governing system with weights on crankshaft.*

of 250 explosions per minute. If the belt suddenly slipped off, relieving the engine of its load, there would be an excessive increase in speed. If, on the other hand, the number of explosions per minute were reduced by some mechanical means to, say, 50, the power output would be correspondingly less and the engine would continue to run at its normal speed of 500 r.p.m.

This system of governing, then, varies the number of explosions or working cycles per time interval so as to maintain a reasonably constant engine speed at any and all loads, the same maximum mixture charge being taken into the cylinder for each explosion.

The governing mechanism (Fig. 15-1) consists of the following parts: weights *W*, sliding collar *B*, detent arm or finger *C*, and notch or catch block *F* on exhaust-valve push rod *E*. The weights, usually located on one flywheel on the crankshaft, are held together by springs, but when rotated are drawn apart against the spring tension by centrifugal force. The greater the engine speed, therefore, the farther they separate. This expansion of the weights slides the grooved collar on the crankshaft, and this sliding movement of the collar reacting on one end of the pivoted detent arm causes the opposite end to catch in a notch on the exhaust

push rod, holding the valve open. This valve being open, a fuel charge
will not be drawn in and compressed and fired on the next cycle. Consequently, the engine will lose speed, and the springs will draw the
weights together owing to the decreasing centrifugal force, thus sliding
the collar back and releasing the detent arm and push rod, and permitting another explosion. Such an engine, when carrying light loads, operates at a more or less uneven or fluctuating speed, but when running
at full load it fires steadily and runs uniformly. The governor weights
in some cases are not located on the crankshaft but are mounted separately and driven by a small spur pinion meshing with the cam gear.

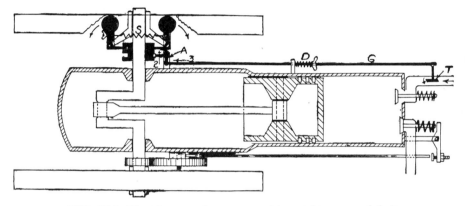

FIG. 15-2. *Throttle governing system with weights on crankshaft.*

Throttle system. The principle of the throttle system of governing is to
permit the engine to fire the maximum number of times, that is, on every
fourth piston stroke, regardless of the load, but to vary the fuel charge
per cycle and the resultant explosion intensity as the load varies. That is,
an engine having a normal speed of 500 r.p.m. would fire 250 times per
minute at any load, the governor functioning in such a manner as to reduce the quantity of fuel mixture entering the cylinder on each intake
stroke at light loads and to increase it with an increasing load.

The mechanism (Fig. 15-2) consists of (1) a set of weights, held together by springs and located on the crankshaft or driven by a special
pinion, (2) a sliding collar, (3) a throttle connecting rod or arm, and (4)
a throttle butterfly. As the engine speed increases, the weights fly apart,
moving the collar and actuating the throttle connecting rod, thus partly
closing the throttle butterfly and cutting off the fuel mixture. If the engine speed decreases with an increased load, the springs counteract the
centrifugal force on the weights, drawing them together and sliding the
collar so as to open the throttle. If the mechanism is well designed and
operates freely, the power output of the engine will be adjusted instantly

to the power required and a uniform speed will be produced and maintained at all loads.

TRACTOR GOVERNING

A governor is necessary on a tractor engine to maintain a uniform speed with varying loads, particularly when operating belt-driven machines. Again, a governor protects the engine against operation at excessive speeds when doing either belt or drawbar work.

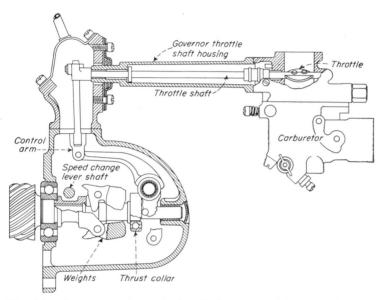

FIG. 15-3. *Throttle governor for multiple-cylinder engine.* (Courtesy of International Harvester Company.)

Governing mechanism. All tractors are equipped with the throttle system of governing, the mechanism being actuated and controlled by centrifugal force by means of rotating weights. A typical layout is shown by Fig. 15-3. Referring to this figure, the essential parts include the weights mounted on the magneto drive shaft, the ball-thrust collar, the throttle-control arm, and the throttle-control rod, which is connected to a hand lever. A governor-control spring (not shown) is connected to the hand lever and control rod and reacts against the expansion of the weights as the engine speed increases. The mechanism operates as follows: With the engine not running and the hand control in the open position, the throttle butterfly is wide open. When the engine starts and gains speed, the weights expand against the control-spring pressure, actuate the control arm and throttle rod, and gradually close the butterfly until a certain speed is established, depending on the load. If the load is very small, the butterfly will be nearly closed. Now if the engine load is increased, the engine speed will tend to decrease. But this, in turn, will cause the weights to contract and thereby open the butterfly. Hence, the original speed will be maintained as long as the load does not exceed the maximum power of the engine. By placing the hand-control lever in any position between the closed or idling position and normal or rated engine speed position, any desired speed may be established and maintained by the governor. It is quite obvious that the control spring tension must be closely correlated with the centrifugal action of the weights in order to provide sensitive speed control.

A perfectly functioning governing mechanism should not permit any appreciable variation in the engine speed between no load and full load. Obviously the natural action is for an engine to run faster without load, with the speed dropping off as the load increases. The total variation will depend largely upon the rated engine speed. If it is a high-speed engine with a rated r.p.m. of 1,500, for example, a variation of 75 to 100 r.p.m. would not be excessive or unreasonable. Poor governor control is usually due to faulty or imperfect design, but may be caused by lack of good lubrication of all working parts, by paint in the lever connections, by a bent, broken, or poorly fitted throttle butterfly, or by incorrect carburetor adjustment. Any tractor governor, in order to function properly, must work freely but with as little lost motion in the connections as possible. Some engines have the entire mechanism completely enclosed and exposed to a mist of oil or continuous lubrication. Hence there should be little friction and wear and good speed control.

It is sometimes possible to adjust a governor to maintain a higher or a lower operating speed by changing the spring tension or the length of the control rod. However, such practice is not recommended because every engine is designed to operate within a certain speed range and any change in this respect is seldom necessary or advisable.

Diesel engine governing. The principles of diesel engine governing and the construction and operation of such mechanisms are fully explained in Chap. 20.

Governor hunting. Frequently when an engine is first started or after it is warmed up and is working under load, particularly in belt work, its speed will become uneven or irregular. It speeds up quickly, the governor suddenly responds, the speed drops quickly, the governor responds again, and the action is repeated. This is known as *hunting*. It is usually caused by an incorrect carburetor adjustment and can be corrected by making the mixture either slightly leaner or slightly richer. It is possible also for the governor itself to cause hunting by being too stiff or by striking or binding at some point so that it fails to act freely.

Automatic or vacuum-type governor. Motor trucks, buses, and automobiles are sometimes equipped with a governor for the purpose, primarily, of maintaining a set maximum road speed, which may be considerably below the maximum speed possible without such a device. An automatic or vacuum-type governor (Fig. 15-4) is used for this purpose. It is a simple device located between the carburetor and the intake manifold and has no mechanical connection to any other parts of the engine.

Referring to Fig. 15-4, the device consists of a housing and a throttle-butterfly valve mounted off center and connected to a spring-controlled

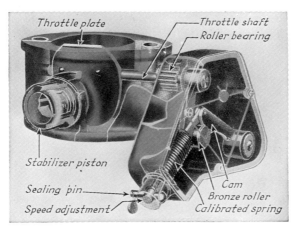

FIG. 15-4. *Vacuum-type governor.*

cam-and-lever mechanism. With the butterfly mounted off center, the longer portion is subjected to the pressure reaction of the gas mixture passing through the device. Thus as the engine speed and resultant suction increase, the reaction tends to close the valve and thereby to maintain a certain maximum speed. As the engine speed and suction decrease, the spring opens the valve. The desired speed range is maintained by a simple adjustment of the spring tension. The successful operation of this type of governor depends largely upon precision of construction, freedom of movement of the parts, and proper installation, adjustment, and adaptability to the engine.

REFERENCES

BARGER, E. L., W. M. CARLETON, E. G. McKIBBEN, and ROY BAINER, "Tractors and Their Power Units," John Wiley & Sons, Inc., New York, 1952.

HELDT, P. M., "High-speed Combustion Engines," 16th ed., Chilton Company, Philadelphia, 1956.

MOSES, BEN D., and KENNETH R. FROST, "Farm Power," John Wiley & Sons, Inc., New York, 1952.

PROBLEMS AND QUESTIONS

1. How would you proceed to compare the operating efficiencies of the governors on two different tractors?

2. What attention and service should be given a tractor governor to ensure proper operation?

3. Explain how the throttle hand lever of a tractor functions to control the engine speed between the idling and fully open setting.

16

Ignition Methods—Fundamentals of Electric Ignition—Magnetism and Induction

In any internal-combustion engine, the fuel mixture must be ignited or "set on fire," so to speak, before the explosion can take place and power be generated. This ignition always takes place near the end of the compression stroke or during the latter part of it. In the development of the internal-combustion engine, four different methods of ignition have been devised, as follows:

1. Open-flame method
2. Hot-tube, hot-bulb, or hot-bolt method
3. Ignition by the heat of compression
4. Electric-spark ignition

Of these four, only the last two named are still in use, and by far the greatest number of engines utilize the electric-spark method in some form or another.

Open-flame ignition. The open-flame arrangement was perhaps the first successful means of ignition. However, it was soon displaced by the other methods mentioned, as they proved more satisfactory for several reasons. This system consisted of two gas jets, one burning continuously on the outside of the engine and a second jet that alternately communicated with the first jet and the combustion chamber. This second jet was extinguished each time by the explosion and, therefore, had to be relighted. It was placed on the inside of a hollow, rotating valve whose one port or opening first registered with an opening near the first jet. This lighted the second jet. Further movement of the valve permitted its port to register with an opening leading to the combustion space just as compression was nearly completed. Thus, the charge coming in contact with the flame was ignited, and an explosion produced. As previously stated, this system of ignition survived only a short time, owing to the immediate development of other more reliable ones.

Hot-tube and hot-bulb ignition. The hot-tube system of ignition originally consisted of a tubelike projection on the end or side of the cylinder.
The outer end of the tube was closed and the other end opened into
the combustion space. It was heated by a torch or flame, and as the
charge was compressed, a certain portion entered the tube and was
ignited by contact with the hot inner surface. The ignition of the charge
in the tube then spread or propagated through the mixture in the cylinder
and produced an explosion. In some cases it was necessary to keep the
torch burning as long as the engine was in operation. In others, the

FIG. 16-1. *Oil engine with hot-bulb ignition.*

flame was taken away once the engine was started, and the hot exhaust
gases which remained in the tube following the explosion served to keep
it hot and ignite the next charge.

The original hot-tube arrangement just described was superseded by a
modification known as the hot bulb (Fig. 16-1). The bulblike projection
on the cylinder head is heated by a torch until the engine starts. In
most cases this torch is then removed or extinguished, the hot exhaust
gases continuing to keep the bulb sufficiently hot to produce ignition.

Some heavy-duty, stationary oil engines are equipped with a bolt or
pin in the cylinder head that projects into the combustion space. This
bolt, when heated by some external means, provides the ignition for
starting the engine. Once the engine is in operation the heating torch
is removed and ignition is produced by high compression. This hot-bolt
or hot-pin arrangement, however, may be considered as another modification of the hot tube.

Ignition by high compression. As explained in Chap. 6, when air or
gaseous material is compressed rapidly and consequently reduced in

volume, work is required that is instantly converted into heat, thereby causing a correspondingly rapid rise in the temperature of the gas compressed. This physical action is utilized in producing ignition in certain so-called compression-ignition engines; that is, the compression pressure is great enough to produce a temperature high enough to ignite the fuel mixture at the proper time without the assistance or use of any special ignition device.

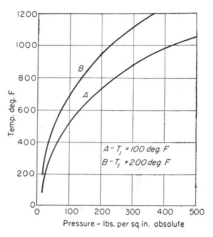

The effect of rapid compression on temperature is shown by the curve in Fig. 16-2. Table 11-3 shows that the ignition temperature of the common internal-combustion-engine fuels varies from 500 to 900°F. Consequently, a compression pressure of 400 to 500 lb. per sq. in. will readily ignite any hydrocarbon fuel mixture. In other words, compression-ignition engines require a compression ratio of 1:15 or higher, while 1:6 or 1:7 is the average compression ratio of ordinary electric-ignition, carbureting-type engines. Since it was Dr.

FIG. 16-2. *Curves showing relationship of compression pressure to cylinder temperature.*

Rudolph Diesel who first demonstrated the possibilities of high compression in producing ignition in internal-combustion engines, all such engines are now usually known as diesel engines.

Electric-spark ignition. Electric-spark-ignition systems vary somewhat in construction and operation, depending upon the type of engine. For example, all automobile and truck engines are equipped with battery ignition, while some tractor, airplane, and other special types of engines are equipped with magneto ignition.

ELECTRICAL DEFINITIONS AND UNITS

Conductors and insulators. Certain materials, largely metals, transmit an electric current readily and are known, therefore, as good *conductors;* that is, they are said to offer a low resistance to the flow of electricity through them. Some of these substances are silver, copper, aluminum, zinc, brass, platinum, iron, nickel, tin, and lead. On the other hand, many materials are very poor conductors, or apparently do not conduct an electric current at all, and are known as *insulators.* Some common insulating materials are porcelain, mica, rubber, glass, fiber, and bakelite.

Electrical units and measurement. The flow of an electric current through a conductor can be compared to the flow of water through a pipe. The quantity of water flowing or rate of flow, usually expressed in gallons per minute, is dependent upon the pressure in pounds per square inch, or head, and upon the resistance offered by the pipe according to its size and length. Likewise the rate of flow of an electric current measured in amperes is determined by the electrical pressure in volts and by the resistance of the conductor according to its size and length and according to the material used.

The usual definitions of the common electrical units are as follows:

Volt. The unit of electrical pressure or electromotive force (e.m.f.). It is the pressure required to send a current of 1 amp. through a circuit whose resistance is 1 ohm.

Ampere. The unit of the rate of flow of an electric current. It is that quantity of electricity which is made to flow by a pressure of 1 volt through a circuit whose resistance is 1 ohm.

Ohm. The unit of electric resistance. It is the resistance offered to the flow of 1 amp. under a pressure of 1 volt.

Ampere-hour. The quantity of current flowing in amperes for a period of 1 hr., or

$$\text{Ampere-hours} = \text{amperes} \times \text{hours}$$

Watt. The unit of electric power or the rate at which work is performed by 1 amp. of current flowing under a pressure of 1 volt, or

$$\text{Watts} = \text{volts} \times \text{amperes}$$

Watthour. The power consumed when 1 watt is used for 1 hr., or

$$\text{Watthours} = \text{volts} \times \text{amperes} \times \text{hours}$$

Kilowatt. One thousand watts.

Kilowatthour. The power consumed when 1 kw. of power is consumed for 1 hr., or

$$\text{Kilowatthours} = \text{kilowatts} \times \text{hours}$$

$$= \frac{\text{amperes} \times \text{volts} \times \text{hours}}{1,000}$$

Ohm's law. As previously stated, the current flowing in an electric circuit is dependent upon the resistance of the circuit and the pressure or voltage. In fact, there is a definite relationship between the current flowing in amperes, the pressure in volts, and the resistance in ohms. This relation, known as *Ohm's law*, is expressed as follows:

$$\text{Current in amperes } (I) = \frac{\text{pressure in volts } (E)}{\text{resistance in ohms } (R)}$$

or, using the common symbols,

$$I = \frac{E}{R}$$

Likewise
$$E = IR$$

and
$$R = \frac{E}{I}$$

This law is of inestimable value, particularly to the electrical engineer, for calculating the voltage required to transmit a certain current a given distance, for determining correct wire sizes, and so on.

SOURCES OF ELECTRICITY

Any electric ignition system is made up of certain parts or units, according to the following outline:

1. Source of current
    a. Chemical—dry cells and storage cells
    b. Mechanical—magnetos and similar electricity-generating devices
2. Coil
    a. Low-tension or make-and-break
    b. High-tension or jump-spark
3. Timing mechanism
4. Sparking device
    a. Igniter
    b. Spark plug
5. Switch and wire connections

Chemical generation of electricity. Electricity for ignition purposes may be generated in two ways, namely, by chemical means or by a mechanical device. Chemical devices for generating an electric current are known as cells or batteries. Correctly speaking, a cell is a single unit, and a battery consists of two or more cells connected together. Such cells for generating electricity are made up of four fundamental parts: (1) the positive material, (2) the negative material, (3) the electrolyte, and (4) the container. That is, a simple cell (Fig. 16-3) consists essentially of two dissimilar materials immersed in a solution called the *electrolyte*. If these materials are connected externally by a good conductor of electricity, such as a copper wire, chemical action takes place between the solution and these materials, and an electric current flows through the wire; that is, chemical energy is converted into electrical energy.

Only certain combinations of materials will generate electricity in this manner. Some of the more common ones and the voltage produced are given in Table 16-1. Combinations *A* and *B* form what are known as primary cells. Combination *C* is the one used in the ordinary lead-type automobile and farm light-plant batteries and forms what is known as a *secondary cell* or *battery*.

Primary and secondary cells. A *primary cell* is one in which the chemical action, going on as the cell discharges, changes one or more of the active materials—particularly the negative element and the electrolyte—in such a way that when the cell is completely discharged or "dead," it can be restored to its original condition only *by renewing the materials that have been so changed*. For example, in Fig. 16-3 the zinc plate is gradually consumed, the zinc replacing the hydrogen in the sulfuric acid. This hydrogen collects on the positive copper plate, which remains unchanged. Consequently, the negative zinc and the electrolyte are gradually broken down and eventually must be replaced.

In a *secondary cell* (Fig. 16-4), the active materials likewise undergo a chemical change during the discharging process, but when the cell becomes completely discharged, a replacement of these materials is unnecessary and it can be restored to its original condition *by sending an electric current through it in a direction opposite to that of discharge*. This process is commonly known as recharging. Of course, this charging and discharging action cannot be carried on indefinitely because these secondary

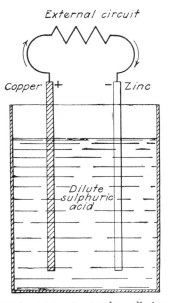

FIG. 16-3. *A simple cell for generating electricity.*

Table 16-1. *Chemical Combinations Used in Different Types of Cells*

	(A) Daniell cell	(B) Leclanché cell or dry cell	(C) Lead-acid storage cell
Positive material....	Copper (Cu)	Carbon (C)	Lead dioxide (PbO₂)
Negative material...	Zinc (Zn)	Zinc (Zn)	Lead (Pb)
Electrolyte..........	Sulfuric acid (H₂SO₄)	Ammonium chloride (NH₄Cl)	Sulfuric acid (H₂SO₄)
Voltage..............	1.0	1.5	2.0

or so-called storage cells gradually lose their strength and efficiency for other reasons. Their life varies from 2 to 10 years or more, depending upon their type, construction, quality of materials, use, care, and other factors.

The dry cell. The common dry cell is nothing more than a primary cell whose principal active materials are carbon, zinc, and ammonium chloride. However, it is made up in such a manner that the electrolyte is in a so-called nonspillable form so that the cell or battery can be car-

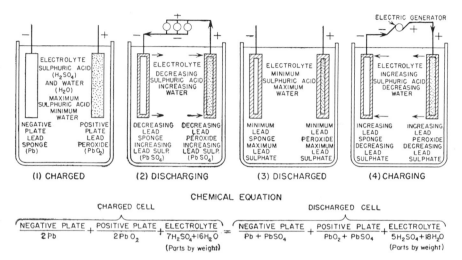

FIG. 16-4. *Action taking place in a lead-acid storage cell during a cycle of discharge and charge.*

ried about or placed in any convenient position without injury to its contents or hindrance to its action.

The dry cell serves as a source of electricity for a number of purposes, including gas-engine ignition, flashlights, doorbells, telephones, radio receivers, and so on. It is made up in different forms and sizes according to the purposes for which it is to be used. For ignition purposes, it is cylindrical in shape, the standard size being $2\frac{1}{2}$ in. in diameter and 6 in. high.

Referring to the cross-sectional view (Fig. 16-5), the construction of a dry cell is as follows:

1. The outer pasteboard carton serves as a protector from moisture and possible short circuits.

2. The zinc cup serves as a container and as the negative material.

3. The carbon stick acts as a conductor to conduct the current from the cell, but does not serve exclusively as the positive material, although it is often erroneously considered as such. This carbon stick has the termi-

nal fastened to it, although the entire stick might be considered as the positive terminal.

4. The filler is a mixture of (*a*) granulated carbon or graphite, which serves as the active positive material; (*b*) manganese dioxide (MnO_2), which is called the depolarizer; (*c*) ammonium chloride (NH_4Cl), in solution, which is the electrolyte; and (*d*) zinc chloride ($ZnCl_2$), which reduces the chemical action between the zinc and ammonium chloride when the cell is not being used.

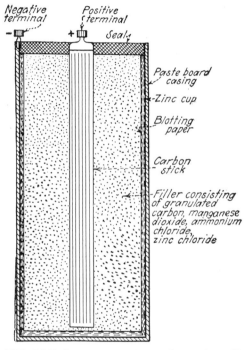

FIG. 16-5. *Construction of an ordinary dry cell.*

5. The blotting paper that completely lines the zinc cup acts as an insulator between it and the positive carbon. This blotting paper, however, permits the electrolyte to permeate it and come in contact with the zinc, thus producing the chemical action and generating an electric current.

6. The top is sealed airtight with some hard waterproof material, usually a pitch or tar compound.

Polarization. The chemical action taking place in a dry cell, as it discharges, results in the liberation of some of the hydrogen of the electrolyte. This hydrogen collects in the form of bubbles on the carbon, which serves as the positive electrode, and has a tendency to act as an insulator, preventing the carbon from receiving its positive charge of electricity and functioning as it should. The current output, or rate of discharge, is thus gradually reduced. This action is known as *polarization* and is more pronounced if the cell is discharged at a high or excessive rate.

The manganese dioxide, mixed with the carbon and electrolyte, acts as a depolarizer; that is, it liberates some of its oxygen, which unites with the hydrogen to form water. The manganese dioxide is probably reduced to a lower oxide.

Testing dry cells. The most practical method of determining the condition of a dry cell is to use a common pocket voltammeter (Fig. 16-6). This instrument is equipped with two stationary contacts labeled "amps" and "volts," a flexible contact, and a double scale. To read the current in amperes, the stationary "amps" contact is placed on the positive terminal of the cell and the negative terminal is touched with the flexible contact. The reading in amperes will be indicated by the hand on the upper 0 to 30 scale. It is important in testing for amperes that the reading be made as quickly as possible when the indicator comes to rest. If the cell shows 20 to 30 amp., it is in good condition. If it shows only 5 to 10 amp., it is practically exhausted and of little value for ignition or other purposes.

FIG. 16-6. *Testing a dry cell with a pocket ammeter.*

To test the voltage of a dry cell, the "volts" terminal of the instrument is placed on the positive terminal of the cell and the flexible contact touched to the negative terminal. The hand will indicate the voltage on the 0 to 12 or "volts" scale. For a good cell, the reading will be 1.5 and will not drop perceptibly until it is nearly worn out. That is, the amperage of a dry cell or battery decreases gradually with use and age but the voltage remains practically constant. Therefore, the condition of a cell should be determined by testing for amperes rather than for volts.

To obtain the best results and maximum service from dry cells they should be stored in a cool place when not in use and kept free from dampness at all times. Dry cells deteriorate and lose their strength even when allowed to stand unused, their maximum life seldom exceeding 1 year under any conditions.

Connecting dry cells. Ignition systems using a battery as a source of electricity require it to have a pressure of at least 6 volts. Since the voltage of the common dry cell is only 1.5 and cannot be increased by increasing the size of the cell, several units must be connected in such a way as to produce this higher pressure. Figure 16-7 illustrates the *series* method of connecting cells, in which the carbon or positive of one is connected to the zinc or negative of the next, and so on. If a voltmeter were placed in the circuit, it would register about 6 volts. On the other hand, if the current reading in amperes were taken, it would show little

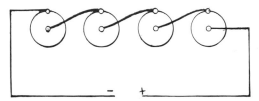

FIG. 16-7. *Series method of cell connection.*

or no increase over that of the individual cell; that is, the series connection produces a total voltage equal to the sum of the voltages of the cells and a total amperage equal, approximately, to the average amperages of the individual cells.

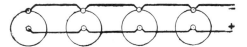

FIG. 16-8. *Parallel or multiple method of cell connection.*

Another arrangement (Fig. 16-8), in which all the positive terminals are connected by one wire and all the negatives by another, is known as the *parallel* or *multiple* method. In this case, the voltage of the set

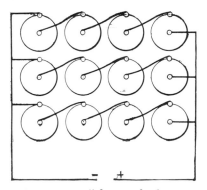

FIG. 16-9. *Parallel- or multiple-series method of cell connection.*

would be about 1.5 or the average of the voltages of the individual cells, but the total amperage would be equal to the sum of the amperages of the separate cells. This method is impractical and seldom used.

Figure 16-9 illustrates a third method of connecting cells, which is known as *parallel series* or *multiple series.* It will be observed that the individual cells are connected in series and the sets in parallel. Such an arrangement is advantageous, particularly under two conditions, namely, (1) when an engine using a dry-cell battery for ignition is operated almost continuously every day (as on a concrete mixer, for example), and (2) when a supply of good dry cells is not available and a number of weak ones must be used.

MAGNETS AND MAGNETISM—INDUCTION

Nature of Magnetism. It has been found that under certain conditions a piece of iron or steel or some iron alloy possesses the property of attracting or repelling other pieces of iron or materials containing this metal. This peculiar action or form of energy is known as *magnetism,* and the metal possessing it is called a *magnet.* Other metals and non-ferrous alloys, such as aluminum, copper, brass, bronze, tin, lead, zinc, and so on, do not have this property and are therefore termed *non-magnetic.*

Soft iron of a more or less pure form absorbs or takes up magnetism readily and in greater quantity, so to speak, but retains this property only

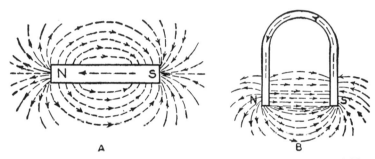

FIG. 16-10. *Steel-bar and horseshoe magnets showing magnetic field.*

while the magnetizing force or medium is very near or acting upon it. In other words, soft or pure iron forms what is known as a *temporary magnet.* Steel and alloys containing iron are not magnetized so readily but, when once so treated, retain this property to a certain degree even after the magnetizing medium has been removed. The common bar and horseshoe magnets (Fig. 16-10) are, therefore, made of hard steel and are known as *permanent magnets.* The well-known magneto magnets are likewise permanent magnets and are made of a very high-grade steel alloy.

Characteristics of magnetism. If a steel-bar magnet is held under a piece of cardboard (Fig. 16-11), on which has been placed a thin layer of iron filings, and the cardboard is tapped gently, the filings will assume a rather definite arrangement and form more or less distinct lines, which radiate from one end of the magnet to the other. The attraction appears to be greater at the ends or poles of the magnet but also exists in the space around it between the poles. This space about a magnet in which there exists more or less attraction for other pieces of iron is known as the *magnetic field.* When iron filings are held over a U-shaped or horseshoe magnet (Fig. 16-12), a similar effect is produced and a magnetic field likewise exists.

If a pocket compass is brought near an ordinary bar magnet, the end of the needle which ordinarily points north will be attracted by one pole of this magnet but will be repelled by the other pole, as shown in Fig 16-13. The end of the magnet attracting the north end of the needle is

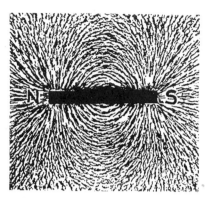

FIG. 16-11. *Lines of magnetic force around a bar magnet as shown by iron filings.*

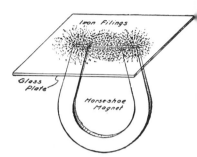

FIG. 16-12. *Effect produced by a magnet held under a glass plate which is covered with iron filings.*

called the *south pole* and the end repelling the north end of the needle is known as the *north pole* of the magnet. It is likewise observed that the lines of force about the magnet flow from north to south.

If the north poles of two steel magnets are brought close to each other (Fig. 16-14) and iron filings are sprinkled on a cardboard held over them,

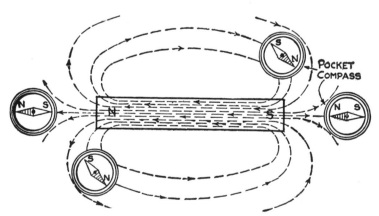

FIG. 16-13. *Polarity of a bar magnet, as indicated by a compass.*

the filings will arrange themselves as shown, indicating that there is a repulsion or repulsing effect. On the other hand, if a north pole of one magnet is brought close to the south pole of the other (Fig. 16-15), there is a very strong attraction and the filings arrange themselves differently.

In other words. it can be said that like poles repel, and unlike poles attract each other.

If a piece of soft iron is brought near to a permanent steel magnet, the soft iron itself becomes a magnet and the lines of force tend to concentrate themselves in it. If the soft iron is removed, however, it does not retain its magnetism. If, instead of a piece of soft iron, a piece of unmag-

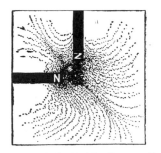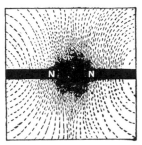

FIG. 16-14. *The repelling effect of like poles.*

netized soft steel is placed near a permanent steel magnet, as previously described, the piece of soft steel, upon removal from the magnet, will, perhaps, retain a small amount of magnetism, known as *residual magnetism*. The ability to retain this residual magnetism is known as *retentivity*.

A piece of very hard steel, unmagnetized, when brought close to a magnetized piece of steel or a strong magnet, will not take the magnetism

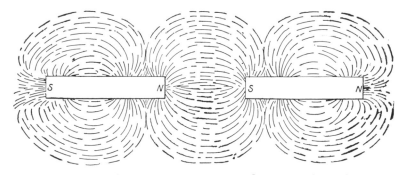

FIG. 16-15. *The magnetic attraction produced by unlike poles.*

so readily as soft iron, but once it becomes magnetized, it retains a considerable amount and is said to have better retentivity than soft iron or soft steel. These characteristics of soft iron, soft steel, and hard steel are very important and useful in connection with the successful operation of numerous electrical devices such as coils, magnetos, and electric generators.

Electromagnetism. Although magnetism and electricity are two entirely different forms of energy, they are more or less connected or re-

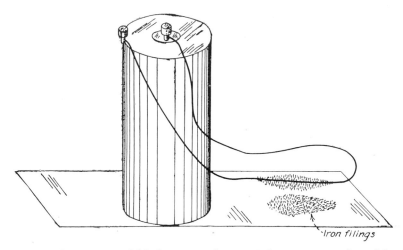

FIG. 16-16. *The magnetic field about a conductor of electricity, as indicated by iron filings.*

lated. For example, if an electric current is passed through a piece of copper or iron wire, and a portion of the latter dipped in iron filings (Fig. 16-16), they will be attracted to it and the wire will have the prop-

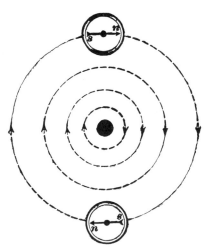

FIG. 16-17. *Direction of lines of force about a conductor of electricity, as indicated by a compass.*

erties of a magnet. When the circuit is broken, the filings drop off. This shows that the conductor of electricity has a magnetic field about it. If an ordinary compass is placed in different positions about a wire carrying an electric current, and the action of the needle observed in these different positions, it will be found that the lines of force form concentric circles about the wire, as shown in Fig. 16-17. Likewise, it has been found that the direction taken by the lines of force is determined by the direction of the current through the wire, as shown in Fig. 16-18.

If a certain length of wire is made into a coil, as in Fig. 16-19, and the current passed through it, the lines of force about each turn of wire in the coil will combine to form a concentrated or strong magnetic field about the entire coil. Such a coil of wire through which an electric current is flowing is known as a *sole-noid* and possesses the same properties as a piece of magnetized steel; that is, it has a north and a south pole and a magnetic field around it. If the current is suddenly broken or ceases to flow, the magnetism likewise disappears.

The polarity of a solenoid depends upon the direction of flow of the current through the wire, and it may be determined as follows if the

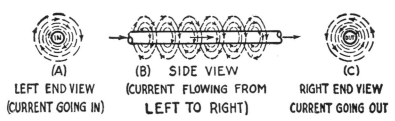

(A)	(B) SIDE VIEW	(C)
LEFT END VIEW	(CURRENT FLOWING FROM	RIGHT END VIEW
(CURRENT GOING IN)	LEFT TO RIGHT)	CURRENT GOING OUT

FIG. 16-18. *Effect of direction of flow of current on lines of force.*

direction of flow is known: Grasp the coil with the right hand, with the fingers pointing around the coil in the direction of the current flow. The thumb will then point toward the north pole. The polarity can likewise be determined by means of an ordinary compass in the same manner as that in which the polarity of the steel magnet is determined (Fig. 16-13).

The electromagnet. If the end of a piece of soft iron is brought near a coil or solenoid, consisting of many turns of insulated wire, and a current is passed through the coil, the iron will be attracted and drawn or

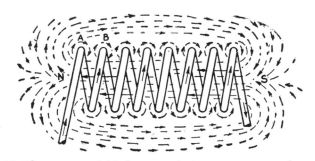

FIG. 16-19. *The magnetic field about a coil of wire carrying an electric current.*

sucked into the center of the solenoid (Fig. 16-20). The soft iron thus becomes magnetized and is known as an electromagnet. It possesses the same characteristics as an ordinary steel-bar magnet. Since the soft iron is extremely magnetic and readily magnetized, the lines of force tend to concentrate in this iron core, and the coil becomes much stronger, magnetically, than without the iron core. If the core of soft iron is withdrawn, this iron will lose its magnetic properties. A steel core would not produce so strong an electromagnet because steel does not take up magnetism as readily as soft iron.

The strength of such an electromagnet depends upon two factors, namely, the number of turns of wire around the core making up the coil, and the quantity of current flowing in the wire in amperes; that is, the greater the number of turns of wire and the greater the current flow in amperes, the stronger the electromagnetic field and the electromagnet produced.

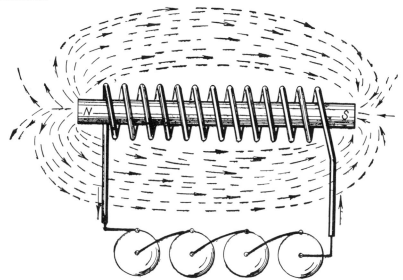

FIG. 16-20. *A simple electromagnet.*

Induction. In the preceding discussion it has been shown that a conductor of an electric current has a magnetic field existing about it as long as the current flows. Now, if the action is reversed and, in some manner, a magnetic field is suddenly set up about a conductor of electricity, an electric current will flow in the conductor just at the instant the field builds up. Again, if a magnetic field existing about a conductor is suddenly reduced in strength or completely broken down, a current will flow in the conductor at the instant the change occurs. This peculiar relationship or interaction of electricity and magnetism is known as *induction.*

It should not be assumed that if a conductor is merely held in a magnetic field of uniform strength a current will flow. Such a current is generated only by a change in the number of lines of force about the conductor. This change may be from a low to a high field strength or from a high to a low field strength.

Electromagnetic induction. The phenomenon of induction is well demonstrated and illustrated by means of an ordinary single-winding coil (Fig. 16-21). If an ordinary 6-volt battery is connected to such a coil as shown and the circuit is closed, a strong magnetic field is built up and exists as long as the current flows. Some of the electrical energy of the battery becomes magnetic energy. Now, if the circuit is quickly broken at some point, an electric spark of considerable size is observed where the break occurs. Bearing in mind that an electric spark is electricity flowing through air and that the latter is a very poor conductor, it is evident that this sudden breakdown of the magnetic field about the coil sets up a

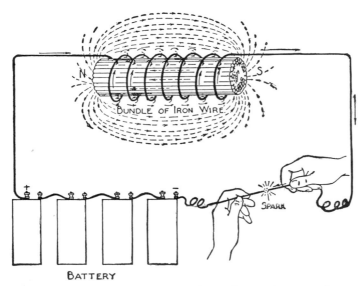

FIG. 16-21. *Action of a simple low-voltage induction coil.*

high voltage in the circuit, which produces an instantaneous flow of current. The magnetic energy is thus dissipated and converted into electrical energy again, and this action is known as *electromagnetic induction*.

The double-winding coil (Fig. 16-22) demonstrates this action in a somewhat more conclusive manner, perhaps, than the single-winding coil. Suppose that the winding attached to the battery, ordinarily known as the *primary*, is made of reasonably coarse wire and has fewer turns than the other or *secondary* winding, which is finer and has many turns. If the primary circuit is closed, current flows through it and sets up a magnetic field, which also surrounds the secondary winding, since it is on the same iron core. Now, if the primary circuit is suddenly broken, a spark will jump the small gap left between the ends of the secondary. Thus the magnetic field which existed about this winding, although created by the primary winding, generates for an instant a current flow in the secondary winding, due to its sudden breakdown or dissipation. This again is called an *induced current*.

The phenomenon of induction, produced in a somewhat different manner than previously described but fundamentally the same in principle, is shown in Fig. 16-23. If the permanent steel horseshoe magnet is first held so that the coil of insulated copper wire is between its poles, a magnetic field exists about the coil. Now, if the coil is jerked away in

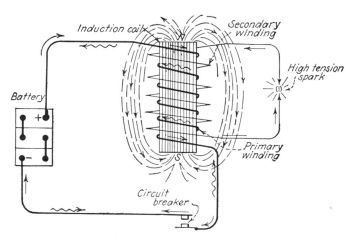

FIG. 16-22. *Construction and action of a two-winding high-voltage induction coil.*

the direction indicated, a voltage and resultant current flow will be generated for an instant, as indicated by a sensitive galvanometer. Likewise, if the coil is quickly returned to the first position, a current will flow just at the instant the coil enters the field. In this device it will be observed that the movement of the magnet and its field away from the coil, or the movement of the coil away from the magnet, results apparently in the lines of force being cut or broken. In fact, the action is often so expressed, and the maximum voltage and current flow occur when the greatest number of lines of force are cut.

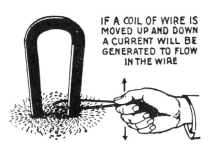

IF A COIL OF WIRE IS MOVED UP AND DOWN A CURRENT WILL BE GENERATED TO FLOW IN THE WIRE

FIG. 16-23. *Principle involved in generating an electric current by induction.*

The voltage and amount of current induced in an electric circuit depend upon three factors, namely, (1) the strength of the magnetic field about the conductor, (2) the number of turns making up the conductor involved, and (3) the speed or rate at which the magnetic field changes or breaks down. In other words, the stronger the magnetic field, the greater the number of turns of wire in the field, and the quicker the field strength changes with respect to the conductor, the stronger the voltage and current induced. The principles of electromagnetic induction, as just described, are important and fundamental to a clear understanding of the action and operation of all ignition coils, magnetos, electric generators of all kinds, transformers, doorbells, alarms, and many similar devices.

Direction of flow of induced current. Just as there is a definite relation between the direction of the current in a solenoid or coil and the polarity of the electromagnet so formed, so there is also a definite relation be-

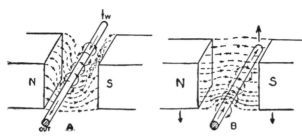

FIG. 16-24. *Effect of polarity and direction of motion of conductor on direction of current flow.*

tween the arrangement of the poles, the direction of movement of the conductor through the magnetic field, and the direction of flow of the induced current. For example, referring to Fig. 16-24A, it will be observed that if the conductor is moved downward through the field between the poles of the magnet, the lines of force are bent or distorted and assume a more or less circular form about the conductor as the latter passes through the field. The direction of the induced current is thus determined by the direction of the circular lines of force about the conductor. In Fig. 16-24B the conductor is shown moving upward through the field, so that the lines of force pass around it in the opposite direction; therefore the induced current flows the other way.

A rule for determining any one of the three conditions involved—namely,

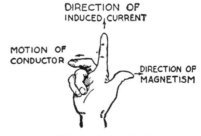

FIG. 16-25. *Right-hand three-finger method for determining direction of induced current.*

the direction of flow of the magnetic lines of force, the direction of motion of the conductor, and the direction of flow of the induced current—when two of them are known is called the *right-hand three-finger rule* and is illustrated by Fig. 16-25.

REFERENCES

The Electrical Characteristics and Testing of Dry Cells, *Natl. Bur. Standards* (*U.S.*) *Circ.* 79.

CROUSE, W. H., "Automotive Electrical Equipment," McGraw-Hill Book Company, Inc., New York, 1959.

MOSES, BEN D., and KENNETH R. FROST, "Farm Power," John Wiley & Sons, Inc., New York, 1952.

WRIGHT, F. B., "Electricity in the Home and on the Farm," John Wiley & Sons, Inc., New York, 1950.

PROBLEMS AND QUESTIONS

1. An electric circuit is carrying two 60-watt, eight 100-watt, and three 200-watt lamps. The power rate is 4 cents per kw.-hr. Neglecting line losses, calculate I and R and the power cost per 10-hr. day.

2. Explain why any type of dry cell should be tested for condition at the time of purchase.

3. Assuming each cell to be fresh, what is R for the circuit in Fig. 18-2 if I is 4.5 amp. when the points are closed?

4. Distinguish between a temporary magnet, a permanent magnet, and an electromagnet.

5. Knowing the polarity of a electromagnet, explain how you determine the direction of the current flow.

6. Explain the meaning of the term electromagnetic induction and just how a voltage is set up in the secondary winding of a two-winding coil.

7. Explain the relationship of polarity, current flow, and direction of motion of the conductor for a simple electric generator.

17

Storage Cells and Batteries

Storage cells or batteries are used extensively for many purposes, some of which are:

1. Automobile and truck ignition, starting, and lighting
2. Farm lighting
3. Train lighting
4. Radio-receiver operation
5. Motor power for vehicles, trucks, mine locomotives, and so on
6. Railway-signal and switch operation

Kinds of storage cells. The two types of secondary cells are the lead-acid cell (Fig. 17-1) and the Edison or nickel-iron alkaline cell (Fig. 17-2). The essential parts of the former are (1) positive plates of lead dioxide (PbO_2), (2) negative plates of sponge lead (Pb), (3) electrolyte of dilute sulfuric acid (H_2SO_4), (4) wood or threaded rubber separators or insulators, and (5) rubber or glass container.

The Edison cell consists of (1) positive plates of nickel oxide (Ni_2O_3), (2) negative plates of iron (Fe), (3) electrolyte of potassium hydroxide (KOH), (4) hard-rubber insulators, and (5) nickel-plated steel container.

The Edison cell. The Edison storage cell is not used so extensively as the lead-acid type for the following reasons:

1. It has a low discharge voltage (1.2 volts); therefore, more cells are necessary to obtain a desired circuit voltage.

2. Its current output and efficiency are greatly reduced at low temperatures.

3. Its maximum, short-interval discharge rate is comparatively low for a battery of given voltage and capacity.

Some advantages of the Edison cell are:

1. It is not injured by remaining in a charged or discharged condition for a long time.

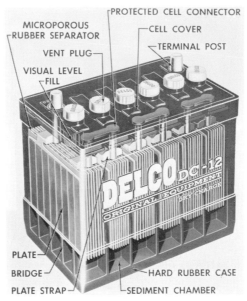

FIG. 17-1. *Lead-type storage-cell construction.* (Courtesy of Delco-Remy Division, General Motors Corporation.)

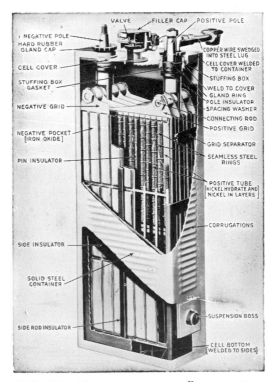

FIG. 17.2. *Edison-type storage-cell construction.*

2. It is rugged in construction and will withstand severe vibration.

3. It does not give off corrosive gases.

4. It is light in weight.

5. It is not injured by excessive charging and discharging rates.

LEAD-TYPE BATTERY CONSTRUCTION AND OPERATION

Plates. The active positive and negative materials in the lead-acid cell are in the form of rectangular plates. A number of positive plates

FIG. 17-3. *Positive plate group for lead-type cell.*

FIG. 17-4. *Negative plate group for lead-type cell.*

FIG. 17-5. *Complete plate assembly for lead-type cell.*

are connected together to form what is known as a *positive group* or element (Fig. 17-3). In a similar manner, a *negative group* is made up of several negative plates (Fig. 17-4). The two groups are then placed together (Fig. 17-5), so that the positive and negative plates alternate. Since it is necessary to have a negative on each side of a positive, there must be one more of the former, and the total plates per cell will be an odd number. Separators or insulators, as described later, are inserted between all plates.

Plate construction and manufacture. Since the active materials in both the positive and negative plates are of a brittle nature and have little mechanical strength, a framework made of some neutral metal is necessary to hold them in place. This cellular frame (Fig. 17-6), made of a lead-antimony alloy, is known as a *grid*. There is

FIG. 17-6. A *plate grid for a Faure-type plate.*

considerable variation in the grid construction as used by different manufacturers, but in all cases the purpose is the same, namely, to prevent the active materials from cracking and falling out of the plate and thereby reducing the cell output.

In manufacturing plates, the active material, in paste form, is pressed into the grid and allowed to harden. The materials as pasted into the grids are red lead (Pb_3O_4) for the positive, and litharge or lead monoxide (PbO) for the negative, mixed with sulfuric acid and water into a stiff paste. When pressed into place the paste hardens like cement and adheres to the ribbed structure. At this stage the positive plate will be bright red in color and the negative a yellowish gray. The plates are then subjected to an electrochemical process known as *forming*, which consists in submerging them in sulfuric acid and water and sending a direct current through them, the current flowing in at the positive plate

FIG. 17-7. A *wood separator for a lead-type cell.*

FIG. 17-8. A *threaded-rubber separator for a lead-type cell.*

and out at the negative. This process converts the active material of the positive plate into lead dioxide, which is chocolate-brown in color, and that of the negative into gray spongy lead.

The size, thickness, and number of plates per cell vary considerably according to the purpose for which the battery is to be used. Further information concerning these items is given in the discussion of battery ratings and capacity.

Separators. The purpose of the separators is to act as insulators between the plates so as to prevent them from coming in contact with each other and creating a so-called internal short circuit. At the same time, they permit the electrolyte to penetrate or pass through and come in contact with the entire plate surface and to circulate freely. Originally, separators were made of chemically treated wood (Fig. 17-7) such as cypress, redwood, or fir. However, even the best wood separators were broken down eventually by the electrolyte. Present-day batteries use porous, synthetic, acid-resistant rubber, or resin-impregnated cellulose fiber separators alone (Fig. 17-8) or in combination with perforated-rubber sheets (Fig. 17-9), or glass-fiber mats as retainer walls. These thin retainer walls retard the loss of active material from the plate surface and improve separator life.

All separators are grooved on one side which is placed next to the positive plate with the grooves vertical. This construction permits any sediment forming on the plates during charging and discharging to settle to the bottom of the container.

The electrolyte. The electrolyte used in the lead-acid cell consists of a mixture of about 2 parts of chemically pure, concentrated sulfuric acid (H_2SO_4) to 5 parts of distilled water by volume. The concentrated acid will have a specific gravity of 1.835, but the diluted mixture of the above proportions will drop to about 1.300 at 70°F. Some types of storage batteries, particularly farm light-plant batteries, use even a weaker solution than this,

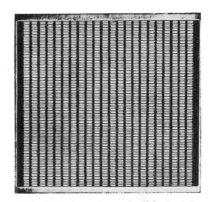

FIG. 17-9. *A perforated-rubber retaining wall for a lead-type cell.*

its specific gravity, when the cells are fully charged, varying from 1.220 to 1.250.

The usual method of determining the strength of the solution is to test it by means of a hydrometer syringe, as shown in Fig. 17-10. The hydrometer itself is placed inside the syringe so that it is only necessary to insert the latter in the cell, draw out some of the liquid, make the reading, and squirt the liquid back into the cell without removing the syringe nozzle. The ordinary battery hydrometer is graduated from 1.100 to 1.300, which is the maximum range of variation of the electrolyte between a completely discharged and a fully charged condition. Table 17-1 gives the conditions present in a battery at different stages of charge, assuming the surrounding temperature to be 70°F.

Container. The container for the lead-acid cell is made either of a hard-rubber composition material (Fig. 17-1) or of glass. For automobile and radio work the former is preferred because it will withstand jars and light shocks when carried about. Glass is preferable for light-plant batteries, which are not moved about and thus subjected to possible cracking and breakage. The glass jar has the advantage of permitting better observation of the cell contents and its condition.

The tops of both the rubber and the glass-jar cells are covered with a rubber-composition material and

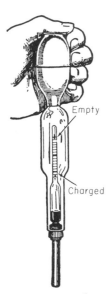

FIG. 17-10. *Hydrometer syringe for determining the gravity of the electrolyte.*

Table 17-1. Characteristics of Lead-acid-type Storage Cells at Different Stages of Charge

Condition of battery	Specific gravity	Cell voltage	Freezing point, °F.
Fully charged.............	1.230–1.300	2.2	−90
Three-quarters charged.....	1.200–1.250	2.1	−60
One-half charged...........	1.190–1.220	2.0	−20
One-quarter charged.......	1.175–1.190	1.9	Zero
Completely discharged......	1.150–less	1.8 or less	20

sealed with a tarry, acid- and waterproof compound. This cover has a vent or opening that permits testing of the electrolyte and refilling the cell. The vent plug is provided with one or more small holes, which allow the escape of gas formed during the charging and discharging action.

Chemical action in the lead-acid cell. As already stated, the active materials in a lead-acid cell, when fully charged, consist of (1) the lead dioxide (PbO_2), or positive material; (2) the sponge lead (Pb), or negative material; and (3) the dilute sulfuric acid solution, or electrolyte (H_2SO_4). If the terminals of such a cell are connected by a conductor so that an electric current will flow, the cell is said to be discharging, and the chemical action takes place as follows:

$$PbO_2 + Pb + 2H_2SO_4 = 2PbSO_4 + 2H_2O$$
(Lead dioxide + lead + sulfuric acid = lead sulfate + water)

Thus, during discharge, the active materials in the plates are changed to lead sulfate, a light gray compound of somewhat greater volume, and consequently the plates swell and tighten.

Likewise, some of the acid is consumed in the formation of the sulfate, and there is an increase in the water content of the electrolyte so that the latter becomes weaker and lower in specific gravity. It is not possible for a cell to keep discharging until all the active materials in the plates are converted to sulfate; the action is confined largely to the surface layer.

The initial voltage of a fully charged lead-acid cell in good condition is about 2.2, while the average cell will show a voltage of about 2. The minimum permissible voltage for a discharged cell is 1.7. Although a further discharge is possible, the current output is low and the life of the cell is apt to be shortened.

The variation in voltage of the lead-acid cell, according to its condition of charge, might seem to offer a convenient means of determining the stage of charge, but such is not the case for the reason that the change is merely a fraction of a volt. Obviously, a very delicate and extremely accurate testing instrument would be required. However, this voltage variation does provide a possible check on the general condition of a cell; that is, the electrolyte, when tested for specific gravity, may indicate that the cell is in a fully or partly charged condition, but, if the voltage is checked and found to be below normal, something else is wrong with the cell. Nevertheless, since there is a marked and uniform drop in the specific gravity of the electrolyte, owing to the formation of water and the absorption of the acid during the discharging process as already described, the measurement of the specific gravity serves as the most convenient, accurate, and satisfactory means of determining the state of charge of a cell or battery.

When a battery is charged, the chemical reaction is opposite to that during discharge, as shown by the following equation:

$$2PbSO_4 + 2H_2O = PbO_2 + Pb + 2H_2SO_4$$
(Lead sulfate + water = lead dioxide + lead + sulfuric acid)

Thus, the electrolyte gradually assumes its former concentration and the stage of charge, whether half charged, full charged, and so on, can be readily determined by means of the battery hydrometer (Fig. 17-10). When a fully charged condition is reached, the specific gravity of the electrolyte will not increase further, and noticeable or violent gassing will take place in the cell as a result of the breaking down of some of the water into hydrogen and oxygen. Excessive gassing and bubbling in a cell or battery are a positive indication that it is completely charged, provided it is in good condition in other respects.

Effect of temperature on specific gravity of electrolyte. In determining the specific gravity of the electrolyte in any storage cell, its temperature should be about 70°F., or else a correction should be made, according to the existing temperature, for the reason that the liquid will expand or increase in volume and have a lower specific gravity at high temperatures, or will contract and have a higher specific gravity at low temperatures. For the lead-acid battery, the specific-gravity readings for cells in various stages of charge, as given in Table 17-1, are always assumed to be taken at 70°F. A variation of 3°F. will produce a variation of 0.001 in the hydrometer reading. The usual rule is as follows: For each 3°F. above 70°F., add 0.001 to the observed hydrometer reading; or for each 3°F. below 70°F., subtract 0.001. The result will be the specific-gravity reading if the temperature of the electrolyte were 70°F. For example, if the temperature of the electrolyte is 85°F. and its specific gravity 1.190, the latter corrected to 70°F. would be

$$1.190 + \frac{85 - 70}{3} \times 0.001 = 1.195$$

Battery voltage. Storage batteries are rated according to (1) voltage and (2) ampere-hour capacity. As already explained, the voltage of either the Edison or the lead-acid cell varies only slightly with its condition of charge, the average discharge voltage of the former being considered as 1.2 and of the latter 2.0 volts. The total voltage rating of a

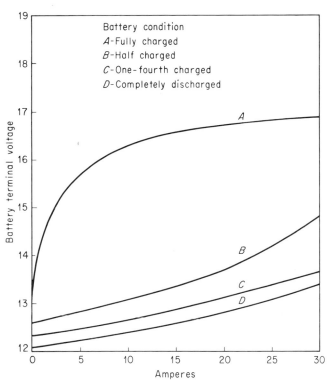

FIG. 17-11. *Effect of battery condition on voltage and charging rate.*

battery, therefore, depends only upon the type of cell and the method used in connecting them; that is, for cells connected in series,

Voltage = number of cells × 2   for lead-acid battery

or   Voltage = number of cells × 1.2   for Edison battery

For a number of cells connected in parallel, the voltage reading would be about 2.0 for the lead-acid battery or 1.2 for the Edison type, regardless of the number of cells in the battery.

The principal factors affecting the voltage of a lead-acid battery are (1) the strength of the electrolyte, (2) the charging or discharging rate, and (3) the existing temperature. For example, Fig. 17-11 shows the relationship of applied voltage and charging rate in amperes, depending upon the condition of charge. In general, the curves show that for any given voltage, the charging rate will be high for a discharged battery and lower for one which is well charged. Figure 17-12 shows that the rate of charge is greatly affected by temperature and that, in general, a higher voltage is needed to charge any battery at a given rate under low-temperature conditions than under high-temperature conditions.

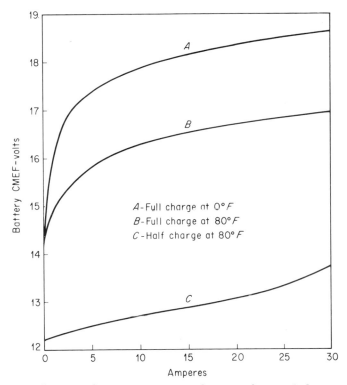

FIG. 17-12. *Effect of ambient temperature on battery voltage and charging rate.*

Ampere-hour rating or capacity. It is frequently convenient and necessary to designate in some manner the size and capacity of storage batteries used for various purposes. This is done by giving them a certain ampere-hour rating. For example, suppose that a given battery is rated at 60 amp.-hr. This means, theoretically, that when in good condition and fully charged, it will deliver 60 amp. for 1 hr., or 30 amp. for 2 hr., or 20 amp. for 3 hr., or 10 amp. for 6 hr., or 7.5 amp. for 8 hr., or 5 amp. for 12 hr., and so on, when it will be completely discharged. In other words, its 1-hr. discharge rate would be 60 amp.; its 2-hr. rate, 30 amp.; its 3-hr. rate, 20 amp.; and so on. Practically, however, the battery would not deliver 60 amp. for 1 hr. or 30 amp. for 2 hr. or even 10 amp. for 6 hr. In other words, the ampere-hour capacity of any storage battery actually varies greatly, depending upon the rate of discharge in amperes per hour. The lower the rate becomes, the longer the period during which it will discharge at that rate and the greater its total ampere-hour capacity up to a certain limit. This is best explained by reference to the curves (Fig. 17-13).

It is the usual practice to base the ampere-hour rating of a battery upon a discharge rate equal to the 10-hr. rate or even less; that is, an

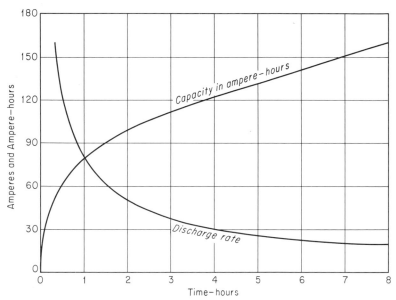

FIG. 17-13. *Curves showing capacity and discharge characteristics of lead-acid storage cell.*

80-amp.-hr. battery, when fully charged, should supply a current of 8 amp. for 10 hr.; a 120-amp.-hr. battery, 12 amp.; a 160-amp.-hr. battery, 16 amp.; and so on, when discharged to a voltage of 1.75 volts per cell. As already explained, a battery may be discharged at a rate greater than the 10-hr. rate, but such a discharge rate should not be maintained for more than a few minutes at a time, for reasons that will be explained later.

Since nearly all storage batteries consist of a number of cells connected in series, the ampere-hour capacity and rating of the battery are the same as the capacity and rating of the individual cells. It is primarily dependent, therefore, upon the size and number of plates per cell, because the greater the size or number of plates or both, the greater the total plate surface and the quantity of active materials available for generating electricity. Other factors affecting the ampere-hour capacity are thickness of plates, porosity of plates and separators, quantity and density of electrolyte, and temperature.

Automobile battery sizes and ratings. Automobile batteries consist of either three or six cells and, therefore, have a voltage rating of six or twelve volts, respectively.

The size is determined by the number of plates per cell, as shown by Table 17-2. This varies from 9 to 23, and the number of plates in turn

Table 17-2. Size and Rating of Automobile Batteries

Volts	Plates per cell	Amp.-hr. capacity, 20-hr. rate	Watt-hr. capacity	300 amp. at 0°F., min. to 1 volt per cell
6	13	70	420	1.5
6	15	100	600	3.3
6	17	115	690	4.5
6	19	135	810	5.3
12	9	60	720	4.8 [1]
12	11	72	864	6.0 [1]

[1] 150 amp. at 0°F. for 12-volt batteries.

determines the capacity in ampere-hours. The present standard method of rating automotive-type batteries as established by the Society of Automotive Engineers is as follows:

Batteries for combined starting and lighting service shall have two ratings except as noted. The first rating shall indicate the lighting ability and shall be the capacity in ampere-hours of the battery when it is discharged continuously to an average final terminal voltage equivalent to 1.75 per cell at the 20-hr. rate for passenger car and motor truck service and at the 6-hr. rate for motor-coach service. The temperature of the battery at the beginning of such discharge shall be exactly 80°F., and an average temperature of 80°F. shall be maintained during discharge with a maximum variation of ±5°F. New batteries shall meet these ratings on or before the third discharge when discharged at a rate in amperes obtained by dividing the rated capacity in ampere-hours by the number of hours at which the rating is specified. The second rating shall apply only to batteries used in passenger car and motor truck starting and lighting service. This rating shall indicate the cranking ability of the battery at low temperatures and shall be (1) the time in minutes when the battery is discharged continuously at 300 amp. to a final average terminal voltage equivalent to 1.0 volt per cell, the temperature of the battery at the beginning of such discharge being 0°F.; and (2) the terminal battery voltage 5 sec. after beginning such discharge. New batteries shall be prepared for this test by

giving them a complete charge followed by an initial discharge for 5 hr. at a
rate in amperes equal to one-sixth of the 20-hr. rate in ampere-hours specified
for the respective sizes and types of batteries. This discharge shall be made
while the battery is at a temperature of 80°F. following which the batteries
shall be fully charged and then placed in an atmosphere of 0°F. ± 1°F. for
not less than 24 consecutive hours prior to discharge at 300 amp. at 0°F.

Battery efficiency. The efficiency of a storage battery, like that of any
similar chemical or mechanical energy-producing device, is the ratio of
the energy output of the battery when discharged to the energy input
when charged. This energy output and input may be expressed either
in ampere-hours or in watt-hours; that is,

$$\text{Ampere-hour efficiency} = \frac{\text{output in ampere-hours}}{\text{input in ampere-hours}}$$

or
$$\text{Watt-hour efficiency} = \frac{\text{output in watt-hours}}{\text{input in watt-hours}}$$

The efficiency of the lead-acid battery depends upon several factors,
such as (1) rate of discharge, (2) condition of plates, (3) temperature,
and (4) internal resistance. For a battery in good condition and discharged at a normal rate and temperature, it may be 80 to 85 per cent.
High discharge rates and low temperatures tend to lower the efficiency.

Battery charging. As previously stated, a secondary cell or battery
is so designated because, when discharged, it can be restored to its original condition or recharged by sending an electric current through it in a
direction opposite to that of the current flow during discharge. Also, as
already explained, the charging process is an electrochemical action
that converts the active materials into their original form. To charge any
battery, the following conditions must be observed:

1. Direct current only can be used. This may be supplied in a number
of ways as described later.

2. The flow of the current through the battery in charging must be
opposite to that during discharge. Therefore, the polarity of the charging
circuit must be known, and its positive and negative terminals connected
to the positive and negative terminals, respectively, of the battery.

3. The voltage of the charging circuit must be greater than that of
the battery, but not excessive. A charging voltage equal to about 2.5
volts per cell is recommended to obtain the correct charging rate in
amperes. If the voltage of the charging circuit is too low, the rate will be
decreased and a longer time required to fully charge the battery. A
charging voltage less than the battery voltage will obviously discharge
rather than charge the battery. A charging voltage greater than 2.5 to 3.0
volts per cell will charge the battery at too high a rate and result in
heating and permanent injury to the materials.

Methods of charging batteries. Some of the usual methods and devices used for charging storage batteries are as follows:

1. By direct-current generator driven by an internal-combustion engine. Examples: (*a*) All automobiles are equipped with a small direct-current generator, which charges the battery whenever the engine is running beyond a certain speed. (*b*) The common battery-type farm-lighting plant usually consists of a small high-speed engine directly connected to a direct-current generator, which may be operated whenever the battery needs charging.

2. By a special battery-charging outfit or motor-generator set consisting of an alternating-current electric motor driven by current from a central power station and connected directly to a direct-current generator, which generates and supplies the necessary charging current.

3. By means of a rectifier in connection with an ordinary alternating-current supply line. The rectifier converts the alternating to direct current. There are a number of different types available including the slow or normal-rate charger and the high-rate type.

Dry-charged batteries. A dry-charged storage battery is manufactured with charged plates and the electrolyte is not added until it is placed in service, the advantage being that the battery does not deteriorate with nonuse and the customer is assured of a good battery. Provision is made for supplying the proper quantity of acid of the correct strength. Dry-charged batteries should be given at least a limited charge immediately before service installation.

Charging rate. The rate in amperes at which the current flows when a storage battery is being charged is known as the charging rate. Obviously, the higher the charging rate for a given battery, the shorter the time required to charge it. On the other hand, an excessively high charging rate may cause permanent injury because of the heating effect on the plates and cell contents.

During the early stages of the charging process, a higher rate of charge is permissible. As the battery becomes partly charged and bubbling or gassing is observed, the rate should be reduced until, near the end and during the last few hours, it is less than one-half the initial rate. A safe rule to follow in the case of a completely discharged battery, if it is in good condition otherwise, is to determine or estimate its ampere-hour rating and start charging it at a rate equal to one-eighth this capacity, continuing until gassing begins and then reducing the rate about one-half and completing the charge. This method will require from 12 to 24 hr. of continuous charging.

High-rate chargers are used largely by service stations to boost the battery rapidly without removal from the vehicle. They are usually constant-potential machines of very high capacity. If such a charger is used, the electrolyte temperature should not exceed 125°F. and excess bubbling and gassing should not continue for any length of time. It is not desirable to charge a battery at a high rate longer than 30 min. to 1 hr.

Hints on battery charging. When a battery is connected to a charging circuit, care must be taken to connect it correctly, that is, the positive terminal of the circuit to the positive of the battery, and negative to negative. If the battery terminals are not marked or otherwise distinguishable, wires may be attached to them and the other ends immersed in a glass of water containing a small amount of common salt in solution. The ends of the wire should not touch. Bubbles will be seen to form on the end of the wire attached to the negative terminal of the battery. If a battery is not properly connected for charging, it will discharge further and the plates will be seriously injured.

It is not advisable to add water to the electrolyte in a completely discharged battery unless the electrolyte is below the top edge of the plates and they are exposed. The charging action increases the volume of the electrolyte; therefore, if too much water is added, the solution may bubble up into the filler opening or even run over.

Each cell in a battery should be tested by means of a hydrometer every 3 to 5 hr. to determine the progress of the charging action. Little change may occur during the first few hours, but if the cell is taking the charge, bubbling will eventually take place, and near the end, excessive bubbling or gassing should develop. When gassing begins, the charging rate should be low and the charge should not be continued more than 1 or 2 hr. longer, unless one or more cells have failed to come up with the others. Continued charging, after gassing begins, lowers the level of the electrolyte, causes heating of the cell, and may injure the plates. A battery is fully charged when all cells are gassing freely and the specific gravity and voltage have reached a high value and show no further change.

BATTERY TROUBLES

Sulfation. The life of any storage battery is dependent upon the care and attention it receives. Maximum service should not be expected from a storage battery of any kind if it is not inspected and checked up periodically. Perhaps the most common cause of short life is sulfation, which results from a protracted discharged condition. As already mentioned, during the normal discharging process, the active material in the plates is changed to lead sulfate ($PbSO_4$), which, in turn, is converted back into lead dioxide and lead when the cell is recharged. However, if the cell or battery is permitted to remain in a discharged condition for any length of time, this sulfate gradually hardens and is not readily converted to its former state. The longer the cell remains uncharged, the more difficult it is to recharge it. A badly sulfated cell or battery can be recharged only with difficulty, if at all, and then seldom regains its original effectiveness.

High charging and discharging rates. Excessive charging or discharging rates for periods exceeding a few seconds or minutes are injurious to storage batteries in that heat is generated, which causes warping or buckling of the plates and thereby loosens the active material and reduces the life and efficiency of the battery. As previously stated, it is important that a battery be charged or discharged only at a certain rate based upon its capacity in ampere-hours.

Other causes of battery troubles. Other common causes of battery troubles are (1) failure to keep electrolyte at proper level and over tops of plates; (2) use of undistilled or impure water for replenishing electrolyte; (3) dirty, badly corroded, or loose connections and terminals; and (4) use of too strong acid for replacement of electrolyte.

REFERENCES

CROUSE, W. H., "Automotive Electrical Equipment," McGraw-Hill Book Company, Inc., New York, 1959.

Facts about Storage Batteries, Electric Storage Battery Co., Philadelphia, 1957.

Operation and Care of Vehicle Type Batteries, *Natl. Bur. Standards (U.S.) Circ. 92.*

"Storage Battery Technical Service Manual," 4th ed., Association of American Battery Manufacturers, East Orange, N.J., 1958.

PROBLEMS AND QUESTIONS

1. Name the two types of storage cells and compare them with respect to adaptability, utility, and economy.

2. State the chemical reaction in a lead-acid cell when charging and when discharging.

3. Why is it necessary to add water rather than acid periodically to a lead-acid storage cell?

4. The electrolyte of a lead-acid cell tests 1.190 at 20°F. What would it test at 80°F.?

5. Given a 16-cell light-plant battery having a rating of 160 amp.-hr., how many 100-watt lamps will it carry without difficulty for several hours?

6. Explain the difference between an auto battery with a 1-year guarantee and one with a 3-year guarantee.

7. Name all precautions to be observed in using and caring for a storage battery.

18

Battery Ignition Systems

All electric ignition systems for internal-combustion engines are either one or the other of two types, namely, (1) the *make-and-break* or *low-tension* system, and (2) the *jump-spark* or *high-tension* system. The current for either system may be generated chemically, that is, by means of a battery of some kind, or mechanically, by means of a magneto or similar electric generator.

The essential functions of any electric ignition system are (1) the generation of a large, hot spark in the cylinder and (2) the production of this spark at the right instant in the travel of the piston. In other words, if a good spark is produced in the cylinder at the right time, the combustible mixture of fuel and air should be properly ignited.

Ignition voltage and requirements. An electric spark is nothing more or less than an electric current passing through air. In any electric ignition system such a spark is produced by making the current flow between two points separated by a small fraction of an inch and forming a part of an otherwise complete electric circuit. Since air and other gases are very poor conductors of electricity, an extremely high voltage is necessary to produce the desired spark in the cylinder of any engine. Furthermore, at the time that the spark is required in the cycle, the gaseous mixture surrounding the sparking points is under compression. Consequently, this mixture is considerably more resistant to the passage of an electric current than if it were at a lower or ordinary atmospheric pressure. The curves (Fig. 18-1) show the relationship of gap voltage to compression pressure.

Again, the greater the width of the spark gap, the greater the voltage necessary to make the current flow across the gap and create a desirable spark. This is clearly shown by reference to the curve in Fig. 18-1. Therefore, to obtain the best results, it is important to use as narrow a gap as possible in the spark plug or igniter and to maintain the highest possible voltage in the circuit.

It has already been explained that the voltage of a single dry cell, a storage cell, or any similar chemical generator of electricity seldom exceeds 2.0 volts. In view of this fact, and since voltages ranging from a few hundred to several thousand volts are required if any electrical ignition system is to function properly, it would seem impractical to attempt to utilize this source of electric energy for ignition purposes. That is, to

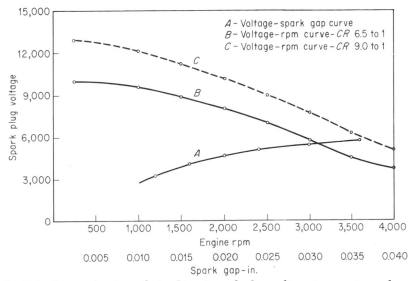

FIG. 18-1. *Curves showing relationship of spark-plug voltage to gap size and compression ratio.*

do so would apparently require a large number of cells connected in series, which would mean excessive cost, weight, and depreciation and, perhaps, considerable trouble. However, since the spark is needed in the cylinder at a certain instant only and need not continue flowing for any length of time, even for a second or less, the source of the electrical energy is not required to supply a steady flow of current, and it is possible to utilize the principle of electromagnetic induction, as previously explained, to increase or "step up" the low voltage of an ordinary three- or four-cell battery to the desired degree.

Make-and-break system. If four dry cells are connected in series and the ends of the two terminal wires are rubbed together, only a very fine spark will be observed. In fact, the current will not flow across even a very minute gap, unless the circuit is first completed and then broken. Now, if this battery is connected properly to a comparatively simple and inexpensive induction coil (Fig. 16-21), a voltage is set up that will produce a much fatter and brighter spark. It is evident, therefore, that the introduction of the coil and the sudden breaking of the electrical circuit result in the generation for an instant of a very high voltage.

It might be said that this spark is produced indirectly and not directly by the battery; that is, the battery current forms the electromagnet, and the sudden or instantaneous collapse of the magnetic field generates a second or induced current of much higher voltage. The quicker the circuit is broken, the larger the spark, for the reason, as previously discussed, that the voltage of an induced current is dependent upon three

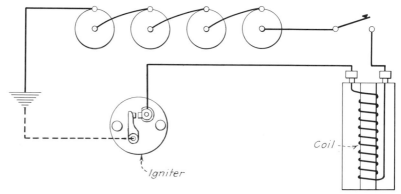

FIG. 18-2. *Wiring diagram for the make-and-break ignition system.*

factors, one of which is the rate at which the magnetic field is cut or broken down.

The make-and-break system of ignition (Fig. 18-2), using a battery as the source of current, operates more or less in the manner just described. The coil is very simple in construction, consisting essentially of a soft-iron core, made up of a bundle of soft-iron wires rather than a solid piece of iron, so that the magnetizing and demagnetizing action will take place as rapidly as possible; a layer of insulating material to bind the iron wires together and separate them from the winding; a single winding consisting of many turns of insulated copper wire; a metal or fiber protective case; and the two terminals that are the ends of the winding.

The device for breaking the circuit and producing the spark in the cylinder is called an *igniter*. As shown in Fig. 18-3, it consists of a cast-iron block or frame, flanged and drilled for bolting to the engine; a stationary pin or electrode, insulated by mica from the igniter block and other parts; and a movable pin, equipped with springs to permit it to snap away or cause a quick separation of the points. The igniter points are held open a fraction of an inch during a greater part of the cycle in order to prevent undue waste of the battery current. Just before the spark is needed in the cylinder, the igniter trip arm (Fig. 18-2) pushes the movable point against the stationary insulated point, and the current flows and builds up an electromagnetic field about the coil. Then, at the instant the spark should occur, the trip arm releases the movable electrode, and a large bright spark is produced at the points as they separate. Most engines equipped with the make-and-break system of ignition have a small hand lever of some kind by which the spark can be retarded for starting.

Adaptability and advantages of make-and-break system. The use of the make-and-break system of ignition is confined principally to stationary low-speed engines. It is simple from an electrical standpoint and gives a good hot spark. On the other hand, it has certain disadvantages that limit its utility for multiple-cylinder high-speed engines: (1) the igniter-tripping mechanism creates more or less noise; (2) frequent adjustment for wear is usually necessary, otherwise the spark gets out of time; (3) the igniter requires a large opening in the cylinder, necessitating the use of a gasket to prevent loss of compression; (4) the igniter cannot be removed so conveniently and easily as a spark plug and is more expensive to replace.

Jump-spark system. The make-and-break system of ignition just described is known as a low-tension

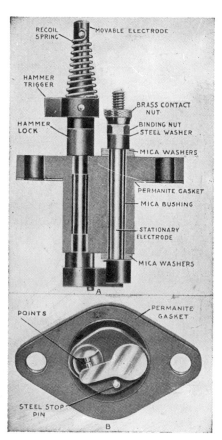

FIG. 18-3. *Igniter construction.*

or low-voltage system because the circuit is first completely closed and then suddenly broken at the igniter points and a spark produced. The momentarily induced voltage is only 300 or 400 volts, which is insufficient to make the current jump the gap of a spark plug, the sparking device used in the jump-spark system. That is, in the jump-spark system a permanent air gap exists between the points of the plug and, with the high compression pressure, a voltage of 10,000 to 15,000 is necessary to make the current flow across this gap and ignite the charge. To set up this high voltage, the principles of electromagnetic induction are utilized as in the make-and-break system, but a somewhat different and more complicated type of coil is necessary.

With reference to Fig. 18-4, the coil is made up of a soft-iron core consisting of a bundle of soft-iron wires, a primary winding of about No. 16 insulated copper wire, and a secondary winding consisting of many thousands of turns of very fine insulated copper wire. In the manufacture of such a coil, the wire itself that makes up the winding is well insulated. Likewise, the different turns of wire are insulated from each other, and the layers forming each winding are well insulated one from the other. This thorough insulation is necessary in order to prevent the excessive voltage generated in the coil winding from breaking through and creating an internal short circuit. In addition to thorough insulation, the coil is surrounded by a moistureproof and waterproof compound and incased in a metal or fiber casing. The ends of the windings are brought through the case and fastened to the terminal pieces or posts.

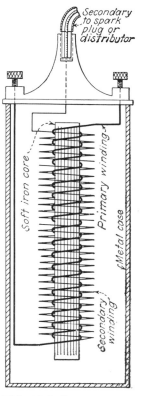

FIG. 18-4. *Construction of a typical nonvibrating coil for jump-spark ignition.*

The operation of such a coil is as follows: If a battery is connected in the primary circuit, as shown in Fig. 16-22, the current flows and forms an electromagnet, as previously described. If this battery current is now suddenly broken, the electromagnetism dies out very quickly and thereby induces a current in the primary winding, and also in the secondary winding, for the reason that it likewise is in the magnetic field. In other words, it is not necessary that the secondary winding have an actual electrical connection with the primary winding to have a current induced in it by the breakdown of the magnetic field. Since the secondary winding consists of many more turns than the primary winding, the voltage induced is very high, and the current flows across the gap and produces a spark. Therefore, if a coil of this kind can be connected to a battery and to the spark plug of the engine, and if some means can be devised by which the primary circuit can be broken just at the instant the spark is needed in the cylinder, the fuel charge will be ignited.

The device (Figs. 18-5 and 18-6) that is used to interrupt or break the primary circuit is known as a *breaker* or *interrupter mechanism*. It consists essentially of three parts: (1) a stationary grounded point, (2) a movable insulated point, and (3) the rotating cam. The cam strikes the movable point and separates it from the stationary one at the instant the spark is desired.

A diagram of the wiring for a single-cylinder engine equipped with the nonvibrating jump-spark system is shown in Fig. 18-7. The primary circuit consists of the battery, the primary winding of the coil, and the breaker mechanism. The secondary circuit consists only of the secondary winding of the coil and the spark plug. If the engine has more than one cylinder, a distributor is needed.

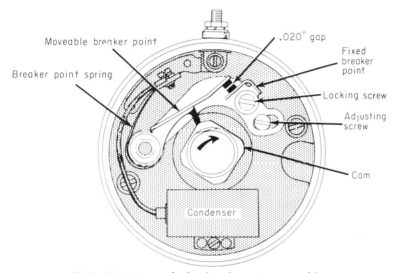

FIG. 18-5. *Four-cylinder breaker-point assembly.*

The condenser. When the breaker points open, a current is induced in the primary as well as in the secondary winding, and a spark will occur at the points, just as it did at the igniter points in the make-and-break system. Since this sparking will soon pit or roughen the points and eventually render them inefficient or inoperative, it is desirable that it be eliminated. This is done by means of a condenser (Fig. 18-8), which consists of alternate layers of tin foil separated and insulated from each other by waxed paper. As shown, it is not possible for an electric current to flow through a condenser as it would through a wire or a coil. The condenser is connected in the circuit as shown in Fig. 18-7. That is, it might be said that it is connected across the breaker points or bridges them.

The condenser action is as follows: The current induced in the primary circuit at the time of the separation of the points, instead of dissipating itself in the form of a spark at the points, surges into the condenser but not through it; then surges outward into the circuit again in the opposite direction; then reverses again and surges backward; and continues until it finally dies out. This action not only eliminates the arcing almost

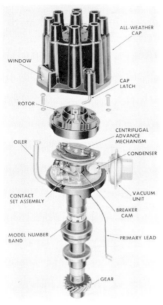

entirely but, in addition, helps to demagnetize the iron core and break down the electromagnetic field much more rapidly than it would be broken down without the condenser. Consequently, the current induced in the secondary circuit is of a much higher voltage, and a better spark is produced. In other words, we might say that the condenser protects the points by eliminating the arcing and intensifies the current in the secondary winding, producing a better spark at the spark-plug gap. The condenser may be built in the coil unit or it may be found near the breaker-point mechanism.

Breaker mechanism. The breaker mechanism (Figs. 18-5 and 18-6) used with the nonvibrating coil system is usually a rather small mechanism with the movable point carefully insulated from the other parts. A small spring holds the movable point against the stationary one when contact is desired. The contact points themselves are usually made of some hard and highly heat-resistant material, such as a tungsten alloy. The

FIG. 18-6. *Complete breaker-point and distributor assembly.* (Courtesy of Delco-Remy Division, General Motors Corporation.)

breaker cam for a single-cylinder engine, or for a four-stroke-cycle engine with any number of cylinders, rotates at camshaft speed or one-half

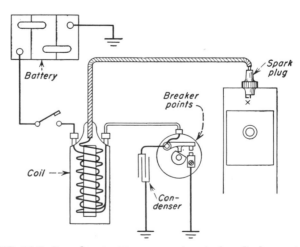

FIG. 18-7. *Complete ignition system for single-cylinder engine.*

crankshaft speed. That is, it is obvious that for a single-cylinder, four-stroke cycle engine, the points must open once in two revolutions of the crankshaft to produce the correct number of sparks. Therefore, if the cam is in time, that is, if it opens the points at the right time in the compression stroke, the ignition system will function correctly.

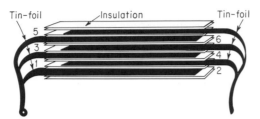

FIG. 18-8. *Construction of a condenser.*

For multiple-cylinder engines the breaker cam, as shown in Fig. 18-9, has as many lobes or projections as there are cylinders and opens the points that number of times per revolution, thereby producing the required number of sparks without increasing its speed with reference to

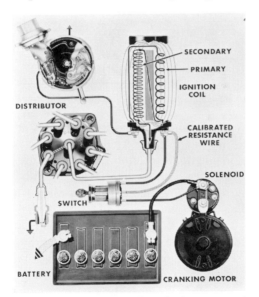

FIG. 18-9. *Complete ignition system for eight-cylinder engine.* (Courtesy of Delco-Remy Division, General Motors Corporation.)

the crankshaft speed. The advancing or retarding of the spark is usually produced by shifting the cam with respect to the breaker points.

Distributor. A distributor (Fig. 18-9) is necessary in any multiple-cylinder ignition system to distribute the secondary current to each spark plug in correct order. The entire mechanism consists of only two parts, the rotor and the cap or cover with its contacts and terminals for the lead wires to the plugs. The rotor is always located just above the breaker cam and is turned by the same gear and shaft. The cover also serves to protect the rotor and interrupter points from dirt, dust, moisture, and oil accumulation.

High-speed ignition systems. The trend toward very high-speed engines with more cylinders and higher compression ratios has necessitated certain modifications in the standard ignition system in order to ensure positive ignition and efficient engine performance. For example, an eight-cylinder engine running at 4,000 r.p.m. fires 16,000 times per min-

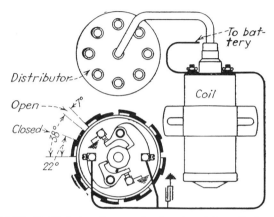

FIG. 18-10. *Multiple-breaker mechanism for eight-cylinder engine.*

ute, or 267 times per second. This means that only a $\frac{1}{267}$ sec. time interval is available for each "spark cycle," that is, closing of the circuit, building up the magnetic field, and then breaking it down and producing a spark. In other words, there is a limit to the minimum time needed by the current flowing in the primary circuit to build up a maximum magnetic flux in the coil core.

Two methods are used to provide the needed voltage under these high-speed conditions: (1) use two sets of interrupter points connected in parallel, one set serving only to close the circuit after the other set has broken it to produce a spark (Fig. 18-10); and (2) use a 12-volt battery and a coil which will generate a correspondingly higher voltage in the same time interval (Fig. 18-9).

The proper functioning of an ignition system using a double breaker mechanism depends upon the proper opening and closing of the points with respect to each other—this being called synchronization—as well as the correct timing of the points with respect to the piston travel. The 12-volt battery system is preferable in that it requires only a single set of breaker points and, also, more power is available for cranking the engine.

Operation of 12-volt ignition systems. The increased secondary voltages available from a 12-volt system are mainly the result of a new ignition coil design which takes full advantage of the higher system voltage. The coil used with the 12-volt system has more primary turns, more secondary turns, and a higher ratio between the two as compared with 6-volt coils of the same size. The increased number of primary turns result in a higher inductance in the primary winding. The increased inductance of the primary circuit along with the other changes makes it possible for the coil to provide a higher secondary voltage output throughout the speed range.

In order to improve ignition performance during cranking and to permit the coil to be built into a container no larger than that used for 6-volt coils, a portion of the necessary coil resistance is built into an ignition resistor. This resistor is connected in series with the primary circuit between the battery and the coil and is wound with wire which changes resistance only slightly with temperature. This characteristic prevents an excessive primary current flow at low temperatures and thus reduces the tendency for the distributor contact points to oxidize during cold weather. It is also noted (Fig. 18-9) that by means of a separate circuit from the battery to the ignition coil through the cranking motor solenoid switch, the resistor is shorted out during cranking and the coil is connected directly to the battery. This makes full battery voltage available which provides a higher voltage during cranking. As soon as the engine starts, the solenoid switch opens this circuit and reestablishes the resistor circuit.

Spark plugs. The spark plug is the device used in the jump-spark system of ignition that provides the gap for the high-voltage current to jump and ignite the charge. Numerous types and styles of spark plugs are manufactured for the many different types of engines that use the jump-spark system of ignition.

Referring to Fig. 18-11, the ordinary spark plug is made up of the following parts: the steel outer shell, which is threaded and screws into the cylinder block; the insulator, usually made of porcelain but sometimes of mica; the copper-asbestos gaskets, between the insulator and the shell, to prevent loss of compression and leakage; the electrodes or points; and the terminal.

The insulator is the most important part of the spark plug and must be made of high-grade material to withstand the high voltage and prevent leakage of the current or a short circuit. It must also withstand high temperatures and pressures. Porcelain is used almost exclusively as the insulating material, but mica withstands heat better than porcelain and, therefore, is a better insulator for spark plugs used under excessively high temperatures.

The spark-plug points must be made of material that will withstand high temperatures and will not be burned away rapidly by the arcing and heat to which they are subjected. They are usually made of some special nickel, tungsten, or chromium alloy with a very small percentage of iron. The gap at the electrode is very important in the effective and efficient operation of the spark plug in an ignition system. In general, this gap should not be less than 0.020 in. or more than 0.040 in.

Sizes of spark plugs. There are five common sizes of spark plugs: the ½-in., with U.S. Standard pipe thread; the ⅞-in. S.A.E. plug; and three sizes of metric plugs. The ½-in. plug uses the same thread as that used on a ½-in. pipe, that is, a pipe whose inside diameter is ½ in. Since a pipe thread is tapered and rather coarse as compared to a bolt thread, this plug, as it is screwed into the cylinder, gradually becomes tighter and is merely screwed in tight to prevent leakage.

The ⅞-in. S.A.E. plug has a thread similar to that used on a ⅞-in. bolt, with 18 threads per inch. Since it does not taper, it cannot be made tight by screwing in farther and farther as with the pipe thread. This plug, therefore, is equipped with a shoulder and a copper-asbestos gasket (Fig. 18-11) and is screwed down until it fits snugly in the cylinder block against this shoulder and gasket. It is very important that the gasket be used. Otherwise oil and gas leakage will invariably occur.

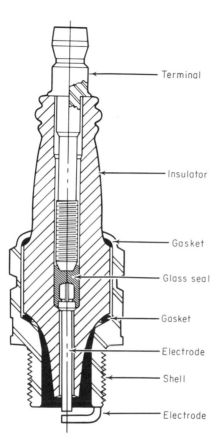

FIG. 18-11. *Typical spark-plug construc-tion.*

(image labels: Terminal, Insulator, Gasket, Glass seal, Gasket, Electrode, Shell, Electrode)

The large metric plug is very similar to the ⅞-in. S.A.E. plug, except that the threaded part, which screws into the cylinder, is smaller, being 18 mm. or about 0.71 in. in diameter. The medium-size metric plug is 14 mm. in diameter and the small metric plug is 10 mm. in diameter.

Spark-plug heat range. Improvements in design and the use of higher compression ratios and faster burning fuels have resulted in higher combustion-chamber temperatures in automotive engines. The discovery was also made that the efficient operation of these engines depended greatly upon the temperature of the spark plugs. If the plug dissipated heat rapidly and remained too cool, combustion was likely to be sluggish and the plug might become fouled. If the plug dissipated heat too slowly and remained too hot, preignition and knocking might occur and the points burned away rapidly. For this reason, not only must any engine use a certain size of plug but it must be of the correct type as related to heat control. The operating temperature of a spark plug is determined by the distance the heat must travel, as shown in Fig. 18-12. The greater this distance, the higher the plug temperature; and the shorter this distance, the cooler the plug operates. In general, high-compression engines operating at high speeds and heavy loads require "cold" plugs, and low-compression engines operating at low speeds and light loads use "hot" plugs. The selection of the correct type of spark plug from the standpoint of heat range for any engine is very important.

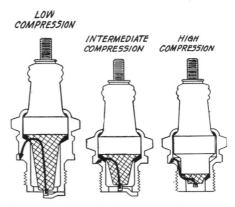

FIG. 18-12. *Spark-plug construction to control heat flow.*

As observed, the heat travels through the spark plug and is transmitted to the cylinder block at the plug shoulder where it seats in the cylinder. Most plugs use a copper gasket as a seal at this point and to improve heat dissipation. However, some engines are equipped with spark plugs having a beveled shoulder which bears directly on the beveled ground seat in the cylinder block. Thus the gasket is eliminated without any reduction in heat dissipation.

Testing and cleaning spark plugs. Spark plugs will usually give very good service if given occasional or periodic attention and cleaning. The gap will gradually increase with use, owing to the burning off of the points; therefore the plug should be removed every few weeks and the gap adjusted. Excessive fouling and carbon deposits result in improper functioning because such deposits produce leakage of the electric current and eventually a short circuit develops. If the fuel mixture is kept correctly adjusted and the engine does not receive an excessive amount of lubricating oil, or the oil does not work past the piston rings, the average spark plug will give very little trouble from fouling. If trouble of this kind develops frequently, it should be remedied by finding its source. The points and the lower end of the insulator are often cleaned by means of a special machine using a blast of sand.

The outside of the spark plug should also be wiped off frequently because the fine dust that often collects on the exposed porcelain absorbs moisture when the air is damp, and eventually the current jumps on the outside of the plug from the terminal to the bushing and, therefore, does not produce a spark at the gap. An occasional wiping of the exposed porcelain surface will prevent this trouble.

Ignition timing. One of the very important factors in the correct operation of any internal-combustion engine is the time of occurrence of the ignition. This is particularly true in multiple-cylinder and variable-speed engines. That is, the combustible mixture of fuel and air must be ignited so that the piston will receive the force of the explosion just as it reaches head dead center at the end of the compression stroke and is ready to start on the power or working stroke. If the spark comes too early, the explosion will take place before the piston reaches the end of the compression stroke, and the result will be a knocking effect and appreciable loss of power. If the spark occurs too late, the explosion will be delayed and the maximum effect will not be received by the piston, resulting in considerable power loss and overheating.

Obviously, the time that the explosion is to take place is determined by the time of occurrence of the spark. If the spark comes too early, the explosion will be too early, and if the spark is too late, the explosion will be late. Furthermore, it should be kept in mind that the occurrence of the spark and the explosion of the mixture are two distinct and separate actions and are not simultaneous as it might appear. This, perhaps, can be best understood by bearing in mind that the fuel mixture when ignited by the spark is "set on fire," so to speak, at one point only. Before an explosion can take place, the ignition must spread throughout the entire mixture. A very short, but nevertheless definite, period of time is required for the propagation of the ignition through the mixture. The rate of ignition is dependent upon several factors, such as the fuel used, the compression pressure in pounds per square inch, the load on the engine, the speed, and the cylinder temperature.

In order to provide for this lapse of time between the ignition of the mixture and its complete combustion by the time that the piston has reached the end of the compression stroke, the spark is advanced as shown by Fig. 18-13; that is, it is made to occur before the piston reaches the end of the stroke by an amount necessary to give the best results. Spark advance is usually designated in degrees of crankshaft travel; that is, an advance of 30 deg. means that the spark occurs when the crankshaft still lacks 30 deg. of being on dead center. A late spark is known as a *retarded spark* and usually occurs on, or very near, compression dead center (Fig. 18-13). A retarded spark is for cranking the engine only, to prevent its kicking back. As soon as the engine is started and reaches its normal speed, the spark should be advanced the necessary amount to give smooth operation.

As previously stated, the amount of spark advance varies with a number of conditions, the most important of which are engine crankshaft speed, kind of fuel, quality of fuel mixture, compression pressure, and

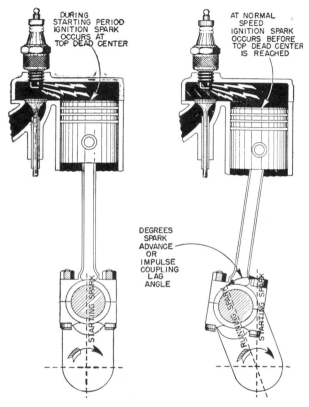

FIG. 18-13. *Spark timing for starting and running.*

cylinder temperature. It is quite evident that with a given fuel and compression pressure, the greater the speed of the engine, the greater the spark advance must be up to a certain point. That is, if the fuel mixture requires a certain fraction of time to be ignited and exploded, the piston will travel farther in a high-speed engine during this small interval of time than it will in a low-speed engine. Again a lean fuel mixture, or a fuel mixture at a low or medium pressure, will not burn so rapidly as a dense mixture or one under higher compression. Consequently, low-compression engines running at light loads require more spark advance than those operating at higher compression pressures and heavy loads.

Spark-timing mechanisms. In the make-and-break system of ignition, the time that the spark occurs is determined by the time that the igniter is tripped. The tripping mechanism is usually operated by the cam gear.

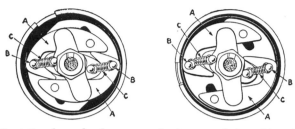

FIG. 18-14. *Centrifugal spark-advance mechanism-retarded position* (*left*) *and advanced position* (*right*).

Consequently, if the exhaust valve is in time, the timing of the spark will be nearly, if not entirely, correct. If it is either too early or too late, it can be adjusted within a range of perhaps 10 to 30 deg. by means of some adjustment on the tripping mechanism or arm itself.

In the jump-spark system of ignition, the time at which the spark occurs is determined by the time at which the breaker points separate. As seen in Fig. 18-6, these points and the distributor rotor are located on the same shaft, which is gear-driven by the camshaft. Usually some provision is made for adjusting the spark timing by slightly rotating the distributor head and breaker points about the breaker cam and shaft. Also the gap setting of the points can affect the timing of the spark. Therefore, they should always be adjusted for the recommended gap setting before the spark timing is checked or changed.

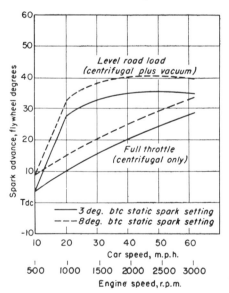

FIG. 18-15. *Spark timing for automobile engine equipped with centrifugal and vacuum control.*

Ignition timing procedure. Most engine manufacturers recommend the use of a timing light (Fig. 27-5) for checking and adjusting the spark setting for high-speed engines. A mark on either the flywheel or the belt pulley of the engine indicates the idle-speed spark setting. When the engine is running at a slow-idle speed, the timing light should flash just as the mark passes a stationary pointer or indicator. If this idle-speed setting is correct, the operating-speed spark setting will be taken care of by the automatic spark advance mechanism.

Automatic spark control. Multiple-cylinder engines using battery ignition are usually equipped so that the spark timing is controlled automatically according to the engine speed and other operating conditions. The most common arrangement consists of a pair of weights held together by two springs and mounted on the distributor shaft just under the breaker points. The weights react against the advance cam, which is a part of the breaker cam, and cause the latter to rotate in the direction it normally turns. At low speeds, the weight springs hold the weights together as shown in Fig. 18-14 so that there is no spark advance. As the speed increases, centrifugal force causes the weights to expand and act on the advance cam, which in turn rotates the breaker cam and thereby opens the breaker points earlier, thus creating an advanced spark.

Tractor engines using battery ignition are equipped only with the centrifugal automatic spark-control device. However, automobile and truck engines use a combination of centrifugal and vacuum control. The vacuum mechanism is actuated by manifold suction and advances or retards the spark according to the engine load as determined by the throttle-butterfly position. A spring-loaded diaphragm is linked to the breaker-point plate and rotates the points with respect to the cam. Figure 18-15 shows how these two types of spark-control mechanisms function with respect to each other and according to engine speed.

REFERENCES

A Discussion of 12-volt Automotive Electrical Systems, *Gen. Motors Eng. J.,* Vol. 1, No. 1.

CROUSE, W. H., "Automotive Electrical Equipment," McGraw-Hill Book Company, Inc., New York, 1959.

HELDT, P. M., "High-speed Combustion Engines," 16th ed., Chilton Company, Philadelphia, 1956.

Matching Compression Ratio and Spark Advance to Engine Octane Requirements, *Gen. Motors Eng. J.,* Vol. 3, No. 5.

MOSES, BEN D., and KENNETH R. FROST, "Farm Power," John Wiley & Sons, Inc., New York, 1952.

OBERT, EDWARD F., "Internal Combustion Engines," 2d ed., International Textbook Company, Scranton, Pa., 1950.

Spark Plugs for Internal Combustion Engines, *Lubrication,* June, 1949.

PROBLEMS AND QUESTIONS

1. Make a complete, detailed sketch of the parts and circuits involved for a six-cylinder ignition system as used in present-day automobiles.

2. What is meant by multiple-breaker ignition system, and what is the basic reason for the use of such a system?

3. An eight-cylinder, four-stroke-cycle engine has a maximum speed of 3,600

r.p.m. At this speed, what is the time in seconds during which the breaker points are closed for each spark, assuming the closed interval is twice the open interval?

4. What specific changes would be necessary to convert a four-cylinder ignition system into a two-cylinder system if the engine had a balanced firing interval? If the firing interval were unbalanced?

5. Name the factors affecting the spark advance needed for an engine and the effects of both a too late and a too early spark setting.

6. Explain the differences in the construction of so-called "cold" and "hot" spark plugs, and state the engine characteristics which determine the use of each.

19

Mechanical Generation of Electricity— Magneto Ignition

Mechanical devices for generating an electric current are termed either electric generators or magnetos. Such devices require a magnetic field. which, as we have seen, can be produced either by a piece of steel permanently magnetized or by means of an electromagnet. Magnetos are distinguished from other electric generators in that they utilize permanent steel magnets for providing the magnetic field, whereas machines ordinarily used for lighting and power purposes have their magnetic. field supplied by electromagnetic action.

Use of magnetos for ignition. The principal use of magnetos is for the mechanical generation of electricity for spark ignition in internal-combustion engines. For many years, magnetos have served as the means of ignition for tractor engines. However, the present trend is toward battery ignition for the reason that most tractors are now provided with electric starting and generating equipment. Magnetos are still used extensively on small stationary farm engines and larger multiple-cylinder power units that can be conveniently cranked by hand or with a battery and electric starter motor. Many small, light-weight, high-speed engines are equipped with flywheel magnetos.

Magneto types and construction. Magnetos for ignition purposes may be classified as (1) either low- or high-tension, (2) either oscillating or rotary, and (3) either unit- or flywheel-type. A low-tension magneto generates a relatively low-voltage current and is used for make-and-break ignition. A high-tension magneto generates a very high-voltage current, such as is needed for a jump-spark or spark-plug system. Most magnetos are gear-driven, and the armature or rotor rotates at some specific speed, usually crankshaft speed. A few single-cylinder, slow-speed stationary engines still use an oscillating, high-tension magneto (Fig. 19-8). In this device, the spark is generated by a limited oscillating movement of the armature. The conventional magneto is a complete, self-contained ignition device, with the exception of the spark plugs, and may be readily attached or detached from the engine; however, many small, single-cylinder, high-speed engines have the magneto built into the flywheel in such a manner that certain essential parts are attached to it and rotate with it. This arrangement provides simplicity and compactness.

Although there is considerable variation in the detailed construction of the different makes and types of magnetos, the basic construction and

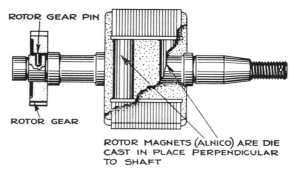

ROTOR GEAR PIN

ROTOR GEAR

ROTOR MAGNETS (ALNICO) ARE DIE CAST IN PLACE PERPENDICULAR TO SHAFT

FIG. 19-1. *Armature construction with rotating magnetic field.* (Courtesy of Fairbanks Morse and Company.)

design of all magnetos are essentially the same. The fundamental parts are (1) a base and frame structure of some nonmagnetic material, usually an aluminum alloy; (2) a permanent alloy steel magnet or magnets; (3) soft-iron field or pole pieces; (4) an armature or rotating member; (5) a winding or windings; (6) breaker points and condenser (if it is a high-tension magneto); (7) a distributor with gears and rotor (if it is a multiple-cylinder engine).

Permanent steel magnets. Magneto magnets must be made of a steel alloy because pure soft iron will not retain magnetism. Alloys containing chromium, tungsten, and cobalt have a high magnetic retentivity, and an aluminum-nickel-cobalt alloy known as Alnico has been developed in recent years and is being used extensively. It is an extremely hard crystalline alloy and cannot be easily machined. Its advantages are greater magnetic energy per volume of material and greater retentivity or stability. It is claimed that Alnico is highly resistant to such demagnetizing forces as stray fields of opposite polarity, high temperatures, and excessive mechanical vibration. The development of this new stronger magnetic alloy steel permits the use of smaller, more compact magnets of any desired shape, as shown by Fig. 19-1.

Generation of an electric current by a simple magneto. The action of any mechanical electric generator is based upon the principle of electromagnetic induction. That is, if a magnetic field is set up about a conductor of electricity and then suddenly weakened or broken down, an electric current will be induced and will flow in the conductor. For example, referring to Fig. 19-2A, with the armature in the position as shown, the magnetic lines of force have a straight path through the

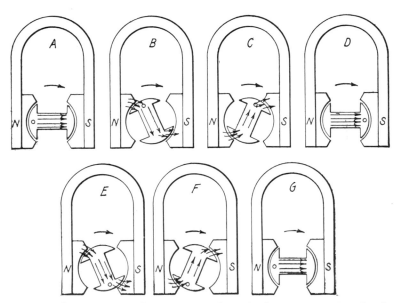

FIG. 19-2. *Path of magnetic lines of force through the armature of a shuttle-type magneto.*

soft-iron portion of the armature; that is, the lines of force flow directly through the armature from the north pole of the magnet to the south pole. If the armature is now rotated a fraction of a turn to the position shown in *B*, it is observed that the lines of force, since they prefer to continue flowing through the soft iron, are stretched. Or it might be said that the number of lines of force passing through the armature from north to south has decreased. Rotating the armature still farther, as shown in *C*, it is observed that the lines of force are flowing through the armature in the opposite direction; that is, the direction of flow is reversed but they still flow from north to south. It is evident, then, that at some point between positions *B* and *C*, the number of lines of force passing through the armature must have decreased to zero. This change in the number of lines of force about the armature winding sets up an induced electric current in it. If the circuit is complete, the current flows through the ignition system. If the armature is now rotated to the position shown in *D*, the lines of force again have a straight path from north to south. Then, as the armature rotates farther, the number of lines of force passing through it decreases as before. When the armature has reached the position as shown in *F*, the lines of force have again reversed their direction of flow with respect to the armature core. At the instant that this change takes place, a second current is induced in the armature winding. If the armature is now rotated to a position shown in *G*, one revolution is completed, and, as we have seen, two currents or impulses have been induced. The greatest voltage and, therefore, the best spark are produced when the armature approaches the position shown by *C* and *F* (Fig. 19-2).

It will be observed that a magneto of the type described does not necessarily generate a continuous flow of current but one which flows in impulses. Also, the two currents induced during the one revolution of the armature will be in opposite directions; hence, an alternating current is generated. This does not mean that it is impractical or useless for ignition purposes. In other words, if the magneto can be so timed to the engine that the armature is in the position at which the highest voltage is set up just when the spark is needed in the cylinder, then the current will flow and ignition will occur.

Shuttle- or armature-wound magnetos. It will be noted that the armature of the magneto just described (Fig. 19-2) has a shuttlelike shape and that the winding is wound about this H-shaped armature and rotates with it. It is, therefore, known as a shuttle- or armature-wound magneto. Since the winding rotates with the armature, it is necessary to take the current off by means of an insulated copper collector ring and a brush. The wire leading to the igniter or spark plugs is attached to a terminal that is a part of the brush and brush holder.

Inductor-type magnetos. Most present-day magnetos are so constructed that the windings are fixed or stationary and the magnets are usually a part of the armature and rotate. Such magnetos are termed inductor types. Figure 19-3 shows the general construction and operation of such a magneto. The winding and its soft-iron core (Fig. 19-4) are mounted on the upper ends of the pole pieces. Since the permanent magnet is a part of the rotor, the magnetic flux or field is forced to change its path of flow through the pole pieces and coil core during rotation as indicated. A change occurs every half revolution, and the maximum induced current impulse comes just at the instant the flux lines through the core are at their minimum value, as in Fig. 19-3B. A complete high-tension magneto of the inductor type is shown by Fig. 19-5. All current models of magnetos use this type of construction.

THE HIGH-TENSION MAGNETO

Construction and operation. A high-tension magneto is one that is used for jump-spark ignition and generates a current of sufficiently high volt-

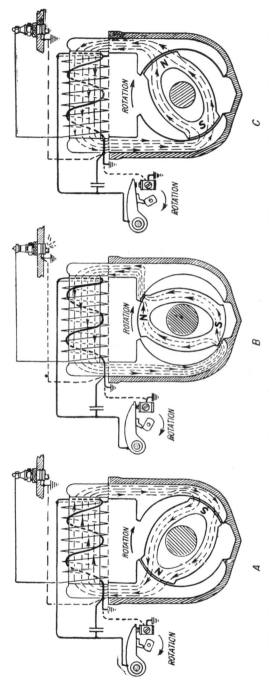

FIG. 19-3. *Generation of current impulse by an inductor-type magneto.* (Courtesy of International Harvester Company.)

age to jump the gap at the spark plug. In fact, such a magneto is a complete jump-spark system in one compact unit with the exception of the spark plugs.

To generate this exceedingly high voltage, the high-tension magneto must be equipped with a number of parts that are not found in the low-tension types. The important parts of such a magneto are as follows: (1) nonmagnetic base and frame, (2) permanent steel magnets, (3) armature, (4) soft-iron pole pieces, (5) primary winding, (6) secondary winding, (7) breaker points, (8) condenser, and (9) safety gap. For

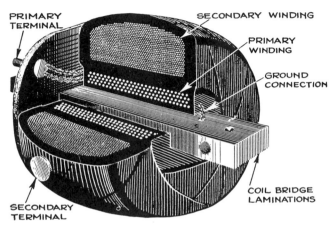

FIG. 19-4. *Core and windings for a magneto.* (Courtesy of Fairbanks Morse and Company.)

convenience and clearness, so that the construction and operation of the high-tension magneto will be readily understood, the electrical circuits and parts involved are shown by Figs. 19-5 and 19-6.

The operation of the magneto is as follows: As the armature rotates and passes through the position at which the lines of force change their path through it, a current is induced in the primary winding of coarse insulated wire. Just as this current is induced in the primary winding, the breaker points, which are in the primary circuit, are separated by a cam, interrupting the current and breaking down the strong electromagnetic field set up by it. This results in the instantaneous induction of a very high voltage in the secondary circuit, which consists of many thousands of turns of very fine wire. Therefore, if the breaker points separate at the correct time in the travel of the engine piston, and the secondary winding can be connected to the spark plug, a spark will be produced and will ignite the mixture.

Breaker points. The breaker points (Fig. 19-5) are similar to those used in the nonvibrating-coil system of ignition with battery. They consist of a stationary insulated point and a movable noninsulated point

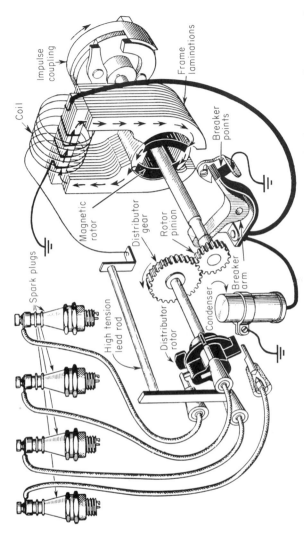

FIG. 19-5. *High-tension magneto construction and circuits.* (Courtesy of Fairbanks Morse and Company.)

277

and arm that comes in contact with the cam. These points are located at one end of the armature. If the magneto is of the inductor type, that is, with stationary winding, the points will be stationary, and the cam that separates them will rotate with the armature. On the other hand, if the magneto is of the shuttle type, the winding and points rotate and the cams are stationary.

The contact points themselves are made of a high-grade alloy steel so that they will not pit up or get rough too quickly. One point is usu-

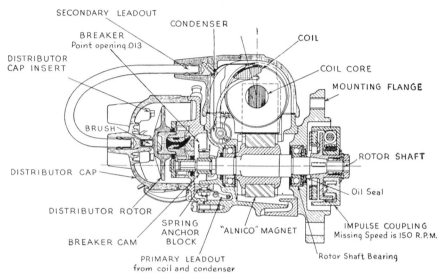

FIG. 19-6. *Cutaway view of International Type H-4 magneto.* (Courtesy of International Harvester Company.)

ally adjustable so that the space between them, when they are separated, can be adjusted. This space should be 0.015 to 0.020 in.

Condenser. The high-tension magneto must be equipped with a condenser similar to that used in a jump-spark coil, for the purpose of eliminating the arcing at the breaker points and intensifying the current in the secondary circuit. The condenser is connected in the primary circuit as shown in Fig. 19-5.

Safety spark gap. If the wire that carries the current from the magneto to the spark plug should become broken or disconnected at any point, it is obvious that the high-voltage current induced in the secondary winding could not take its regular path and, therefore, might dissipate itself by breaking through the insulation in the winding on the armature. This would create a permanent short circuit and, therefore, make the magneto useless until it could be rewound. To eliminate the possibility of such injury in case of a broken secondary circuit, all high-tension magnetos are equipped with what is known as a safety spark gap. This gap consists of a point fastened to that side of the secondary winding that leads to the spark plug or the collector ring, and another point exactly opposite the first and grounded to some metal part of the magneto. It must be about $\frac{1}{4}$ to $\frac{3}{8}$ in. wide, which is somewhat greater than the spark-plug gap. Otherwise the current would have a tendency to jump at this point at all times, rather than at the spark plug.

Distributor. A high-tension magneto for a multiple-cylinder engine, in addition to the parts named, requires a distributor and rotor to distribute the secondary current to the different spark plugs in the correct order, just as the nonvibrating coil system of ignition with battery requires a distributor to distribute the secondary circuit to the spark plugs in the case of an engine with two or more cylinders.

Wires attached to the distributor terminals conduct the current to the spark plugs in the correct order. From these plugs the current returns through the engine to the base of the magneto, and thence to the grounded end of the secondary circuit. In other respects, the magneto is exactly the same as that used for a single-cylinder engine. The different makes of high-tension magnetos vary somewhat in detailed construction and operation, but the same general principles are followed in all makes. The greatest improvement that has been made is the complete enclosure of the working parts, thus providing greater protection from dust, dirt, and moisture.

Flywheel magnetos. Many small high-speed engines used on washing machines, lawn mowers, small garden tractors, and motorboats have the magneto built into the flywheel. In a typical flywheel magneto (Fig. 19-7) the magnet is located in the outer rim of the flywheel, which revolves around the stationary coil, condenser, and breaker-point assembly. As the ends of the magnet pass by the pole pieces, an alternating magnetic flux is created around the coil and a current is generated in the primary winding as long as the breaker points remain closed. At the instant the primary current is strongest, a cam on the crankshaft opens the points and instantly breaks the circuit and causes a collapse of the magnetic field. This induces a very high-voltage current in the secondary winding, which in turn results in a spark at the plug. This type of magneto is very simple, has few moving parts, and requires very little attention or servicing.

Oscillating high-tension magnetos. Figures 19-8 and 19-9 show the Wico high-tension magneto, which is used extensively on single-cylinder farm engines. Referring to the sketch (Fig. 19-9), this magneto is constructed and operates as follows: The permanent steel magnet consists of several small straight bars clamped together and bridging the ends of two laminated soft-iron core members, which might also be called pole pieces. The opposite ends of these two core members are bridged by a laminated soft-iron yoke, which is moved up and down on a guide and is really the armature of the magneto. Two windings, a primary and a secondary, are placed on these core members, one-half of each winding being placed on each core member and so connected that the current generated in each of the two halves will flow in the same direction. One end of the primary winding is grounded to the magneto frame. The other end is connected to the fixed contact (insulated from frame) of the breaker points or interrupter. Since the moving contact is attached to the armature and is thereby grounded, there is a complete electrical circuit when the points are closed.

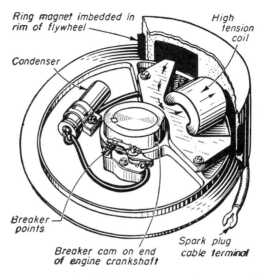

FIG. 19-7. *Construction of a flywheel-type magneto.* (Courtesy of Fairbanks Morse and Company.)

As in any other high-tension magneto, the secondary winding consists of many turns of very fine wire. One of the ends is grounded to the magneto frame. The other end is connected by a heavily insulated lead wire to the spark plug. Thus the secondary circuit is completed through the engine.

In generating a high-tension current, the armature is held firmly in contact with the ends of the poles by magnetic attraction. The lines of magnetic force now have a complete soft-iron path from north to south, as indicated by arrows in Fig. 19-9. The breaker points are also in contact. Now, if the armature is suddenly pulled downward away from the pole pieces, the magnetic path will be broken and the lines of force will be reduced in the two core members; and the farther the armature is removed from the poles, the greater will be the reduction in the lines of magnetic force. This decrease in lines of magnetic force induces a current in the primary circuit. As soon as a current flows in the primary circuit, it acts as an electromagnet producing lines of magnetic force in the core in the same direction as those of the permanent magnet. Thus, it will be seen that the total magnetic lines of force will not be reduced as much as they would without the primary winding. As soon as the armature has moved far enough away from the poles to allow a consid-

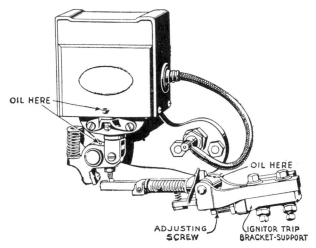

FIG. 19-8. *Wico high-tension oscillating magneto and tripping mechanism.*

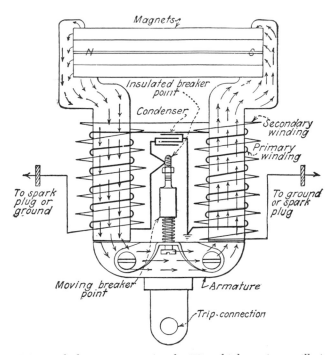

FIG. 19-9. *Wiring and electric circuits for the Wico high-tension oscillating magneto.*

erable reduction of the lines of magnetic force, and at such a point that the sustaining action of the primary is still adequate, the breaker points are opened (thus breaking the primary circuit), which removes all the sustaining action and allows the lines of magnetic force to decrease instantly to a very small value. This rapid changing of the lines of magnetic force induces a current in the secondary winding of sufficiently high voltage to jump the gap in the spark plug. A condenser is connected across the breaker points to produce a quick break of the primary current when the breaker points are opened and, incidentally, prevents arcing at the points.

Impulse-starter couplings. Since most engines are of such a size that in cranking they can be turned only a fraction of a revolution at a time

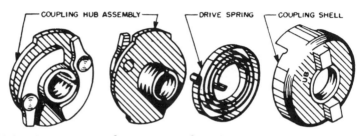

FIG. 19-10. *Automatic impulse-starter coupling.* (Courtesy of Fairbanks Morse and Company.)

or rotated very slowly at best, a special provision of some kind is necessary to permit the magneto to supply a strong spark at this cranking speed. The device used for this purpose is known as an impulse-starter coupling, since it always serves as a part of the magneto-drive coupling. All magnetos are equipped with impulse starters that engage automatically whenever the speed drops below 150 r.p.m. Such a device is shown by Fig. 19-10. The action is dependent upon centrifugal force, which causes certain weighted members to move outward sufficiently to disengage the coupling when the proper speed is attained.

It is observed that all impulse starters are made up of certain small moving parts whose free movement is essential to the proper functioning of the device. If lubrication is neglected, or if dust and dirt gum up the parts, poor action is likely. Most of the wear takes place in the catch block, catch notch, and catch release. The catch block, when released, is under considerable pressure. Consequently, the end of the catch and the notch holding it are subject to a certain amount of wear. Eventually the catch may fail to engage or may slip out of its own accord. Also the starter may function normally when the engine is cranked but release the moment firing starts. The engine fails to pick up and must be cranked again. All impulse starters have a distinct click when working properly. Therefore, if this click is not heard or is weak, the trouble is likely to be due to the causes mentioned.

Since the spark made by an impulse starter is for starting the engine, it must always occur just as the piston reaches the end of the compression stroke. In other words, an impulse spark is always a retarded spark regardless of the position of the spark advance and retard lever, provided, of course, that the magneto is correctly timed.

Magneto mountings. Magnetos must be mounted rigidly on engines to provide positive drive and accurate timing. Until recent years all magne-

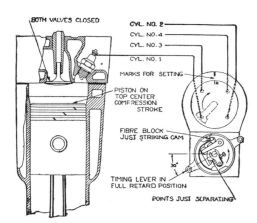

FIG. 19-11. *Timing a high-tension magneto.*

tos were base-mounted on a small platform bracket on the cylinder block. An adjustable, flexible coupling is used to connect the drive shaft to the armature shaft and provides a means of adjusting the timing.

The flange type of mounting (Fig. 19-6) is now used extensively on tractors and similar engines. The flange of the magneto fits directly to a mating flange on the governor housing or crankcase of the engine, thereby enclosing the entire magneto drive assembly within a dustproof housing. A flexible coupling eliminates any difficulty from drive misalignment. Timing adjustment is provided by using slotted holes for the flange bolts. By loosening the two bolts, the entire magneto can be turned in either direction about the armature to give a timing adjustment range of about 20 deg.

Spark advance and retard. The advancing and retarding of the spark on engines equipped with high-tension magnetos are accomplished by changing the time at which the breaker points are opened. That is, if the magneto is of the shuttle-wound type, the cams are stationary and are carried on a ring (Fig. 19-11). If this ring is shifted or turned slightly, the breaker points will hit the cams later, and therefore the spark will come later. If the magneto is of the inductor type, the points themselves are shifted, so that the rotating cam hits the movable point sooner or later. A stop screw and slot of some kind usually serve to limit the range of spark advance and retard.

Since all magnetos are now equipped with an impulse starter coupling, a spark-advance and -retard device is unnecessary. The reason for this is that, if the magneto is correctly timed, the impulse or starting spark must occur at or very near dead center. As soon as the engine starts and speeds up, the impulse coupling is thrown out and the spark is not delayed but occurs earlier in the piston travel.

Timing high-tension magneto with engine. When a magneto is disconnected and removed from an engine, it is essential that it be correctly timed when replaced, so that the spark will come at the right instant in the piston travel. The following procedure for timing a high-tension magneto is applicable to any engine (Fig. 19-11), regardless of the number of cylinders:

1. Place piston 1 on head dead center at the end of the compression stroke.

2. Select or determine the distributor terminal to be connected to spark plug 1. Unless the wires are already cut to an exact length and fitted, any terminal may be chosen for spark plug 1.

3. Place distributor rotor on terminal brush or segment 1. To do this it is usually necessary to remove the distributor cover.

4. See that breaker mechanism is in the retard position.

5. Slightly rotate or move armature in driven direction until breaker points are just opening. In doing this, the amount of rotation should not be sufficient to disturb the position of the distributor rotor.

6. Without moving the armature, place magneto in position on the engine and connect the drive coupling.

7. Check the timing by turning the engine over very slowly. See that the breaker points open just as the piston reaches head dead center at the end of the compression stroke. If the magneto is equipped with an impulse starter, it should snap just as piston 1 reaches compression dead center. If it snaps slightly before or after, carefully disconnect the coupling, rotate the armature a trifle forward or backward as the case may be, and again connect and recheck.

8. Connect the wires to the distributor and spark plugs in the proper manner according to the firing order of the engine.

High-tension-magneto care and adjustment. High-tension magnetos require very little attention and should seldom give any trouble. They are well enclosed and almost completely dustproof and moistureproof. This does not mean that they do not require even reasonable care. Occasional lubrication, according to the manufacturer's instructions, and prevention of excessive dirt accumulation around the magneto are important.

The parts of a high-tension magneto requiring lubrication are the armature bearings and the distributor rotor. Since practically all magnetos have ball bearings for the armature, very little oil is needed. From 2 to 5 drops of a very light grade of machine oil placed in the small oil openings at either end about once a month, or after 100 hr. of operation, is all that is necessary. A heavy oil or an excessive amount should be avoided by all means, as gumming, short circuits, and other troubles will develop.

In a few cases the bearings are packed in a light grease and so enclosed that it cannot escape. These require no further lubrication.

If it is desirable to clean the distributor rotor, brush contacts, breaker points, and collector ring at any time, only a clean rag and gasoline should be used.

Breaker-point adjustment. The proper functioning of a high-tension magneto is largely dependent upon the breaker points. An occasional inspection should be made and the following noted:

1. The contact points should be smooth, flat, and free from dirt, oil, or moisture and should make a good full contact. If they are rough, use only a very fine file, and file off as little as possible.

2. The points should have the required opening, namely, about 0.015 or $\frac{1}{64}$ in.

3. The movable point should hinge freely on its pivot. Corrosion caused by moisture may develop sluggish action, which usually results in the magneto failing to spark.

REFERENCES

Fundamentals of Magneto Ignition, *Bull.* FM-123, Fairbanks, Morse and Co., Beloit, Wis.

Moses, Ben D., and Kenneth R. Frost, "Farm Power," John Wiley & Sons, Inc., New York, 1952.

PROBLEMS AND QUESTIONS

1. Explain fully the theory of generation of an electric current by a magneto with a rotating magnet.

2. Make a complete detailed sketch of the essential parts and circuits for a high-tension magneto for a four-cylinder engine.

3. Explain fully how a flange-mounted magneto equipped with an impulse coupling can be properly timed to a four-cylinder engine.

4. Enumerate the specific sources of magneto trouble most likely to occur, and tell how the operator might remedy or avoid them.

5. If the crankshaft speed of a six-cylinder, four-stroke-cycle engine is 2,400 r.p.m., what are the armature and distributor speeds of the magneto?

20

Diesel-engine Construction and Operation

For a number of years following the efforts of Dr. Rudolph Diesel in successfully developing the compression-ignition engine in 1898, only a limited number of such engines were manufactured, and these were heavy-duty slow-speed stationary models. Eventually, however, the possibilities of the utilization of the diesel principle in smaller, higher speed, single- and multiple-cylinder engines of both the stationary and automotive type were given consideration. During the past three decades there has been a marked expansion of the application of the diesel principle of ignition and operation to various types of internal-combustion engines.

PRINCIPLES OF OPERATION

As explained in Chap. 16, the diesel engine differs from a carbureting-type engine primarily in two ways, namely, (1) only air is taken in on the intake stroke of the piston, the liquid fuel being injected directly into the combustion chamber at the end of the compression stroke; and (2) the fuel mixture is ignited by high compression, and no special ignition device or mechanism is needed. On the other hand, all diesel engines operate on either the two- or the four-stroke-cycle principle like other internal-combustion engines.

Two-stroke-cycle diesel. The principles of operation and events involved for a two-stroke-cycle engine are shown by Fig. 20-1. The cycle begins with the upward movement of the piston from its C.D.C. position. The intake and exhaust ports are closed and the charge of fresh air is compressed to approximately 500 lb. per sq. in. At the same time the crankcase volume is increasing and air enters the crankcase through an automatic suction valve. This air is sometimes called *scavenging air.* When the piston reaches H.D.C., a charge of fuel is injected into the combustion space. The high temperature existing ignites the mixture

286

of atomized fuel and air, and combustion takes place in such a manner that a constant pressure equal to the compression pressure is maintained as the piston moves downward on the power stroke. Expansion continues until the exhaust port is opened and the burned gases are released. The intake port is likewise uncovered immediately after the exhaust port, and the air in the crankcase, which is now under pressure, bypasses into the cylinder, thus completing the cycle.

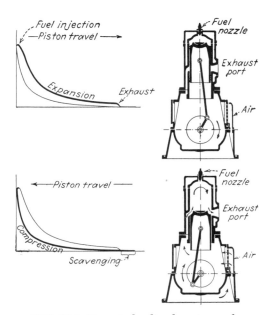

FIG. 20-1. *Two-stroke diesel-engine cycle.*

Four-stroke-cycle diesel. Figures 20-2 and 20-3 show the principles of operation of a four-stroke-cycle diesel engine. It will be observed that the events take place in the same manner as in the ordinary four-stroke-cycle carbureting-type engine (see Chap. 8) with the exception that air alone is drawn in on the intake stroke and the liquid fuel is injected into the cylinder at or near the end of the compression stroke. Obviously, two valves, intake and exhaust, operated by a gear, camshaft, and the usual mechanism, are necessary.

Fuel injection. The proper injection of the fuel into the combustion chamber against the high pressure is one of the most difficult problems encountered by the diesel-engine designer. Since the mechanism involved must supply a fuel charge sufficient only for a single explosion, it is obvious that it must be carefully designed to operate with the utmost precision. The principal requirements of a diesel fuel supply and injection mechanism are (1) that it positively supply a correct fuel charge to each cylinder according to the engine load and speed; (2)

that it inject the fuel at the correct time in the cycle; (3) that it facilitate efficient fuel utilization by atomizing the charge at the time of
injection; and (4) that it not be subject to undue wear or require fre-

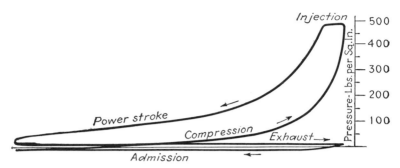

FIG. 20-2. *Pressure diagram of a four-stroke diesel-engine operation.*

quent adjustment or servicing. Considering these factors, it is obvious
that for engines having limited piston displacement and high speed the
utilization of the diesel principle becomes increasingly difficult.

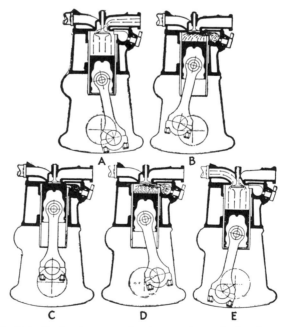

FIG. 20-3. *Cycle of events of a four-stroke-cycle diesel engine.*

The two systems of fuel injection are *air injection* and *direct or solid
injection*. The former utilizes a stream of air under high pressure (1,000
to 1,200 lb. per sq. in.) to force the fuel from the injector nozzle into

the combustion chamber. Direct or solid injection involves the direct application of high pressure to the liquid fuel by a pump (Figs. 20-4 and 20-5) to force it into the fuel nozzle and thence to the combustion chamber. The air-injection system is adapted only to very large, stationary, four-stroke-cycle engines and is becoming obsolete because of the necessity of an air compressor, heavy bulky air-storage tanks, and other parts.

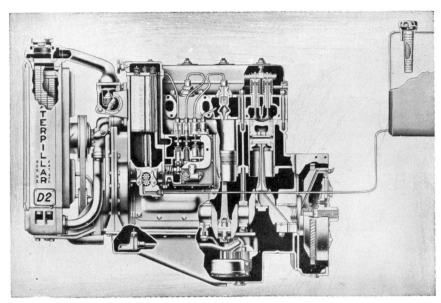

FIG. 20-4. *Diesel tractor engine showing complete fuel supply and injection system.* (Courtesy of Caterpillar Tractor Company.)

Direct or solid injection. In the solid-injection system (Figs. 20-4 and 20-5) the fuel is first pumped from the main supply tank to an auxiliary chamber by means of the transfer pump. The high-pressure injection pumps receive the fuel from the auxiliary chamber and force the proper charge to the injector in the cylinder head. The timing of the charge is controlled by timing the stroke of the injector pump with the crankshaft and piston position.

Direct-injection systems may be divided into three types, namely, (1) single-unit type with pump and injector nozzle built together in a single unit mechanism, (2) two-unit type with individual pumps and injectors for each cylinder, and (3) two-unit type with one master injector pump but with distribution valves and injectors for each cylinder.

Figure 20-7 shows the operating mechanism for the single-unit system, and Fig. 20-8 shows the detailed construction of the injector. This system is used in the GM two-stroke-cycle diesel engine.

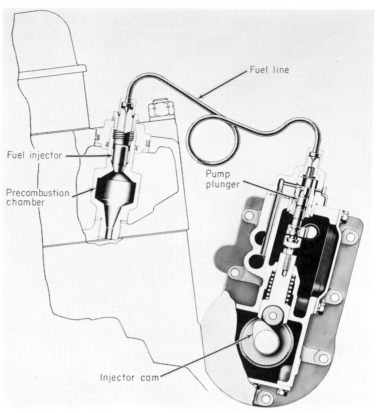

FIG. 20-5. *Two-unit fuel-injection system.* (Courtesy of Caterpillar Tractor Company.)

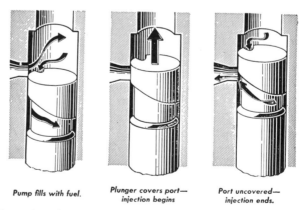

Pump fills with fuel.　　Plunger covers port—injection begins　　Port uncovered—injection ends.

FIG. 20-6. *Operation of an injection pump.* (Courtesy of Caterpillar Tractor Company.)

290

Figure 20-5 shows the construction and operation of the injection pump and valve for a two-unit system. In this case a cam operates each plunger, forcing the necessary fuel charge to the valve and into the pre-combustion chamber. In the third system (Fig. 20-9) a single master

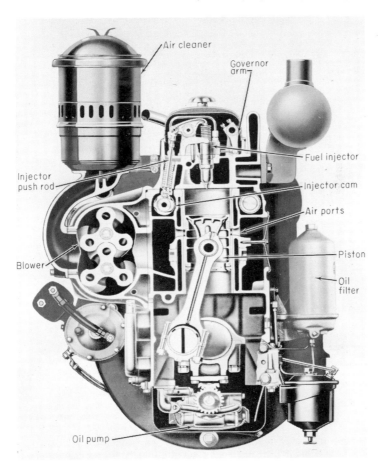

FIG. 20-7. *Cutaway view of a high-speed two-stroke-cycle diesel engine showing air blower and injection mechanism.* (Courtesy of Detroit Diesel Engine Division, General Motors Corporation.)

pump supplies the pressure to force the fuel to all cylinders, the distribution and timing of the charges to the cylinders being controlled by individual valves and cams as shown.

Figure 20-10 shows another type of master pump fuel-injection system which incorporates all the essential parts, including transfer pump, injection plungers, fuel-charge distributor, and governor in one compact unit. Figure 20-11 shows how the fuel is fed to the injection plungers and then, in turn, forced to the injectors in proper order.

Most injection valves operate as shown by Fig. 20-12. The valve is held to its seat by a spring. The fuel pressure developed by the injection pump overcomes the spring pressure and lifts the valve. Most diesel engines of this type use the precombustion-chamber type of injector as shown. As the fuel is sprayed into this small chamber, the highly heated

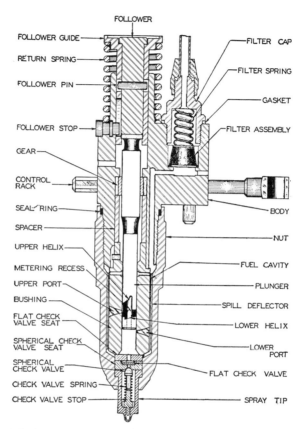

FIG. 20-8. *Cross-sectional view of a unit-type fuel injector.*

air causes a small portion of the fuel to ignite. As injection continues, the fuel is enveloped by flame, becomes gaseous, and, as a result of the high pressure developed, rushes at high velocity into the main combustion chamber where complete combustion takes place. The use of a precombustion chamber rather than direct injection into the main combustion chamber does not require so high an injection pressure. Furthermore, it permits the use of an injector having a large single jet rather than several small jets, which would clog more readily.

Diesel governing. The principle involved in governing diesel engines is not unlike that used in other types; that is, the reaction of centrifugal force produced by revolving weights is utilized to control the quantity

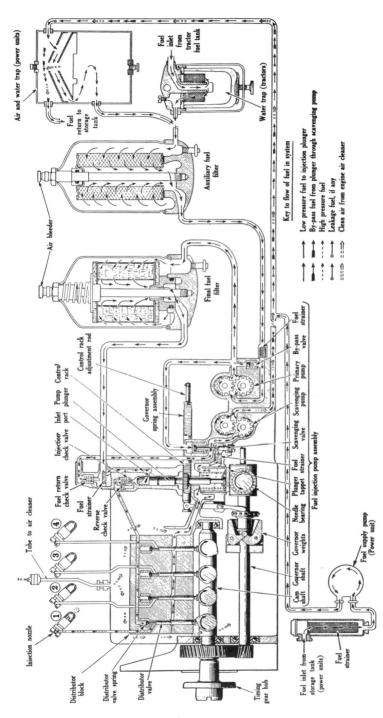

Air and water trap (power units)

Fuel return to storage tank

Fuel inlet from tractor fuel tank

Water trap (tractors)

Air bleeder

Auxiliary fuel filter

Final fuel filter

Key to flow of fuel in system

→ Low pressure fuel to injection plunger
⇒ By-pass fuel from plunger through scavenging pump
--→ High pressure fuel
○ Leakage fuel, if any
⇛ Clean air from engine air cleaner

Control rack adjustment rod

Pump Control plunger rack

Inlet port

Injection check valve

Governor spring assembly

Fuel return check valve

Fuel strainer

Reverse check valve

By-pass valve

Primary pump

Scavenging pump

Scavenging valve

Fuel strainer

Tube to air cleaner

④ ③ ② ①

Injection nozzle

Distributor block

Distributor valve spring

Distributor valve

Timing gear hub

Fuel injection pump assembly

Plunger tappet

Needle bearing

Governor weights

Cam Governor shaft

Fuel supply pump (Power unit)

Fuel inlet from storage tank (power units)

Fuel strainer

FIG. 20-9. *Complete fuel-supply and fuel-injection system for a four-cylinder engine using a master pump with distribution valves.* (Courtesy of International Harvester Company.)

of fuel injected according to the engine load. However, no attempt is made to vary the air charge, and it remains constant at all loads. Figures 20-13, 20-14, and 20-15 show how such a governor operates. Referring to Fig. 20-14, the governor rack is connected to and actuated by the governor. This rack revolves the pump gear 2, which is attached to the bottom of the pump plunger 3. As the gear is turned by the rack, the plunger is turned and lifted so that it closes the inlet port 4, to which

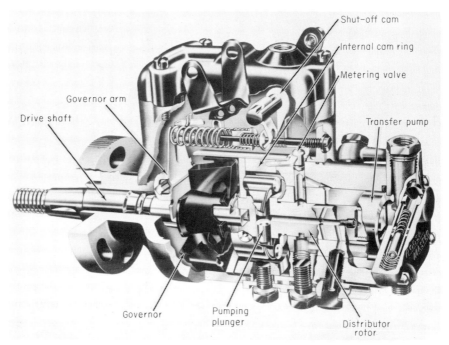

FIG. 20-10. *Roosa Master diesel injection pump and fuel distribution unit.* (Courtesy of Hartford Machine Screw Company.)

fuel is fed from manifold 10. This operation traps the fuel in the compartment 5 above the plunger, in the groove 6, and in the space below the scroll 7. Here a pressure is created, and as the plunger is raised by the camshaft, the fuel is forced through the line 9 into the injection valve. As the scroll edge 7 reaches the fuel-inlet port 4, pressure is relieved, causing check valve 8 to close. Thus the position of the scroll with respect to the inlet port, as shown in Fig. 20-15, determines the size of the fuel charge trapped above the plunger and consequently forced to the injector.

Figure 20-16 shows a diesel engine governor which is actuated by the air flow in the intake manifold rather than by a centrifugal mechanism. The velocity of the air flow varies with the changes in engine load and power output. Hence a throttle valve located in the air manifold creates

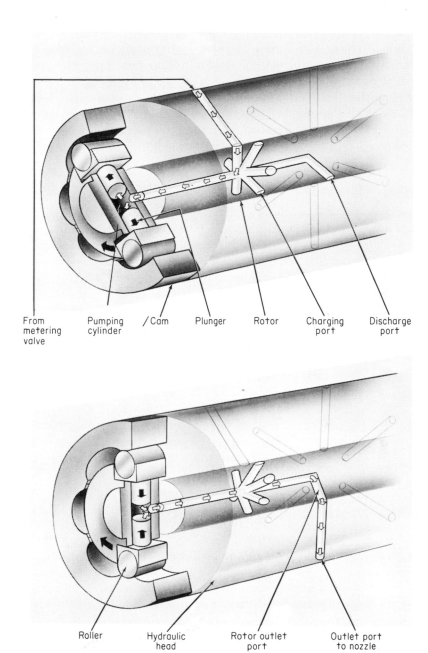

From · Pumping · /Cam · Plunger · Rotor · Charging · Discharge
metering · cylinder · · · · port · port
valve

Roller · Hydraulic · Rotor outlet · Outlet port
· head · port · to nozzle

FIG. 20-11. *Detailed construction and operation of Roosa Master injection mechanism.*
(Courtesy of Hartford Machine Screw Company.)

a varying pressure on a spring-loaded diaphragm whose movement, in turn, controls the amount of fuel injected, depending upon the engine speed and power.

Diesel starting methods. One of the disadvantages of a diesel engine, regardless of size or number of cylinders, is the amount of energy required to crank it when starting, because of the very high compression pressure. Hand cranking is usually out of the question, and, in most cases, some type of mechanical starter is used.

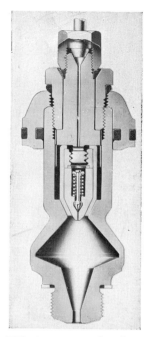

FIG. 20-12. *Diesel fuel-injection valve and precombustion chamber.* (Courtesy of Caterpillar Tractor Company.)

The following methods are used for cranking diesel engines: (1) hand cranking by temporarily releasing or reducing the compression pressure (adaptable only to engines of limited displacement, such as automotive-type diesels), (2) use of compressed air from a high-pressure air-storage tank, (3) use of a small auxiliary starting engine, and (4) use of a storage battery and electric starting motor.

The International diesel engine is an example of a hand-started automotive-type diesel engine. It is equipped with an auxiliary combustion chamber (Fig. 20-17) that is connected to the main combustion chamber by a special valve. Likewise, there is a high-tension magneto with spark plugs and a gasoline carburetor and manifold. To start this engine, lever 1 is rotated one-fourth of a turn. Through linkage 2, valve 3 is opened into the auxiliary compression chamber 4 which reduces the compression ratio for gasoline operation. The magneto is also put into operation, air valve 6 is closed to shunt the air through the carburetor 8, and a shut-off valve in the carburetor is opened. The engine is then hand-cranked or cranked with a battery and starter motor and is allowed to warm up for a few minutes. Lever 1 is then tripped, resulting in a change-back of all parts to full diesel operation.

Compressed-air starting is used only for stationary diesel engines. Air under high pressure is stored in a tank that is connected by a pipe to the cylinder head. Opening a valve permits the air to act on the piston and turn the engine until firing begins. Such engines must be equipped with an air compressor to replenish the air supply.

Some diesel-tractor engines are equipped with a small high-speed auxiliary gasoline-burning starting engine (Fig. 20-18). This engine is cranked either by hand or by an electric starter motor and then engaged with the tractor-engine flywheel by a special starter-drive coupling. The

FIG. 20-13. *Governing mechanism for diesel tractor engine.* (Courtesy of Caterpillar Tractor Company.)

drive is by means of a small spur gear that meshes with teeth on the flywheel. In starting the tractor engine, the compression pressure is released by locking the exhaust valves open. As soon as the engine is turn-

ing over properly, the compression-release lever is disengaged, the fuel-injection pumps are engaged, and firing begins, after which the starter engine is disengaged and stopped.

The small, independent, gasoline cranking engine is particularly advantageous under low-temperature conditions in that it has sufficient power to spin the diesel engine as long as necessary under full compression.

Most automotive-type diesel engines are equipped with a storage battery and electric starting motor for cranking (see Fig. 20-19). Usually a 12- or a 24-volt system is necessary, particularly for large

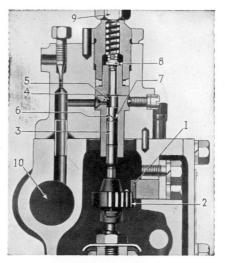

FIG. 20-14. *Caterpillar diesel governing mechanism.* (Courtesy of Caterpillar Tractor Company.)

engines. Starting is accomplished by closing a switch connecting the battery to the starting motor. As the latter begins to rotate, a small spur pinion on the armature slides into engagement with the teeth on the flywheel, and the engine turns. When firing begins, the gears automati-

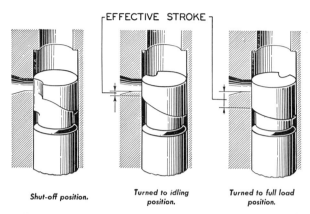

Shut-off position.   **Turned to idling position.**   **Turned to full load position.**

FIG. 20-15. *Method of measuring fuel charge by pump plunger.* (Courtesy of Caterpillar Tractor Company.)

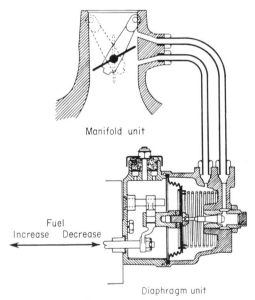

FIG. 20-16. *Pneumatically operated diesel governing mechanism.*

cally disengage and the starter switch is opened. A generator is also needed to keep the battery charged.

Diesel engines using the electric starting system require certain aids when the ambient temperature is 32°F. or lower. One such aid consists of an electrically heated glow plug (Fig. 20-19) which preheats the precombustion chamber. Another method is the use of ether capsules or bombs. A simple, manually operated device punctures the capsule and releases sufficient ether fluid to the cylinders to produce the necessary explosions and starting power.

Diesel-engine design and construction. Because of the higher pressures and strains to which certain parts of a diesel engine are subjected, consideration must be given to designing these parts heavier and stronger or

FIG. 20-17. *International diesel engine showing auxiliary combustion chamber for starting.* (Courtesy of International Harvester Company.)

of special materials. Also, extreme precision in manufacturing and assembly is important. Some concrete examples relative to this problem are (1) heavier, special carbon-steel crankshafts, (2) large precision-fitted bearings of special-quality bearing metal, (3) correctly designed and fitted pistons with a sufficient number of rings to retain compression, (4) alloy-steel heat-treated valves, carefully ground and fitted to eliminate leakage and withstand high temperatures, (5) positive lubrication of all moving parts, (6) efficient cooling under all operating conditions, and (7) positive and reliable fuel-supply and injection system and fuel-filtering devices. As a rule diesel-type engines are somewhat heavier and cost more per horsepower than spark-ignition engines of the same type.

The outstanding operating characteristic of any diesel engine as compared with an electric-ignition engine is its lower fuel consumption per horsepower-hour. Referring to Fig. 5-18 it will be observed that a diesel engine uses from 0.45 lb. per hp.-hr. at full load to approximately 0.90

lb. at one-fourth load. A similar electric-ignition engine burning gasoline consumes from 0.50 lb. per hp.-hr. at full load to 1.20 lb. at one-fourth
load. This lower fuel consumption combined with the lower first cost of
the diesel fuel itself means a pronounced saving in operating costs. For

FIG. 20-18. *Caterpillar diesel starting engine.* (Courtesy of Caterpillar Tractor Company.)

example, the cost of the fuel per hour for a 50-hp. diesel engine, using
fuel costing 15 cents and weighing 7 lb. per gal., would be

$$\frac{50 \times 0.45 \times 15}{7} = 48.2 \text{ cents}$$

For an electric-ignition engine of the same size, using gasoline costing 20 cents and weighing 6.15 lb. per gal., the fuel cost per hour would be

$$\frac{50 \times 0.50 \times 20}{6.15} = 81.3 \text{ cents}$$

Multiple-cylinder automotive-type diesel engines show a somewhat different torque characteristic as compared with similar electric-ignition engines. The difference in this respect is such that a diesel engine is

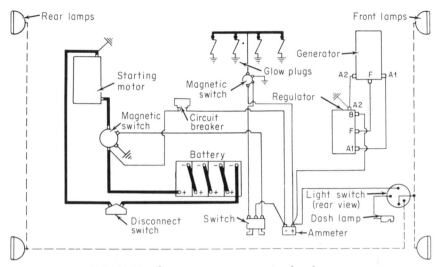

FIG. 20-19. *Electric starting system for diesel engine.*

said to have better "lugging" ability; that is, it hangs to the load and continues to pull even though the speed drops off perceptibly. This characteristic is probably brought about by the time and duration of the fuel injection and by the fact that the subsequent combustion process is somewhat slower and lacks the more spontaneous explosive action characteristic of the electric-spark-ignition engine.

Diesel fuels. Diesel fuels and their characteristics are discussed in Chap. 11. A diesel engine, to give satisfactory service, not only must operate on a fuel of proper specifications, but also must be equipped with efficient strainers and protective devices to prevent the slightest trace of foreign matter of any kind reaching the fuel-injection mechanism. This mechanism, being extremely delicate and sensitive in construction and operation, might have its proper performance noticeably affected by a minute particle of dirt, moisture, or other apparently harmless material. For this reason the tank and fuel systems of all diesel engines are equipped with filters and moisture and sediment traps, as shown in the preceding illustrations, to catch any foreign material. These filtering devices should be cleaned and serviced regularly. In addition only clean fuel should be placed in the tank, the tank should be kept closed, and all fuel lines should be kept tight.

REFERENCES

ARMSTRONG, L. V., and J. B. HARTMAN, "The Diesel Engine," The Macmillan Company, New York, 1959.

HELDT, P. M., "High-speed Diesel Engines," 6th ed., Chilton Company, Philadelphia, 1956.

Improved Diesel Engine Provides Increased Fuel Economy, *Gen. Motors Eng. J.,* Vol. 6, No. 1.

LICHTY, L. C., "Internal Combustion Engines," 6th ed., McGraw-Hill Book Company, Inc., New York, 1951.

MALEEV, V. L., "Diesel Engine Operation and Maintenance," McGraw-Hill Book Company, Inc., New York, 1954.

MOSES, BEN D., and KENNETH R. FROST, "Farm Power," John Wiley & Sons, Inc., New York, 1952.

OBERT, EDWARD F., "Internal Combustion Engines," 2d ed., International Textbook Company, Scranton, Pa., 1950.

PROBLEMS AND QUESTIONS

1. Explain the difference between the cycle of events for a spark-ignition engine and that for a diesel engine.

2. Name the three types of solid-injection systems, and explain the operation of each.

3. A four-cylinder, four-stroke-cycle engine develops 45 hp. at 1,200 r.p.m. If its fuel consumption is 0.48 lb. per hp.-hr., what is the weight of the fuel required for a single power impulse in any cylinder?

4. Explain the basic principles involved in diesel-engine governing, and compare with spark-ignition engine governor operation.

5. Discuss diesel-engine starting systems.

6. A spark-ignition engine develops 35 hp. and uses 0.60 lb. of gasoline per hp.-hr. A diesel engine develops the same power but uses 0.48 lb. of fuel per hp.-hr. Gasoline weighs 6.15 lb. per gal. and diesel fuel weighs 7.00 lb. per gal. If the diesel tractor costs $375 more than the spark-ignition engine, and if diesel fuel and gasoline cost 12 and 18 cents, respectively, how many additional service hours will be required for the saving in fuel cost to equal the additional first cost of the diesel engine?

21

Electric Generators—Starters—Lighting

For many years nearly all tractor engines were cranked by hand, the ignition spark being supplied by a magneto equipped with an impulse coupling. Tractors were seldom operated at night; hence lighting equipment was unnecessary. However, as tractors were improved and made more versatile, and as they came into more extensive use, the advantages and convenience of electric starting and lighting equipment were recognized. Therefore all tractors are regularly provided with electric starting and lighting equipment.

Lighting and starting equipment. If lights alone are desired for a tractor, the current may be obtained directly from a storage battery or from a generator. The use of a battery permits burning the lights without operating the engine, whereas, if a generator is used alone, light is available only when the engine is running. A combination generator and battery arrangement is most satisfactory and eliminates the necessity of periodically removing the battery for recharging. Starting equipment consists essentially of a starter motor, switch, and cables. A complete lighting and starting system (Fig. 21-1) consists of (1) battery, (2) generator, (3) starter motor, (4) generator output control, (5) lamps, (6) ammeter, (7) switches, and (8) fuse and wires.

Generator construction and operation. The purpose of the generator is to keep the battery charged and to supply current for lights, ignition, and other electrical accessories. The generator (Fig. 21-2) produces a direct current and consists of a frame and soft-iron pole shoes, field winding, armature with commutator and winding, bearings, commutator brushes, brush holders and springs, field and armature terminals, and drive pulley.

The theory of generation of an electric current by a generator is much the same as for a magneto, as described in Chap. 19. Figure 21-3 shows

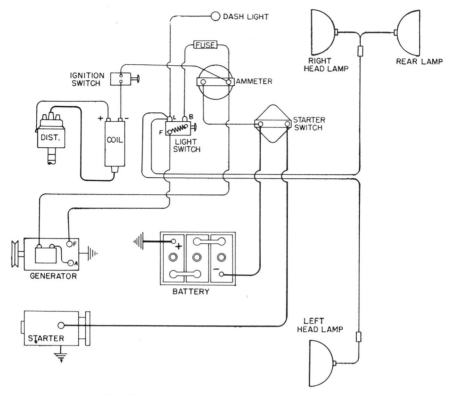

FIG. 21-1. *Complete electrical system for a tractor.*

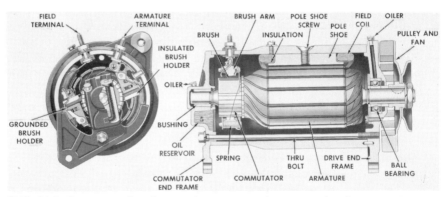

FIG. 21-2. *Cutaway and end view of a generator.* (Courtesy of Delco-Remy Division, General Motors Corporation.)

the construction of a simple direct-current generator and how it operates. The principal distinction is that the magnetic field is produced by a current passing through the windings on the pole shoes. Hence these particular windings constitute the field circuit or winding as contrasted with the armature and main supply circuit. Furthermore it will be observed that the field current is self-produced by the generator; hence, the field strength will vary according to the armature speed and other factors. It is obvious that a small amount of magnetism must be present in the pole shoes at all times in order to create an initial current build-up. This limited permanent flux is known as residual magnetism. Generators are

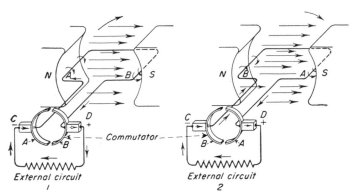

FIG. 21-3. *Operation of a simple direct-current generator.*

rated according to voltage as 6, 12, 24, and so on, in accordance with the voltage of the battery and the voltage specifications of the other electrical equipment. The actual generated voltage at normal speeds must slightly exceed the battery voltage in order to force current into the battery. This explains the noticeably brighter lights when the generator is running.

Two types of generators are in common use. The first is known as a third-brush type (Fig. 21-4) because a separate or third brush is used to transmit the field current from the commutator to the field winding and circuit. The second type (Fig. 21-5) uses only two brushes with both the field and external circuits coming from the same brushes. It will be noted that the field circuit is in parallel with the main supply circuit; hence, such a generator is usually called shunt-wound.

Cutout relay. Any generator-battery charging circuit must be equipped with a device that will automatically make and break the circuit, depending on whether the generator is operating or not and on the voltage differential at low speeds. This device (Fig. 21-4) is known as a cutout relay. It automatically closes the circuit when the generator voltage exceeds the battery voltage, and it opens or breaks the circuit when the generator stops running or its voltage is low. If such a device were not used, the battery would discharge through the generator when the engine was in-operative or idling.

This relay consists essentially of a small iron core, the fine or voltage winding, the coarse or current winding, and the points. As noted, when

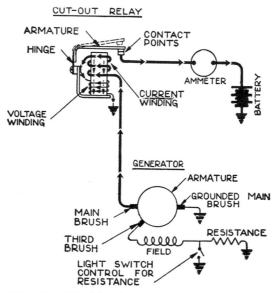

FIG. 21-4. *Third-brush generator and cutout relay.*

the generator is not operating the points are held open by a small spring. As the generator starts operating, a voltage is built up in the shunt-field winding. The fine or voltage winding of the relay, being a part of the

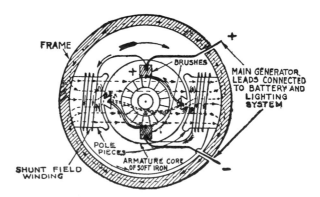

FIG. 21-5. *Principle of a shunt-wound generator.*

field circuit, thereby carries a weak current that magnetizes the relay core and pulls the movable point into contact with the stationary point. The main or charging circuit is thus completed, and the stronger current now flowing through the heavy winding on the relay core holds the points firmly in contact. If the generator speed drops sufficiently to permit the generator voltage to fall below the battery voltage, there is a reverse flow of current, the core is demagnetized, and the points open again. The cutout relay may be connected as a separate unit but is usually a part of the generator-charging-rate control unit, if such a device is used.

Generator types and control methods. In any simple shunt-wound generator, the tendency is for the voltage to vary more or less directly with armature speed; nevertheless a constant voltage is essential, if possible, over a considerable speed range. A slightly low voltage gives poor lights or a low battery-charging rate, whereas a slightly high voltage may burn out the lights or charge the battery at too high a rate. Automotive-type generators, therefore, utilize a number of different methods of controlling the voltage and corresponding current output, as follows:

A. Third-brush generator
    1. Adjustable third brush only
    2. Adjustable third brush and light-switch control
    3. Adjustable or fixed third brush and voltage control
        a. Using step-voltage control
        b. Using vibrating relay
    4. Adjustable third brush and current-voltage control
B. Two-brush shunt generator
    1. Vibrating voltage-control relay
    2. Vibrating current-control relay
    3. Combined current- and voltage-control relays

Third-brush generator operation. A third-brush generator is one which uses a special or third brush to connect the field windings to the commutator. As a result of this construction, the field strength not only varies with the armature speed but also shifts with respect to the armature and pole shoes as the speed changes. Referring to Fig. 21-6, with the armature revolving at a low speed, the flux lines created by the field current flow straight across through the armature from N to S. A current is generated in the armature winding as the turns pass through the flux lines. This armature current, in turn, magnetizes the iron of the armature and the resulting flux lines travel at right angles to the normal field flux. As the armature speed increases, the armature and field currents increase and produce a corresponding increase in the two magnetic fields. Furthermore, the combined reaction results in a shifting of the field strength with respect to the armature and pole shoes, as shown in Fig. 21-6. This is called field distortion. There is, therefore, a certain speed at which the field strength reaches a maximum and the current output is greatest. A further increase in speed distorts or shifts the field with respect to the windings so that the field and generated currents decrease in value.

Figure 21-7 shows characteristic output curves for a third-brush generator and a shunt generator.

The maximum output of a third-brush generator may be changed by shifting the third brush through a limited range with respect to the com-

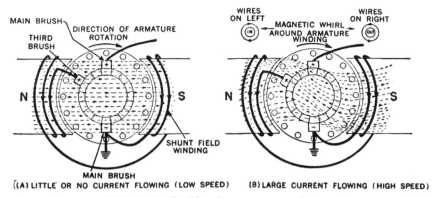

FIG. 21-6. *Third-brush generator regulation.*

mutator and armature rotation. Moving the brush as far as possible in the direction of the armature rotation will give a high current output because a greater voltage is set up in the field circuit. Moving the brush

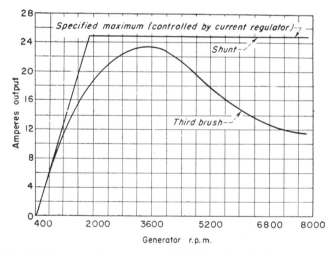

FIG. 21-7. *Output characteristics of third-brush and shunt generators.*

against the armature rotation as far as possible will give a low current output.

Plain third-brush generators without any other means of output control are objectionable for a number of reasons. First of all, should the external circuit become broken or disconnected from the battery, an extremely high voltage and current will be built up in the field windings, which in turn would damage them by overheating. Also a high voltage would be impressed upon the lights and other parts if the battery became disconnected. A second objection is that there is too much variation in output with respect to speed, and it is difficult to adjust this output to the needs of the battery. In fact, a plain third-brush generator without other means of control will have a high output if the battery is fully charged and a low output if the battery is discharged. This is exactly opposite to the requirements.

THIRD-BRUSH CONTROL METHODS

Adjustable third brush. As previously explained, the third brush of this type of generator may be adjustable; that is, by loosening a bolt or

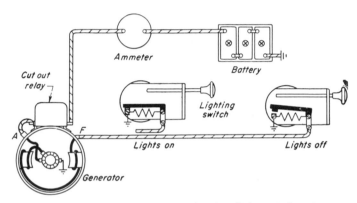

FIG. 21-8. *Generator output control using light-switch resistance.*

screw, the third brush can be moved a limited amount about the commutator which, in turn, changes the field strength with respect to the armature speed and thereby increases or reduces the generated amperage. It is a simple method of control, but it does not provide reliable and precise control under such variable conditions as generator speed, battery conditions, and output requirements.

Light-switch control. A method commonly used to control the output of tractor generators involves the insertion of a resistance in the light switch (Fig. 21-8) so that when the lights are off the output is reduced because of this resistance in the field circuit. When the lights are turned on, the resistance is cut out and the generator output is considerably increased to care for the additional load without reducing the charge to the battery. A third position provides for a high-rate battery charge when the lights are off.

Field-voltage control. One of the most reliable and effective methods of obtaining close regulation of generator output is by means of special electric devices attached to the generator and operating automatically to maintain a constant generator field voltage. One such device uses a vibrating relay, while the other automatically changes the field resistance according to the condition of charge of the battery.

The vibrating-type voltage control (Fig. 21-9) consists of an iron core with two windings. The shunt winding consists of many turns of fine wire, and the series winding consists of fewer turns of heavy wire connected in series with the field circuit when the regulator points are closed. When the generator voltage reaches a certain value, the magnetic field

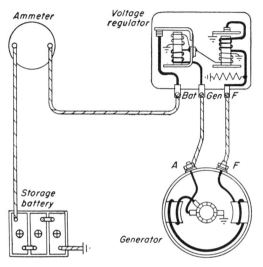

FIG. 21-9. *Third-brush generator with voltage regulator.*

produced by the two windings overcomes the armature spring tension, pulls the armature down, and separates the contact points. This breaks the series circuit, inserts resistance into the generator-field circuit, and reduces its voltage. This, in turn, weakens the magnetic field, the armature is released, and the points again make contact and close the series field circuit and permit an increase in voltage. Thus it is observed that a continuous making and breaking action goes on because the armature actually vibrates rapidly. This vibration maintains the voltage at a constant value and permits the generator to supply varying amounts of current to meet the varying states of battery charge and electrical load.

A similar but slightly different type of voltage regulator is known as the two-charge or step-voltage control device (Fig. 21-10). It has two shunt windings assembled on two cores, above which is a flat steel armature. When the points are in contact, the generator-field circuit is directly grounded so that there is no control of the generator output. When the load demand is high and the battery charge is low, the generator and circuit voltage will be low and the control will remain inoperative. This will permit a high output according to generator speed and third-brush setting. However, if the load is decreased or the battery becomes well charged, the circuit voltage will increase and thereby increase the field strength about the control windings and cores. When the voltage reaches the value for which the device is set, the armature will be pulled downward toward the cores and the points will be separated. This causes a resistance to be inserted into the generator-field circuit so that the out-

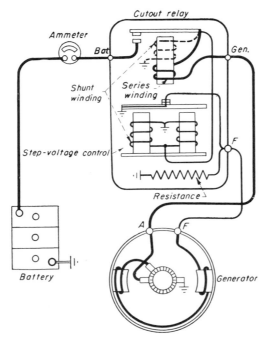

FIG. 21-10. *Third-brush generator with step-voltage control.*

put is considerably reduced. There is no vibrating action, and the resistance remains in the field as long as the battery remains in a fully charged condition and the electrical load is small. Again if the load increases and the battery becomes partly discharged, the generator voltage will drop and the magnetic pull will decrease and release the armature. This will close the points and permit a high generator output.

Current-voltage regulator. Figure 21-11 shows a type of regulator very similar to the vibrating-relay voltage regulator (Fig. 21-9). However, it will be noted that there are three windings on the core, one of which is in series with the battery-charging circuit. On the other hand, the load circuit produced by lights and ignition is independent of this winding. This regulator is adapted particularly to tractors and power units that are operated continuously for many days without any appreciable battery and generator load, for the reason that it provides much closer control of the battery-charging rate and the circuit voltage under conditions of extreme temperature variation.

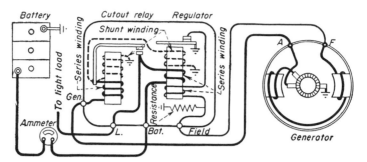

FIG. 21-11. *Third-brush generator with current-voltage control.*

TWO-BRUSH SHUNT-GENERATOR CONTROL

As previously explained, one of the disadvantages of the third-brush generator is that the output is largely dependent upon speed and tends to taper off at very high speeds. The two-brush or shunt generator provides a high output at lower speeds and will also give a maximum output, when required, at high speeds.

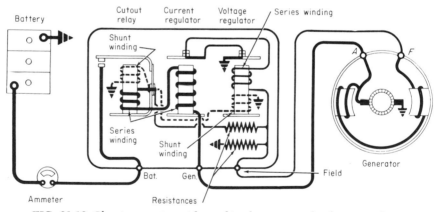

FIG. 21-12. *Shunt generator with combined current and voltage regulator.*

Shunt generators are coming into extensive use because they supply a relatively high output, which is essential for autos, trucks, and tractors equipped with numerous electrical accessories, as well as lights. Since the current output of a shunt generator increases in direct proportion to its speed, some external device must be used to limit the maximum output to a safe value. This is done by means of a combined current and voltage regulator (Fig. 21-12). It will be noted that the device consists of three distinct units: (1) the cutout relay, (2) a voltage regulator, and (3) a current regulator. The operation of the first two has already been discussed. The current regulator has a series winding of a few turns of heavy wire, which carries the entire generator output. With the relay points closed, the generator-field circuit is completed to the ground through the current-regulator points in series with the voltage-regulator relay points. When the load demand is heavy, as when electrical devices are turned on and the battery is in a discharged condition, the voltage may not increase sufficiently to cause the voltage regulator to operate. Consequently, the generator output will continue to increase until the

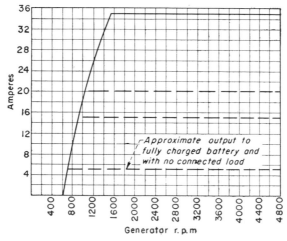

FIG. 21-13. *Output characteristics for a shunt generator with current and voltage regulator.*

generator reaches its rated maximum which is the current value for which the regulator is set. At this point, the magnetism in the core will pull the regulator armature down and open the points. With the points open, resistance is inserted in the field circuit and the output is reduced. As the output drops, the spring tension on the armature pulls it away from the core, the points again make contact, and the output increases. Thus this cycle continues; that is, the armature vibrates rapidly as long as the output remains at a maximum. When the electrical load is reduced or the battery becomes charged, the voltage increases and causes the voltage regulator to operate. This tapers off the generator output and prevents the current regulator from operating. The two regulators never operate simultaneously. The operating characteristics are shown by Fig. 21-13.

It will be noted that there are two resistances in the regulator and that they become connected in parallel in the generator field circuit when the current regulator operates. When the voltage regulator operates, only one resistor is inserted in the field circuit. The reason for this is that a higher value of resistance is required to reduce the generator output, when the voltage regulator operates, than is required when the current regulator operates to prevent the generator from exceeding its rated maximum.

Regulator adjustment. As a rule, the means of output regulation provided by the manufacturer for the generator on any engine is adequate to meet any normal requirements without the need for any further adjustment. However, it is occasionally desirable to readjust the generator output if possible. We have already observed that for adjustable third-brush generators, the shifting of the third brush will usually take care of the situation. For fixed third-brush and two-brush generators, the output can be changed only by making certain adjustments in the regulator relays. Such adjustments are usually based upon changing the tension of the relay-armature spring and should be made only if absolutely necessary and only by a skilled and trained mechanic.

STARTER MOTORS

Practically all automobile, truck, and tractor engines and many stationary power units and other types of engines are cranked and started electrically by means of a battery and a special electric motor. These motors vary somewhat in size and type and are usually equipped with a convenient switch, according to the service requirements.

Starter-motor construction. Starter motors are similar to generators, with the exception that they have a series-wound instead of a shunt-wound field circuit, as shown by Fig 21-14. Also, both the field and armature windings (Fig. 21-15) are of very coarse low-resistance wire, which will allow a high-amperage current to flow. A starter motor must exert a strong turning effort or torque. To provide this, a heavy current must flow through the circuits and create a very strong magnetic field and consequent pronounced reaction between the armature and the field.

The principal variation in different starters is in the number of poles and brushes. For small engines, two-pole starters with two brushes are usually used. Larger engines use four- and six-pole starters with four or six brushes. Otherwise the construction and operation are the same.

Starter drives. The starter drive is the device that connects and transmits the power to the engine flywheel. A small spur pinion on the armature shaft meshing with teeth on the flywheel is the usual means of transmitting the power. However, the drive must embody some convenient means of disengaging as well as engaging the pinion, and the device must be one that will not give trouble or injure the starter motor when the engine begins to fire or if it kicks back.

Three common types of starter drives are the Bendix (Fig. 21-16), the overrunning-clutch type (Fig. 21-17), and the Dyer type (Fig. 21-18). In the Bendix, the construction is such that engagement of the pinion takes place as soon as the starter switch is closed and the armature begins to rotate. A threaded sleeve on the armature shaft carries this pinion and permits it to move along the shaft and into and out of engagement. If the armature starts turning, the thread carries the pinion into engagement with the flywheel gear. As soon as the engine fires and turns the pinion faster than the armature shaft is turning it, the pinion is carried out of engagement by the threads. The device is equipped with a heavy spring

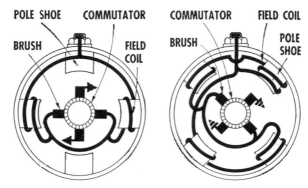

FIG. 21-14. *Circuits and windings for a starter motor.*

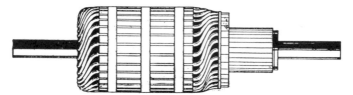

FIG. 21-15. *Starter-motor armature.*

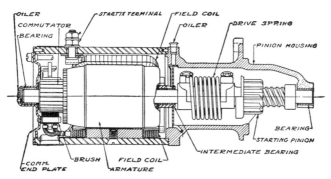

FIG. 21-16. *Sectional view of a starting motor using Bendix-type starter-drive mechanism.*

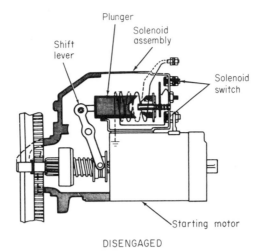

DISENGAGED

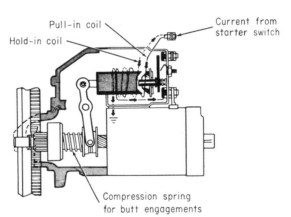

PINION PARTIALLY ENGAGED

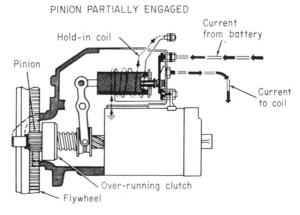

PINION FULLY ENGAGED AND
STARTING MOTOR CRANKING

FIG. 21-17. *Manual-type starter drive equipped with solenoid-actuating mechanism.*

to absorb the shock as the pinion comes into mesh with the flywheel or when the engine kicks back.

In the overrunning-clutch starter drive, pressure on the starter foot lever first slides the pinion into mesh with the flywheel gear. Pushing the foot lever still farther then closes the switch, and the armature rotates and cranks the engine. To prevent damage to the starter motor when the engine begins to fire and turn the pinion at a higher speed than the armature is turning it, an overrunning clutch is built into the pinion and connects it to the armature shaft in such a manner that the pinion is auto-

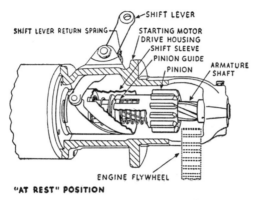

FIG. 21-18. *Dyer-type starter drive.*

matically disconnected from the armature even though the foot lever is not released.

The Dyer drive (Fig. 21-18) is a special type of drive combining some of the features of both the Bendix and overrunning-clutch drives. It was designed particularly for starter motors for diesel and heavy-duty types of engines. It provides for positive engagement of the drive pinion with the ring gear before the cranking-motor switch is closed and thus before the armature starts to rotate. This eliminates clashing and the possibility of broken or burred teeth on either the pinion or the gear. As soon as the engine starts, the pinion is automatically demeshed by the reversal of torque so that the armature will not be subjected to excess speeds.

Cranking motor controls. The cranking circuit of any electric starting outfit must be equipped with a convenient, easily operated, heavy-duty switch. This switch may be operated manually through a foot- or hand-operated lever or semiautomatically by means of a solenoid switch or a magnetic switch. The usual method (Fig. 21-17) is to combine the ignition switch and starting switch in such a manner that the latter, when turned to a certain position, closes a circuit which energizes the pull-in coil of the solenoid. As the solenoid plunger moves inward, it slides the starter pinion into engagement with the flywheel gear and finally closes the main starter switch.

REFERENCES

CROUSE, W. H., "Automotive Electrical Equipment," McGraw-Hill Book Company, Inc., New York, 1959.

FRAZEE, IRVING, and EARL L. BEDELL, "Automotive Electrical Systems," American Technical Society, Chicago, 1956.

PROBLEMS AND QUESTIONS

1. Make a sketch showing the essential parts and circuits for a complete lighting, starting, and ignition system for a four-cylinder engine.

2. Explain the fundamental differences between a generator and a starter motor with respect to both construction and operation.

3. Prepare sketches showing the detailed construction of (a) a third-brush generator, (b) a two-brush generator, (c) a cutout relay, and (d) a voltage-control relay.

4. Explain the meaning of (a) light-switch control, (b) voltage control, (c) current control, and (d) combined current-voltage control, and give advantages, if any, of each method.

5. If the current output of a two-brush generator is excessive, how might it be reduced? Explain in detail.

6. It is estimated that the maximum power required for cranking an engine is 4 hp. If a 24-volt starting system is used which has an efficiency of 70 per cent, what is the discharge rate for the battery when this engine is cranked?

7. Name and briefly describe two types of starter-motor drives.

8. Name two reasons why the Bendix starter drive might fail to turn the engine even though the armature turns.

22

Lubricants and Lubricating Systems

Lubrication plays an important part in the design and operation of any type of automotive machine. The life and service given by an automobile or a tractor are dependent largely upon the consideration and care given to its lubrication, both in the design of the system and during its use and operation. The fundamental purpose of lubrication of any mechanical device is to eliminate friction and the resulting wear and loss of power. Other important functions of lubrication of an internal-combustion engine are (1) to absorb and dissipate heat, (2) to serve as a piston seal, (3) to act as a cushion to deaden the noise of moving parts, and (4) to assist in keeping the engine working parts clean and free of dirt, gum, corrosive acids, and other contaminants.

In the internal-combustion engine, lubrication is even more difficult than in other machines, for the reason that a certain amount of heat is present, particularly in and around the cylinder and piston, as a result of the combustion of the fuel. The lubrication of these heated parts is a somewhat more difficult problem than it would be if the heat were not present.

Friction. Whenever two materials of any kind move against each other, a certain amount of a force known as *friction* tends to oppose the movement. For example, when a liquid or a gas is made to flow through a passage such as a pipe or a conduit, the flow is more or less retarded by the friction between the liquid or gas and the inner surface of the pipe. Such friction is undesirable. On the other hand, the transmission of power by belts and pulleys is entirely dependent upon the friction between the belt and the pulley surfaces. The greater the frictional contact, the more effective the arrangement and the lower the power loss.

The friction due to metal parts of machines moving in or against each other is usually highly undesirable, not only because of the power required to overcome it, but also because of rapid wear. Likewise, it often results in the generation of a certain amount of heat, which may damage the parts or produce a fire hazard. This friction cannot be completely eliminated, but it can be reduced to such an extent by the use of a suitable lubricant that the operation of the machine is greatly improved and its life lengthened.

LUBRICATING OILS AND GREASES

There are a large number and variety of lubricants available for the many different lubrication requirements. Each particular kind, quality, or type of lubricant has a comparatively limited use.

Automotive equipment such as automobiles, trucks, and tractors normally requires three general type of lubricants, namely, (1) a relatively thin, free-flowing oil for the engine, (2) a heavier high-viscosity oil for the transmission gears and bearings, and (3) various types of slow or nonflowing materials termed "greases" for wheel bearings, spring shackles, water pumps, universal joints, and the like. As a result of the many changes and improvements being made in automotive machinery, oil refineries have found it necessary to develop many new and special types of lubricants having properties that better adapt them to operating conditions.

Practically all lubricants are derived from one or the other of three sources, namely, animal, vegetable, or mineral matter.

Animal lubricants. The oils and greases obtained by rendering the fat of animals, such as swine, cattle, sheep, fish, and so on, are utilized to a very limited extent for the lubrication of mechanical devices. Some of the common animal lubricants are lard oil, tallow, sperm oil, and fish oil. The principal disadvantage is that they cannot stand heat and readily combine with oxygen, becoming waxy or gummy. Also, under certain conditions, fatty acids that are harmful to the machine parts are liberated.

Vegetable lubricants. The oils obtained from vegetable materials, such as seeds, fruits, and plants, are likewise limited in their utility for general lubrication purposes for the reason that they also have a tendency to oxidize readily and become gummy. Some common vegetable oils are castor oil, cottonseed oil, olive oil, and linseed oil. Only castor oil has ever proved of any value for engine lubrication. It has been used to a limited extent in some types of airplane and marine engines because it does not congeal except at low temperatures, it does not mix readily with engine fuels, and it retains its lubrication properties at high temperatures.

Mineral lubricants. Crude petroleum, obtained from the earth and therefore usually classed as a mineral, serves as the greatest source of lubricating materials as well as fuels for internal-combustion engines. Petroleum lubricants not only are more plentiful and therefore less expensive than animal and vegetable oils, but also retain their lubricating properties when subjected to abnormal temperatures and other conditions.

Crude petroleum varies in quality, character, and chemical make-up, according to its geographical source. For example, some crude oils contain a high percentage of lighter products, such as gasoline and kerosene, and are therefore more valuable as a source of fuel. Other crudes, usually heavier in gravity, are low in these lighter products but contain a higher percentage of products that, when refined, produce lubricating oils and greases. The so-called paraffin-base crudes are usually lower in specific gravity and yield a high percentage of fuel products when distilled. The asphalt-base crudes are usually higher in specific gravity, darker in color, and yield a high per cent of lubrication products.

Considerable argument has been put forth in the past concerning the relative merits of lubricants produced from different crude oils. Owing to the great development and advance made in the refining process, however, it is doubtful if any conclusive and consistent proof can be shown in favor of any particular crude-oil base as a base for a lubricant for a particular engine or purpose.

Manufacture of lubricants. Crude oil consists of a mixture of many hydrocarbons having different boiling points. Therefore, the first process in the conversion of any crude oil into its various products consists in heating it and distilling off the lighter fractions, such as gasoline, kerosene, gas oil, and so on (see Fig. 11-2). When a temperature of 350 to 400°C. is reached, the heavier fractions, suitable for lubricants, distill over. If it is desired to secure a large quantity of lubricating oil from the crude, steam is introduced into the stills and they may be operated under a partial vacuum in order to prevent these heavy fractions from cracking or breaking up into lighter hydrocarbons. The lubricating-oil distillates may be redistilled with steam under a vacuum and thereby separated into heavy and light oils. Following distillation, the oils are subjected to a further rather complex refining process in order to obtain products which are adapted to every possible operating condition. Two processes have been used, the acid process and the solvent-extraction process. The former involves treatment with sulfuric acid, followed by washing with water and neutralization with an alkali. The solvent-extraction process is now used very extensively and involves six steps, as follows: (1) deasphalting, (2) dewaxing, (3) solvent extraction, (4) redistillation, (5) filtration, and (6) blending. Additional processes and treatments must be used in the preparation of certain special lubricants and greases.

ENGINE-OIL TESTS

The market is flooded with hundreds of brands and grades of oils of varying quality. Consequently, the owners and operators of gas engines, automobiles, trucks, tractors, airplanes, and so on, realize the great importance of choosing the best possible oil for the engine. The price should not be more than a minor determining factor. During the early development and use of these machines, the selection of the correct lubricant was, in many cases, left with the operator. As time went on, the engine manufacturer realized the important part played by lubrication and lubricating oil in the satisfaction and service rendered by his product and, consequently, assumed the responsibility for determining and recommending the proper grade of oil to be used. As a rule, thorough tests are made either by the engine manufacturer or by the oil refiner, before any definite lubrication recommendations are offered. Such being the case, the user and operator of any type of internal-combustion engine should adhere closely to such advice. However, some knowledge of the fundamental factors involved in the choice of an engine oil is valuable and important.

Essentials of a good lubricating oil. As a general rule, the majority of the standard or better known brands of engine oil now on the market are reliable products and will give good results provided the correct grade is used. There are no hard and fast rules or specifications by which one may choose the proper oil to use in a given case. Likewise, there are no simple chemical or physical tests that the average individual may apply to an oil to determine its character. Such things as the color, feel, and general appearance mean nothing.

Thomsen [1] states that in order to satisfy certain fundamental lubricating requirements, a lubricant:

1. Must possess sufficient viscosity and lubricating power—oiliness—to suit the mechanical conditions and conditions of speed, pressure, and temperature. Too little oiliness means excessive wear and friction; too high a viscosity means loss of power in overcoming unnecessary fluid friction.
2. Must suit the lubrication system.
3. Must be of such a nature that it will not produce deposits during use when exposed to the influence of the air, gas, water, or impurities with which the oil may come into more or less intimate contact while performing its duty.

Tests of lubricating oils. There are a large number of physical and chemical tests to which an oil may be subjected for the purpose of determining its quality and adaptability to a given purpose. Many of these, however, are of minor importance except to the oil refiner, the chemist, or the lubricating engineer. In a bulletin published by the

[1] Thomsen, "Practice of Lubrication," McGraw-Hill Book Company, Inc., New York, 1937.

American Society for Testing Materials and entitled "The Significance of Tests of Petroleum Products," the following statements are made:

The rapid growth of the petroleum industry has been accompanied by the development of a variety of physical and chemical methods for the testing of petroleum products.

Physical tests are more widely used than chemical tests. This is natural, in view of the fact that the utility of petroleum products depends to a large extent upon their physical characteristics. Some of these physical tests are of little value except as they serve the refiner in controlling manufacturing processes, while others are useful both to consumer and to manufacturer as an index of the value or fitness of products for particular uses.

Such chemical tests as now exist serve principally to protect against impurities or undesirable constituents. This is because petroleum is an extremely complex raw material, varying greatly in composition in the various producing fields, with each new field bringing its own problems.

Some of the more important tests, together with their definition or meaning, the recommended procedure followed in making them, and their significance and value, are as follows:

Gravity. In testing oils for gravity, the same method is followed as that discussed in Chap. 11, in connection with the gravity of fuels. The A.S.T.M. bulletin previously referred to states: "The property of gravity is of importance in the control of refinery operations. It is of little significance as an index of the quality or usefulness of a finished product and its use in specifications is to be avoided."

Regarding other tests of lubricating oils of more or less importance, the above-mentioned bulletin states as follows:

Color. The color of petroleum products is described and defined in terms of color by reflected light or by transmitted light. Color requirements of lubricating oils are frequently overemphasized as color does not necessarily indicate quality. A fallacy, which is prevalent among consumers, is that pale color indicates low viscosity.

Cloud and pour points. Petroleum oils become more or less plastic solids when sufficiently cooled, due either to partial separation of wax or to congealing of the hydrocarbons composing the oil. With some oils the separation of wax becomes visible at temperatures slightly above the solidification point, and when that temperature is observed, under prescribed conditions, it is known as the "cloud point." With oils in which wax separation does not take place prior to solidification, or in which the separation is not visible, the cloud point cannot be determined. That temperature at which the oil just flows under prescribed conditions is known as the "pour point," irrespective of whether the cloud point is observable. Oils vary widely in these characteristics depending upon the source of the crude oil from which they are made, upon the grade or kind, and upon the method of manufacture.

The cloud point is of value when the oil is to be used in wick-feed service, or when a haze or cloud in the oil above a given temperature would be objectionable for any reason. However, the test may give misleading results if the oil is not dry, due to the separation of water, and the test should always be interpreted with this fact in mind. In general, the cloud point is of more limited value and narrower in range of application than the pour point.

The pour point gives an indication of the temperature below which it might be dangerous to use the oil in gravity lubricating systems. No single test can be devised which can be taken as a positive and direct measure of the performance of an oil under all conditions of service, and the pour test should be regarded as giving only an indication of what may be expected. Consequently, cloud and pour points should be interpreted in the light of actual performance under the particular conditions of use.

Carbon residue. The Conradson carbon residue test is a method of determining the amount of carbon residue left when a given sample of oil is heated and evaporated under specified conditions. It is assumed that there may be some correlation between the carbon-forming tendency of an oil in an engine and its carbon residue test value, but it is also recognized that other factors affect carbon deposits. In recent years, this test is used to indicate the character rather than the quantity of carbon which will be produced by a given oil.

Flash and fire tests. The flash point of a product may be defined as the temperature to which it must be heated in order to give off sufficient vapor to form an inflammable mixture with air. The fire point may be defined as the temperature to which a product must be heated in order to burn continuously after the inflammable air-vapor mixture is once ignited. The fire point test is less frequently used than the flash point test. Flash point tests were originally employed to indicate the fire hazard of petroleum products. Their use has, however, been extended and they are frequently employed to give other information. For lubricating oils, flash point is determined largely for purposes of identification and classification. As a general rule, it may be said that the flash point of a lubricating oil bears no direct relation to its usefulness. Flash point tests are useful to refiners in controlling the manufacturing process.

Viscosity. The viscosity of a fluid is the measure of its resistance to flow. In most commercial work an expression involving the time in seconds required for a measured volume of oil to flow, under specified conditions, through a carefully standardized tube, is known as the viscosity of the oil. In practice, at least three different instruments must be employed in commercial testing: one for light distillates, one for lubricating oils, and one for heavy fuel and road oils. As viscosity changes rapidly with temperature, a numerical value of viscosity has no significance unless both the temperature and the instrument are specified.

Viscosimeters for lubricating oils. The Saybolt Universal Viscosimeter (Fig. 22-1) is now used almost universally in the United States for determination of the viscosity of lubricating oils. The apparatus consists of a central cylindrical reservoir in which the oil to be tested is placed. This reservoir is surrounded by a water bath to control the temperature. The viscosity of the oil sample is determined by taking the time in seconds required for 60 cc. to pass through a small orifice of specified size in the bottom of the reservoir. On the lighter oils the measurements are made at 100 or 130°F., and on the more viscous oils at 210°F. The instrument gives reliable results at any temperature between about 31 and 210°F., provided the oil is not near its solid point or its flash point. Above 210°F., radiation losses become so large that the results are not satisfactory.

Significance of viscosity. The significance of viscosity depends upon the purpose for which the oil is to be used. For lubricating oils, viscosity is the most important single property. In a bearing operating properly, with a fluid film separating the surfaces, the viscosity of the oil at the operating temperature is the property which determines the bearing friction, heat generation, and the rate of flow under given conditions of load, speed, and bearing design.

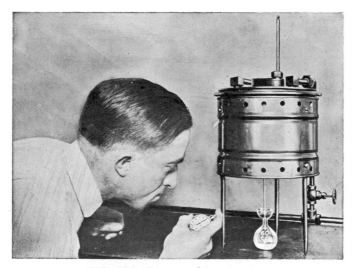

FIG. 22-1. *Testing oil for viscosity.*

The oil should be viscous enough to maintain a fluid film between the bearing surfaces in spite of the pressure tending to squeeze it out. While a reasonable factor of safety is essential, excessive viscosity means unnecessary friction and heat generation. Since the rate of change of viscosity with temperature varies with different oils, viscosity tests should, in general, be made at that standard temperature which approximates most closely the temperature of use.

Viscosity index. As previously explained, temperature is a vital factor in oil viscosity and the viscosity of any oil varies inversely with temperature. Furthermore, even though two oil samples may have the same viscosity at a certain temperature, say 130°F., yet there may be a considerable variation in their viscosities at temperatures lower or higher than 130°F. An ideal oil would be one which would have a desirable viscosity at some optimum temperature and whose viscosity would show little change at appreciably lower or higher temperatures. Unfortunately, very few oils have such a quality and the Saybolt Universal viscosity test of any oil at one temperature is not a true indicator of its viscosity at all temperatures. For this reason, a method was devised whereby this rate of change of viscosity of an oil with respect to temperature could be designated and the viscosity temperature characteristics

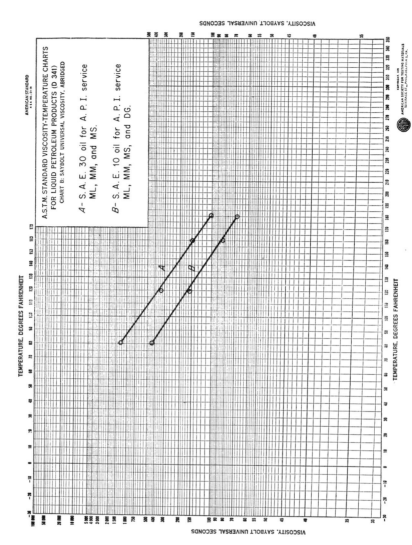

FIG. 22-2. *A.S.T.M. Standard viscosity-temperature chart.* (Chart B Saybolt Universal viscosity, abridged, courtesy of American Society for Testing Materials.)

of different oils compared. This designation is called Viscosity Index and is based upon the general observation that paraffin base oils show a relatively limited change in viscosity and are given an index of 100 while asphaltic base oils show a relatively high change in viscosity and are given an index of 0. Figure 22-2 shows an A.S.T.M. chart which can be used to determine the viscosity characteristics of engine oils. If the oil sample is tested for viscosity at two temperatures, such as 70 and 210°F., and the values are plotted on the chart and connected by a straight line, the slope of the line indicates the relative viscosity index of the oil and viscosities at other temperatures can be determined.

S.A.E. viscosity classification. In order to provide some standard means of designation of motor-oil grades, the Society of Automotive Engineers, cooperating with the oil refiners and automotive manufacturers, has worked out an oil-grading system based upon viscosity numbers as indicated by Table 22-1. As

Table 22-1. S.A.E. Crankcase-oil Classification System

S.A.E. viscosity number	Viscosity range, S.U.S.			
	At 0°F.		At 210°F.	
	Min.	Max.	Min.	Max.
5W		4,000		
10W	6,000 [1]	Less than 12,000		
20W	12,000 [2]	48,000		
20	. . . . .	. . . . .	45	Less than 58
30	. . . . .	. . . . .	58	Less than 70
40	. . . . .	. . . . .	70	Less than 85
50	. . . . .	. . . . .	85	110

[1] Minimum viscosity at 0°F. can be waived, provided viscosity at 210°F. is not below 40 S.U.S.

[2] Minimum viscosity at 0°F. can be waived, provided viscosity at 210°F. is not below 45 S.U.S.

noted, the measured viscosity in seconds by the Saybolt Universal Viscosimeter (Fig. 22-1) is taken at 0 and 210°F. to provide a knowledge of the relative change in fluidity between average operating crankcase temperatures. The oil manufacturer designates the various grades by means of numbers instead of in the usual manner, the number being stamped on the container. The user, knowing the viscosity number recommended by the engine manufacturer, selects the oil accordingly.

Saybolt Universal viscosity is usually determined at temperatures of 100 and 210°F. Viscosity at lower temperatures such as 0°F. is determined by extrapolation on a standard viscosity-temperature chart (Fig. 22-2). Summer-grade motor oils such as S.A.E. 20 or 30 are based on viscosities at 210°F., while winter-grade oils such as S.A.E. 10W are based on viscosities of 0°F. Since the S.A.E. viscosity classification system is based on viscosities at these two different temperatures, it becomes possible for a single oil, if properly formulated, to meet the viscosity requirements of more than one S.A.E. grade. For example, an oil having a viscosity of 10,000 sec. at 0°F. and 59 sec. at 210°F. falls within the S.A.E. 10W range of 6,000 to 12,000 sec. at 0°F. and also the S.A.E. 30 range of 58 to 70 sec. at 210°F. It has become the practice to identify such an oil as S.A.E. 10W-30. Similarly, it is possible to make such combinations as 5W-20, 20W-20, and 20W-40, for example. The principal advantage of multigraded oils is that, other factors being equal, they allow the engine to be operated safely over a wider range of atmospheric temperatures.

A.P.I. motor-oil service classification. In order to provide a more definite means of specifying the quality of engine oils and their adaptability to different types of engines and service, the American Petroleum Institute has recommended the following classifications and definitions:

For gasoline engines

Service ML, service typical of gasoline and other spark ignition engines used under light and favorable operating conditions, the engines having no design characteristics sensitive to deposit formation.

Service MM, service typical of gasoline and other spark ignition engines used under moderate to severe operating conditions but presenting problems of deposit or bearing corrosion control when crankcase oil temperatures are high.

Service MS, service typical of gasoline and other spark ignition engines used under unfavorable or severe types of operating conditions and where there are special lubrication requirements for deposits, wear, or bearing corrosion control due to operating conditions or to engine design or fuel characteristics.

For diesel engines

Service DG, service typical of diesel engines in any operation where there are no severe requirements for wear or deposit control due to fuel, lubricating oil, or engine design characteristics.

Service DM, service typical of diesel engines operating under severe conditions or using fuel of a type normally tending to promote deposits and wear but where there are design characteristics or operating conditions which may make the engine either less sensitive to fuel effects or more sensitive to residues from lubricating oils.

Service DS, service typical of diesel engines operating under very severe conditions or having design characteristics or using fuel tending to produce excessive wear or deposits.

Engine performance tests. The fact has been recognized for a number of years that the performance of oils in engines cannot be predicted from the results of certain chemical and physical tests and the only real measure of oil quality is its performance in service. Some engine manufacturers and certain allied agencies have developed exhaustive engine test procedures to determine the specific performance characteristics of oils but no standard test procedure has been adopted. Nevertheless these tests have provided much valuable information which has aided the oil refiners in improving their products.

ENGINE-OIL ADDITIVES

Changes and improvements in the design of certain types of engines created new problems, which were attributed largely to inadequate lubrication. Some of these were ring sticking, ring and piston scuffing, and excessive bearing corrosion and wear. These difficulties were encountered particularly in the high-speed diesel engines and other heavy-duty types used in tractors, trucks, and busses. As a result of the efforts of oil technologists and engine designers, it was found that certain chemicals, when added to a well-refined motor oil, would improve its lubricating properties and eliminate specific troubles. Most oil refiners are now producing a special grade and quality of motor oil containing chemicals to improve its lubricating properties, particularly under heavy-duty conditions. The term *additives* is usually applied to these chemicals.

Some lubricating-oil additives prevent or retard oil oxidation and thereby control carbon deposits and corrosion, while others improve such physical properties of the oil as its pour point, viscosity index, or film strength. The principal additives and their specific action are listed as follows:

1. *Antioxidants.* Organic compounds increase the resistance of an oil to oxidation and thereby reduce the formation of certain acidic products that may cause the corrosion of certain types of bearings.

2. *Anticorrosives.* Certain compounds containing sulfur, phosphorus, or nitrogen may be added to an oil for the purpose of forming a protective film on the bearing surfaces, thus preventing corrosion from any acids present in the oil. Such chemical additives are called corrosion inhibitors.

3. *Detergents.* Certain compounds, when added to a motor oil, prevent the building up of carbon and gummy or carbonaceous deposits on the pistons and under the rings or on other engine parts.

4. *Dispersants.* Certain chemicals, when added to an oil, cause any finely divided insoluble particles of carbon to remain in suspension in the oil rather than to separate out and form sludge deposits. The action of detergents and that of dispersants appear to be closely allied.

5. *Extreme-pressure agents.* Under certain conditions of high pressure and temperature, an ordinary lubricant, even with a high viscosity, will not provide sufficient oil film between the metal surfaces to control wear. The best example of this is the hypoid gear drive of the modern automo-

bile. A special lubricant has been developed for this type of gear by adding certain chemical agents to an oil of proper viscosity. These additives enable the lubricant to withstand the unusual pressure and temperature conditions developed by hypoid gears and yet give satisfactory lubrication.

6. *Foam inhibitors.* Some types of motor oils have a tendency to absorb air when agitated vigorously, thus forming a foam. Certain chemicals, when added to such oils, accelerate the rate of breakdown of the foam but may not actually prevent foaming.

7. *Pour-point depressants.* Certain chemicals, when added to oils, improve their pour-point characteristics at low temperatures, even though the lubricant has not been fully dewaxed in the refining process.

8. *Viscosity-index improvers.* Under certain conditions it is found desirable to use an oil whose viscosity does not increase excessively at low temperatures. Chemicals have been found which, when added to these oils, aid in retarding this tendency to thicken as the temperature drops. They are therefore called viscosity-index improvers.

9. *Graphite lubricants.* Graphite is a form of carbon found in nature or made artificially. Pencil lead is a good example of graphite. It is frequently added to lubricants to adapt them better to certain conditions. The theory is that it forms a very smooth coating on the bearing-metal surfaces by filling the pores and rough spots. The graphite may be in the lubricant in a flake form or in colloidal form. The so-called upper-cylinder lubricants are light oils containing colloidal graphite. When this substance is added to the fuels, it is claimed that valve and cylinder lubrication is improved. A similar material may be added to the crankcase oil.

Greases. Greases are semifluid or semisolid lubricants and are used primarily for slow-moving parts when pressures are high and for parts that are concealed or inaccessible such as wheel bearings, spring shackles, axle bearings, universal joints, and water pumps. Many different kinds of greases have been developed to meet the specific requirements of automobile, truck, and tractor chassis lubrication.

A grease is a mixture of a metallic soap and a mineral oil. Certain chemicals may be added to provide stabilization, oxidation resistance, rust prevention, tackiness, and other desirable characteristics.

Soap serves as a thickening agent for a lubricant, particularly at certain temperatures. Soap is produced by the chemical action between an alkali such as calcium hydroxide and a fat—usually animal or vegetable —or a fatty acid. The process is called saponification. The characteristics and specific properties of a grease are determined by the fat or fatty acid, the alkali, and the mineral oil used in producing it.

Greases may be classified according to type of soap used as (1) lime-base, (2) sodium-base, (3) aluminum-base, and (4) mixed-base. Lime-

or calcium-base greases are general-purpose greases and are limited to use at temperatures below 175°F. They are water-repellent but, at high temperatures, have a tendency to separate into oil and metallic soap. Sodium-base greases are fibrous and stringy in appearance and well adapted to high speeds and temperatures. They are not water-resistant and are used for wheel bearings, universal joints, and spring shackles. Aluminum-base greases have certain advantages of both lime- and sodium-base greases. They are transparent in appearance, very adhesive, water-resistant, and adapted to high-speed gear-lubrication and similar uses. Mixed-base greases are usually mixtures of mineral oils and certain combinations of lime and soda soaps, lime and aluminum soaps, and potassium and lime soaps, for the purpose of obtaining a special type of grease such as water-pump grease, ball-bearing grease, and so on.

Additives such as graphite, talc, asbestos, and certain chemicals may be incorporated in greases to provide extreme-pressure characteristics, oxidation resistance, rust prevention, and tackiness.

Greases are classified according to consistency as fluid, No. 0; very soft, No. 1; soft, No. 2; medium, No. 3; and hard, No. 4. They are also classified according to use as cup greases, ball- and roller-bearing greases, gear greases, chassis greases, and so on.

Transmission and axle lubricants. A gear or transmission lubricant is a heavy-bodied, dark-colored oil. It must have sufficient body to cushion and sustain the sudden high-pressure loads transmitted to the gear-teeth surfaces and yet cling to these teeth. Also, it must not create undue resistance to motion and should flow in ample quantity to the shaft bearings. Gears such as the hypoid type require a lubricant having the highest possible load-carrying capacity. Such oils are referred to as extreme-pressure (E.P.) lubricants and contain certain additives. Table 22-2 gives the S.A.E. viscosity recommendations for transmission lubricants. The American Petroleum Institute has specified four types of transmission lubricants and their applications as follows:

Regular-type gear lubricant. This term designates gear lubricants generally suitable for use in automotive transmissions and in most spiral-bevel and worm-gear differentials.

Worm-type gear lubricant. This term designates gear lubricants generally suitable for use in truck-type worm-gear rear axles under very severe conditions of service.

Mild-type E.P. gear lubricant. This term designates gear lubricants having load-carrying properties suitable for many automotive transmissions and spiral-bevel differentials under severe conditions of speed and load.

Multipurpose-type gear lubricant. This term designates gear lubricants having load-carrying properties suitable for hypoid gear and other types of differentials and many transmissions.

Table 22-2. S.A.E. Transmission and Axle Lubricants Classification System

S.A.E. viscosity number	Viscosity range, S.U.S.				Consistency, must not channel in service at
	0°F.		210°F.		
	Min.	Max.	Min.	Max.	
75	. . . . .	15,000	. . .	. . .	−40°F.
80	15,000 [1]	100,000	. . .	. . .	−20°F.
90	. . . . .	. . . . . .	75	120 [2]	−10°F.
140	. . . . .	. . . . . .	120	200	20°F.
250	. . . . .	. . . . . .	200		

[1] The minimum viscosity at 0°F. may be waived if the viscosity is not less than 48 S.U.S. at 210°F.

[2] The maximum viscosity at 210°F. may be waived if the viscosity is not greater than 750,000 S.U.S. at 0° (extrapolated).

Hydraulic torque converter and automatic transmission fluids. Torque-converter and fluid-coupling drives and automatic transmissions require a special fluid and lubricant usually having a viscosity range varying from 5W to 20 or 20W. Such fluids must serve as a lubricant, a coolant, a hydraulic medium, and a power-transmitting medium and possess good temperature characteristics, oxidation stability, and antiwear characteristics.

ENGINE LUBRICATION

The lubrication of an engine may be considered under two distinct heads, namely, (1) the choice and use of the correct kind and grade of lubricant; and (2) the choice, design, construction, and operation of the system with which the engine is equipped. A good lubricating system must be efficient in operation, reliable, troubleproof, and simple. Yet, even though it possesses all these important features, if a poor-quality lubricant or one of incorrect grade is used, unsatisfactory service is likely to result.

As previously stated, in selecting the oil to be used, satisfactory results are more likely to be obtained if the advice and recommendations of the engine manufacturer are followed. Then, having selected a suitable oil, one should familiarize oneself with the construction and operation of the lubrication system of the engine itself and see that it functions properly at all times.

Parts requiring lubrication. The most important parts of a gas engine requiring lubrication are as follows:

1. Cylinder walls and pistons
2. Piston pin
3. Crankshaft and connecting-rod bearings
4. Camshaft bearings
5. Valves and valve-operating mechanism

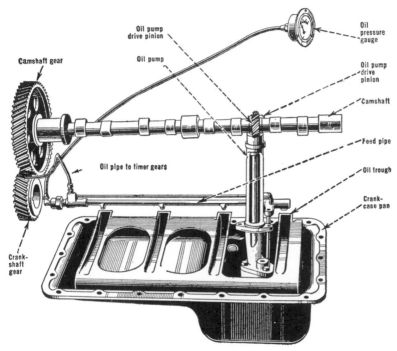

FIG. 22-3. *Circulating-splash oiling system using pump to circulate the oil.*

6. Other moving parts, such as cooling fan, water pump, ignition mechanism, and so on

In general, engine-lubrication systems may be classified as (1) simple circulating-splash, (2) internal force-feed and splash, and (3) full internal force-feed.

Circulating-splash system. In the circulating-splash system the lubrication of all the principal engine parts is dependent directly upon the splashing and spraying of the oil by the connecting rods dipping into it. The one important requirement for its successful operation is the maintenance of a uniform oil level under the rods. This is done by maintaining a continuous flow of oil from the sump or reservoir into a splash pan that has a depression or trough under each rod as shown by Fig. 22-3. A gear pump, driven from the camshaft, pumps the oil from the reservoir up into the splash pan. A dial-type indicator shows whether the pump is working or not. A fine screen around the pump inlet prevents sediment and dirt from being circulated.

Internal force-feed and splash system. In this system (Figs. 22-4 and 22-5) the oil is forced directly to the main crankshaft, connecting-rod, and camshaft bearings. Drilled passages in the crankshaft carry the oil

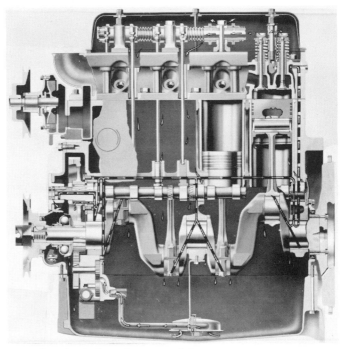

FIG. 22-4. *Combined splash and pressure lubrication system.* (Courtesy of Massey-Ferguson, Inc.)

from the main bearings to the connecting-rod bearings as shown. The oil oozing out of these bearings creates a spray that lubricates the cylinder walls, pistons, and piston pins. The connecting rods do not dip in the oil, and a splash pan is unnecessary. A pressure indicator shows whether the pump is working and pressure is being maintained. The valve mechanism is also oiled by pressure from the crankcase as shown.

Full internal force-feed system. This system goes a step farther and forces the oil not only to the main crankshaft, connecting-rod, and camshaft bearings, as previously described, but also to the piston-pin bearings through tubes or passages that lead from the connecting-rod bearing up the connecting rod to the piston pin, as shown in Figs. 22-6 and 22-7. The cylinders and pistons receive their oil from the piston pins and from the mist created by the oil issuing from the various bearings. The valve mechanism likewise is oiled by pressure feed as indicated.

Oil circulating pumps—oil pressures—relief valves. Two types of pumps are used for circulating the oil in engines equipped with either the circulating-splash, the internal force-feed and splash, or the full

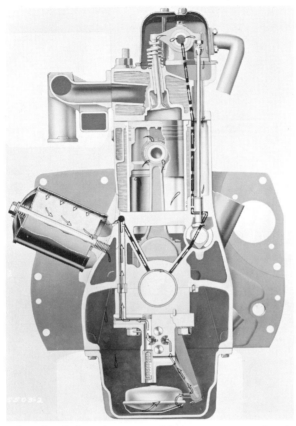

FIG. 22-5. *Combined splash and pressure lubrication system showing full-flow oil filter.* (Courtesy of Massey-Ferguson, Inc.)

internal force-feed system. The most used type is the gear pump (Fig. 22-8). It consists of two small spur gears held in a horizontal position and enclosed in a close-fitting, oiltight housing. A vertical shaft from the camshaft of the engine drives one pump gear, and it in turn drives the second gear. The oil enters on that side of the housing on which the gear teeth are turning away from each other, or going out of mesh, and is carried between the teeth and the inner surface of the housing around to the opposite side and discharged.

The force or pressure applied to the oil by the pump depends largely upon the lubrication system. A plain circulating-splash system requires very little pressure, usually from 2 to 5 lb. per sq. in. On the other hand, a full force-feed system requires that the oil be pumped a greater distance through numerous tubes and passages and in sufficient quantity at all times to ensure the proper lubrication of the various parts. Therefore, in different engines, a higher pressure ranging from 10 to 40 lb. is necessary.

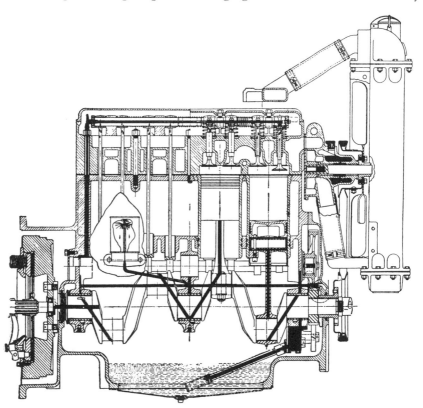

FIG. 22-6. *Full-pressure lubrication system.*

In order to maintain the correct pressure and control the quantity of oil circulated, a relief valve (Fig. 22-9) is connected to the oil-distribution system at some point, usually near the pump-discharge line. This valve consists essentially of a ball held in place over an opening by an adjustable spring. The valve operates in such a way as to permit a certain amount of the oil to bypass back to the oil reservoir as it leaves the pump. That is, if the spring tension is decreased, more oil will bypass and less will be forced through the system. If the tension is increased, less oil will go by the valve and back to the reservoir and more will be forced through the system.

FIG. 22-7. *Horizontal two-cylinder tractor engine equipped with full internal force-feed lubrication system.*

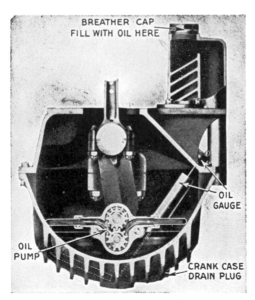

FIG. 22-8. *A gear-type oil pump.*

Oil gauges and indicators. Any engine having an enclosed crankcase and using a circulating-splash or an internal force-feed system of lubrication must have two oil indicators, as follows:

1. An oil-level indicator
2. An oil-pressure or circulation indicator

The oil-level indicator shows the quantity of oil in the crankcase sump or reservoir and whether it is low, half full, or full, and so on. The usual types are (1) test cocks, one for low level and one for high level, and (2) bayonet gauge (Fig. 22-10). In any case the oil level should not be al-

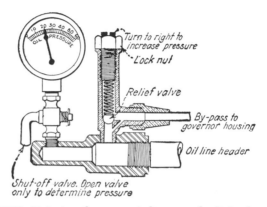

FIG. 22-9. *An oil-pressure indicator and relief valve.*

lowed to drop very much below the upper or full point. The lower the level, the less the quantity of oil being circulated and the greater the rate of circulation and absorption of sediment and heat.

The maintenance of the correct pressure in any internal force-feed system is very important. For most engines a pressure of 25 to 40 lb. is recommended. As the bearings and cylinders wear, there will be a slight drop in pressure. Should this drop become appreciable, the correct pressure can usually be restored by adjusting the relief valve (Fig. 22-9). If the drop develops suddenly rather than gradually, the engine should be stopped immediately and the cause determined. The trouble may be:

1. Too thin oil
2. Lack of oil
3. Oil too cold or too heavy to flow
4. Broken pump parts or oil lines
5. Clogged oil screen or oil line

An oil-pressure gauge of some kind, connected to the distributing lines, is usually placed at some convenient external point to show the operator that the oil is being circulated and to indicate the pressure being maintained.

Oil pollution—carbon deposits. Foreign matter may find its way into the engine crankcase in a number of ways. Metal particles are being constantly worn or broken off from bearings and other parts. Dust and dirt particles will be drawn in through the breather opening if the latter is not provided with an effective screen or filter. The principal objection to this solid foreign matter is that it is apt to clog the oil lines or scratch the cylinder and piston surfaces.

FIG. 22-10. *The bayonet-type oil-level gauge.*

A breather is a necessary part of an enclosed-crankcase engine for the reason that the pistons create a pumping action and, therefore, an uneven pressure, which might otherwise force the oil out through the crankcase joints or upward past the pistons and into the combustion chamber. The breather also usually serves as the oil-filler opening.

Water that may find its way into the oil is likely to cause rusting and corrosion of the working parts. It also forms an emulsion with the oil and renders the latter less effective. Water accumulating in the crankcase is usually indicated by the rising oil level and its appearance in the bottom of the crankcase when the drain plug is first removed.

Dilution of the lubricating oil by the liquid fuel may take place because of (1) a poor carburetor setting that permits too rich a mixture to enter the engine, (2) excessive choking in an attempt to make the engine start, particularly in cold weather, or (3) loose, badly worn piston rings that permit the fuel to pass into the crankcase and condense.

Many engines are equipped with a system of crankcase ventilation (Fig. 22-11), which assists in controlling and eliminating trouble caused by water and fuel vapors in the crankcase.

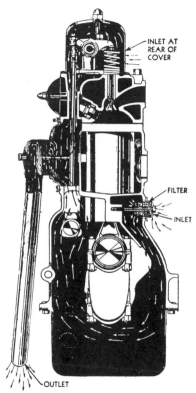

FIG. 22-11. *Crankcase ventilating system.*

A certain amount of carbon and carbon residue eventually forms and becomes deposited on the closed end of the piston, in the ring grooves, and in the cylinder head, as a result of the burning and decomposition of small quantities of lubricating oil in the normal operation of the engine. This carbon is undesirable for several reasons: (1) it often gets very hot and causes preignition of the fuel mixture; (2) it may cause the piston rings to wear rapidly or stick in the grooves; (3) particles work their way into the lubricating oil and contaminate it; (4) particles may get under the valves or cause them to stick or fail to function; and (5) it may accumulate around the spark plug or igniter and result in the failure of the sparking device to ignite the fuel charge.

The use of the correct grade, quality, and amount of lubricating oil and the replacement of worn piston rings and badly worn or damaged pistons and cylinders are the most important requirements in the prevention of excessive carbon deposits.

Oil filters. All tractors are regularly equipped with an oil filter, and it ranks with the air cleaner as a most important accessory for the purpose of reducing engine wear. The purpose of an oil filter is to remove sand, soil, and metal particles, carbon, moisture, and all other undesirable foreign matter from the engine oil during operation.

Oil filters vary considerably in general operation and filtering principle, size, direction of flow, and type of element. Most of them are of the bypass type, and only a limited portion of the oil passes through the filter at any time. The following discussion of typical filters will explain these variations.

Figure 22-12 shows a filter consisting of a cylindrical metal container filled with cotton waste. The oil enters at the base, flows upward through the central tube, and then passes downward through the filtering element to the outlet. When the element becomes saturated the entire unit must be replaced.

Figures 22-5, 22-13, and 22-14 show a popular type of filter with a replaceable filter element. The element consists of one or more accordion-

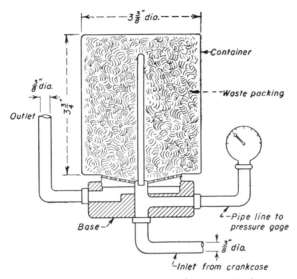

FIG. 22-12. *Replaceable cartridge-type oil filter.*

folded sheets of resin-impregnated creped cellulose (a special kind of heavy paper). The oil entering the filter case completely envelops the element surfaces and finally seeps through the material, passing out to the parts to be lubricated. After a service period of 60 to 150 hr., the case cover is removed and the element is replaced with a new one.

Figure 22-15 shows an engine-lubricating system equipped with a dual filtering system. It will be noted that the oil first passes through a full-flow filter and is then refiltered by a bypass-type filter. Figure 22-16 shows a triple-unit oil filter with a connection to a cooling radiator. Each filter has an edge-type metal element surrounding an absorbent-type element. As shown, the oil filtered by the outer element goes to the bearings, while the oil filtered by the inner element is returned through the metering hole in the stud to the oil pan. Most oil filters are provided with a bypass valve to permit circulation of the oil in case the filter becomes clogged and the oil cannot pass through it.

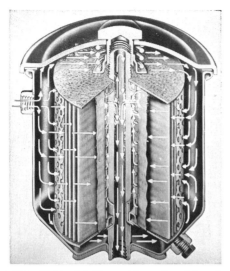

FIG. 22-13. *Oil filter with replaceable cellulose element.* (Courtesy of Purolator Products, Inc.)

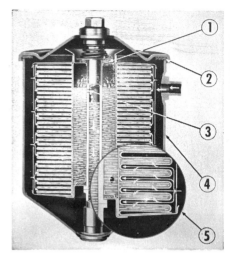

FIG. 22-14. *Oil filter with replaceable element.* (Courtesy of A-C Spark Plug Division, General Motors Corporation.)

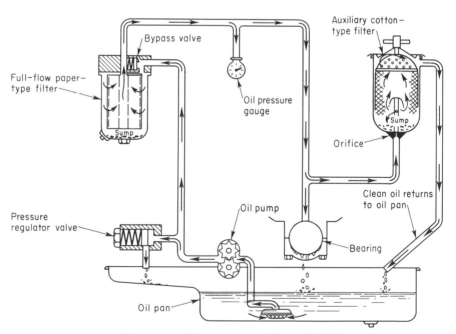

FIG. 22-15. *Lubrication system using dual filters.*

Engine lubrication troubles. As already stated, the primary require-ments for the proper lubrication of an engine under all operating con-ditions are (1) the design and construction of a dependable system of oil circulation and distribution and (2) the selection of a lubricant of the correct grade and quality. However, the satisfactory operation of the

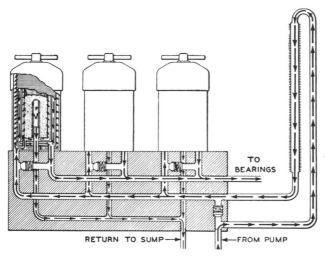

FIG. 22-16. *Oil filtering and cooling system for a diesel tractor.* (Courtesy of Cater-pillar Tractor Company.)

engine from the standpoint of lubrication is also dependent upon certain other conditions. Some of these are:

1. Periodic and regular changing of the oil.

2. Careful observation and regulation of the oil-reservoir supply and the quantity distributed or fed to the parts requiring lubrication.

3. Regular servicing of the oil filter according to instructions.

4. Prevention of pollution of the oil from any or all of the following sources:

    a. Solid matter of a foreign nature, such as dust, dirt, seeds, par-ticles of vegetable matter, iron and steel particles, and so on, which may get into the reservoir through unprotected openings or by carelessness in handling the oil or working around the engine.

    b. Water from leaks in the cooling system or through unprotected openings.

    c. Liquid fuel which may be taken into the cylinders in an un-vaporized condition and, remaining unburned, may get by the piston and rings, diluting the oil.

    d. Particles of carbon due to excess carbon deposits in the combus-tion space and the piston-ring grooves.

Changing oil. Regular and periodic changing of the crankcase oil is very important, not only because it may become polluted as outlined above, but because it becomes thinner and less oily, so to speak, owing to exposure to the high engine temperature and the resultant partial decomposition. No set rules can be laid down and applied to any and all types of engines concerning the best procedure to follow. However, the following general suggestions are more or less uniformly applicable:

1. Change the oil in new or recently overhauled vehicle engines after 500 to 1,000 miles of running, depending on whether it is an automobile, truck, motorcycle, etc.

2. In used or so-called run-in vehicle engines, change the oil every 1,500 to 3,000 miles.

3. In new or recently overhauled tractors, change the oil after 20 to 40 hr. of operation.

4. In used or run-in tractors, change the oil after 60 to 250 hr. of operation according to the manufacturers' instructions.

5. Always drain the engine when hot, as the oil is thinner and will drain out more quickly and more completely.

6. When changing the oil, flush the crankcase, using only a special flushing oil or a similar thin grade of oil. Do not use kerosene for flushing, because it lodges in depressions and pockets and thins the fresh lubricant. In flushing an engine, put in the required amount of flushing oil and operate engine from 30 sec. to 1 min. before draining it out.

7. Clean or change oil-filter element and pump screen, if removable, at recommended interval.

8. In geographic areas experiencing extremes of seasonal temperature, the viscosity of the engine oil should conform to the recommendations of the manufacturer.

Oil consumption. One of the most vital problems connected with the satisfactory lubrication of any internal-combustion engine is that of oil consumption. A limited or reasonable oil consumption commensurate with satisfactory engine performance under all operating conditions is the goal of the designer and the demand of the user.

Oil is consumed or lost in several ways as follows:

1. By working past the piston into the combustion chamber and being burned

2. By escaping from the crankcase as a mist or vapor

3. By leakage

The important factors affecting the oil consumption of a given engine are:

1. Engine speed

2. Engine design and changes due to wear

3. Oil characteristics

Engine speed is the most important factor affecting oil consumption, as indicated by numerous tests as well as actual experience. The reasons for increased oil consumption at increased engine speeds are (1) the higher oil temperature decreases the oil viscosity; and (2) more oil is thrown on the cylinder walls because of the greater pumping pressure and the increased centrifugal force of the crankshaft.

The loss of oil that works past the pistons is commonly termed *oil pumping*. A limited loss in this manner can be expected unless the engine is new or nearly so and is in almost perfect mechanical condition. As the period of service lengthens, the oil loss by pumping increases, because the piston rings and cylinder become worn and carbon accumulates in the ring grooves. The use of special oil-control piston rings and the drilling of small holes in the lower ring grooves appear to be the best means of reducing oil pumping.

Oil viscosity has an important bearing upon oil consumption. However, the practice of using an oil having a viscosity higher than is ordinarily recommended for a given engine, in order to reduce pumping losses, is to be discouraged for the reason that such an oil may prove too heavy to provide proper lubrication, particularly at low temperatures.

Very often two different brands of oil of the same viscosity specifications will vary in their loss characteristics. This variation is probably due to a difference in volatility. Regarding the volatility of lubricating oils and its effect on losses, Wilson [1] states as follows:

Volatility of an oil is a quality which depends very largely upon the process of refining the oil. Even some of the higher priced oils contain an appreciable amount of volatile material.

Since the advent of crankcase ventilation, the matter of volatile material in the oil has become more important because of its effect upon oil consumption. And not all the loss through the ventilating outlet is in the form of vapor, for the draft of air carries along some oil in the form of fog or mist. The amount so carried away depends upon the driving speed. The amount of volatile material, which is lost at high speed, is not only the volatile material contained in the new oil, but also the amount resulting from any breaking up of the oil due to the high temperature reached by that which comes in contact with hot surfaces or gases. Volatility is of little consequence until the oil temperature exceeds 170°F.

Oil leakage. Loss of oil by leakage is usually insignificant unless there is excessive wear in the valve stems and guides and in the outer main crankshaft bearings, or the oil pan gaskets are damaged, or the bolts are not tight. Defective or improperly installed seals for the crankshaft bearings also permit oil leakage and loss.

[1] *Bull. Univ. Wisconsin Eng. Expt. Sta. Ser.* 78.

Worn valve stems and guides encourage excessive oil consumption, because the oil can easily work past the stem and escape around the valve head. In the case of an intake valve, the oil would enter the cylinder and be burned, thus creating carbon deposits. Leaky exhaust valve guides let the oil escape with the exhaust gases into the atmosphere. It is desirable and recommended that a relatively close precision fit be maintained between the valve stem and its guide and that the parts be replaced whenever there is an appreciable increase in this clearance. A recent development to control valve-guide leakage is the use of special neoprene rubber seals located on the spring side of the regular guides.

Clutch and transmission lubrication. Since tractor transmissions consist of alloy-steel gears and precision ball and roller bearings, and since the gear-tooth and bearing pressures are very high, proper lubrication is extremely essential. Clutch lubrication is usually limited to the release or throwout bearing. In some cases, this bearing is grease-packed and permanently lubricated. If periodic lubrication is needed, the lubricant should be applied sparingly in order not to permit excess grease to get on the clutch linings and contact surfaces, where it would create slippage.

Since all tractor transmissions are enclosed in oiltight, dustproof, cast-iron housings, lubrication is accomplished by maintaining an oil level such that all parts either will operate directly in the lubricant or will have it thrown onto them. Plugs are provided for putting in fresh oil, for draining the used oil, and also for testing or indicating the proper level.

The instructions of the manufacturer should be followed in the selection of the lubricant to be used in a tractor transmission. All machines use the regular transmission lubricant recommended for automobiles, trucks, and tractors.

Changing the oil in the transmission is not so important as changing the engine oil. It is not subjected to such high temperatures and, therefore, retains its body more or less indefinitely. Likewise, if proper precautions are taken, very little solid matter should find its way into the oil. Unless the tractor is used almost continuously for tractive work, it is unnecessary to change the transmission lubricant more than once or twice a year. In exceptional cases, however, where the tractor is used extensively under adverse conditions, it may be advisable to change it more often. Best results will be secured by draining the oil when the tractor is warm or, if necessary, by warming up the transmission housing thoroughly with a blowtorch or similar heating arrangement.

Chassis lubrication. There are a number of points on any tractor which cannot be reached or conveniently lubricated by the engine or transmission oil but which require at least periodic lubrication. These are found largely on the so-called chassis parts and include axle bearings, front wheels, steering mechanism including steering rods, knuckles, arms, pins and spindles, and control-lever bearings.

The usual procedure in chassis lubrication is to apply a semifluid lubricant or a soft grease to the bearing by means of a compression grease gun. The high-compression greasing system requires a fitting of some kind at each point to be lubricated. A grease gun, when applied to the fitting, forces the lubricant under great pressure to the bearing. Front-wheel bearings are frequently lubricated by packing the bearings with grease, as in automobiles.

REFERENCES

Additives with a Purpose, *Lubrication*, March, 1957.
Engine Oil Pressure, *Lubrication*, March, 1951.
Extreme Pressure Lubricants, *Lubrication*, June, 1957.
Filters and Purifiers for Oil Circulating Systems, *Lubrication*, March, 1954.
Gear Oil Additives, *Lubrication*, April, 1951.
General Purpose Greases, *Lubrication*, October, 1956.
GEORGI, CARL W., "Motor Oils and Engine Lubrication," Reinhold Publishing Corporation, New York, 1950.
Grease Analysis, *Lubrication*, January, 1956.
LICHTY, L. C., "Internal Combustion Engines," 6th ed., McGraw-Hill Book Company, Inc., New York, 1951.
Low Temperature Sludge in Automotive Gasoline Engines, *Lubrication*, December, 1944, and November, 1945.
Lubricating Oil Additives, *Lubrication*, January, 1946.
Modern Automotive Engine Oils, *Lubrication*, January, 1952.
OBERT, EDWARD F., "Internal Combustion Engines," 2d ed., International Textbook Company, Scranton, Pa., 1950.
Oil Filters for Internal Combustion Engines, *Univ. Nebraska Agr. Expt. Sta. Bull.* 334.
Oil and Gasoline Information for Motorists, *Bull. Univ. Wisconsin Eng. Expt. Sta. Ser.* 78.
Passenger Car Trends Affecting Fuels and Lubricants, *Lubrication*, February, 1958.
The Action of Extreme Pressure Lubricants, *Lubrication*, August, 1944.
Viscosity, *Lubrication*, January and February, 1961.

PROBLEMS AND QUESTIONS

1. Discuss the refining process as it applies to the production of the various kinds of engine oils and other lubricants.

2. Name the various tests that might be made to determine the quality of an engine oil, and state which tests are of greatest significance, particularly to the user of an oil.

3. Explain the meaning of oil viscosity and viscosity index, and describe how each is measured or determined.

4. Explain the A.P.I. motor-oil classification system and the S.A.E. system of designating viscosity.

5. Explain the meaning of lubricating-oil additives, and name the most important of these additives and their specific action.

6. What is a grease, and what are some of the principal types as to composition and adaptability?

7. Describe the systems of engine lubrication most commonly used for automotive-type engines.

8. Describe the common type of oil filter and how it should be serviced.

9. Discuss engine-oil consumption and its causes and control.

23

Tractor Clutches and Transmissions

Some means of disconnecting the power unit from the transmission gears and drive wheels of an automotive vehicle are necessary because (1) the internal-combustion engine must be cranked manually or by a special starting mechanism; (2) this type of engine must attain a certain speed before it will have any power; (3) shifting of the transmission gears must be permitted for the purpose of securing different traveling speeds; and (4) stopping the belt pulley must be permitted without having to stop the engine. All these can be taken care of by placing a clutch between the engine and the transmission gears and belt pulley.

Types of clutches. A number of different kinds of clutches used in tractors in former years are now obsolete. The most important of these are the contracting-band clutch, the cone clutch, and the expanding-shoe clutch. All present-day clutches are of the disk type, and the trend is toward a simple device such as the twin-disk and the single-plate clutch rather than the multiple-disk type.

A satisfactory tractor clutch must fulfill the following requirements: (1) it should not slip, grab, or drag; and (2) it should be convenient, accessible, and easy to operate, adjust, and repair.

Multiple-disk clutch. A multiple-disk clutch (Fig. 23-1) consists of a number of thin metal plates, arranged alternately as driving and driven disks. One set is attached to the flywheel and the other to the clutch shaft and transmission. If the plates are firmly pressed together, the clutch is said to be *engaged* and power is transmitted. This pressure is secured by means of a housing and a set of heavy springs as shown. The clutch throwout collar is attached to the rear part of the housing so that the depression of the operating lever slides the housing backward and compresses the springs. This enlarges the plate space and permits one set to rotate free and independent of the other set.

In the dry-type multiple-disk clutch (Fig. 23-1), the driven plates are faced on each side with friction material. The only part requiring lubrication is the throwout collar. The plates should be kept clean and dry. If slippage develops owing to wear, it can be overcome by increasing the tension of the three springs by tightening up on the nuts.

Single-plate clutch. The single-plate clutch (Figs. 23-2 and 23-3) is a disk-type clutch in which a single, thick, iron plate, faced with friction material on both sides, serves as the driven member. It engages directly with the flywheel on one side and with an unlined iron driving plate

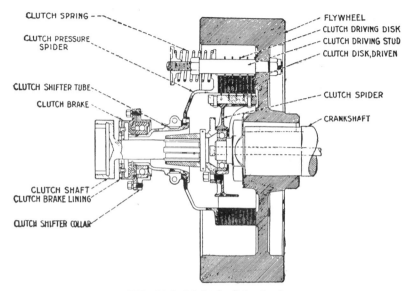

FIG. 23-1. *Multiple-disk clutch.*

on the other. The pressure produced by a number of springs, located between the driving plate and the housing, which is bolted to the fly-wheel, holds the friction surfaces firmly in contact. Three arms are hinged to the housing and have their outer ends connected to eyebolts that screw into the driving plate. When the inner ends of the arms are pushed toward the flywheel by the throwout collar, the driving plate is pulled away from the driven member and the clutch is thereby disengaged.

Dual-type plate clutch. Figure 23-17 shows a cutaway view of a tractor transmission equipped with a dual clutch. This clutch consists of a forward (primary) pressure plate and a dry cushioned disk which is attached to the transmission input shaft and a rearward (secondary) pressure plate and dry disk which is attached to the hydraulic pump and power take-off input shaft. Each pressure plate is spring-loaded by an annular Belleville-type spring which is located between the clutch cover and pressure plate for the secondary disk and the false flywheel ring and pressure plate for the primary disk. The false flywheel ring is interposed between and integrated with the primary and secondary clutch subassemblies and is secured to the flywheel by the same cap screws that attach the clutch cover. In operation, the clutch springs exert pressure against the clutch pressure plates, and this, in turn, transmits the pressure through the disks to the false flywheel ring for the secondary clutch and to the engine flywheel for the primary clutch, thus establishing a firm frictional contact between the respective disks and flywheel faces.

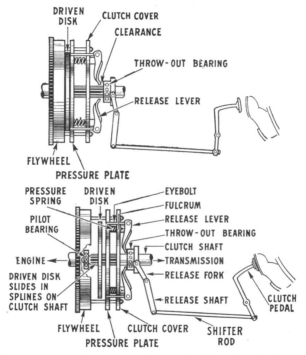

FIG. 23-2. *Construction and operation of a single-plate clutch.* (Courtesy of International Harvester Company.)

FIG. 23-3. *International single-plate clutch.* (Courtesy of International Harvester Company.)

Depressing the clutch pedal through the first range moves the clutch-release fork, which, in turn, contacts the clutch-release bearing, moving it forward on the retainer and bringing it in contact with the clutch-release fingers. The fingers are assembled to the clutch cover. The bearing depresses the fingers which, in turn, cause the primary pressure plate to retract from the disk and release the pressure on it. This inter-

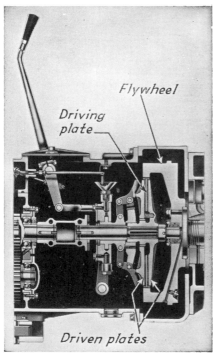

FIG. 23-4. *Caterpillar hand-lever-operated clutch.*

rupts the power flow to the transmission. Depressing the clutch pedal further through the second range causes the same release fingers to move the primary pressure plate to a point where it contacts and causes the secondary pressure plate to retract from its respective disk, thus releasing the frictional contact between the disk and the false flywheel ring face. This interrupts the power flow to the hydraulic pump and power take-off input shaft.

Hand-lever-operated clutches. The single-plate clutch shown in Fig. 23-4 differs in certain respects from those previously described. Instead of using spring pressure to produce positive plate contact, it utilizes short bell-crank levers that press the plates together. Instead of a foot pedal, a hand lever connected to the throwout collar actuates the bell cranks and thereby releases or engages the clutch. Unlike a foot-operated spring-compressed clutch, this clutch when disengaged will remain so without the operator's holding the lever. Another name applied to this clutch is "over center" because the pressure fingers are so linked to the lever and hinged that they snap over center when the clutch is fully engaged.

Figure 23-5 shows another hand-lever-operated clutch, this one having one driving and two driven plates. The flywheel itself does not serve directly as a driving member but has the plate pinned to and rotating with it. The two unlined driven plates carry the power to the transmission. The driving pressure in all clutches of this type is obtained by bell cranks and a sliding cone-shaped collar rather than by heavy springs. Some light springs placed between the driven disks are used merely to ensure the prompt release of the disks when disengagement is desired. The clutch fingers or bell cranks are attached to the threaded adjusting collar. Turning this collar to the right brings the fingers closer to the movable clamping disk and thus compensates for any wear of the lining. The spring-controlled lockpin fits into any one of a series of closely spaced holes and provides for any amount of adjustment desired.

Figure 23-6 illustrates a special, heavy-duty, hand-lever type of clutch which is completely sealed and operates in oil. A special self-contained

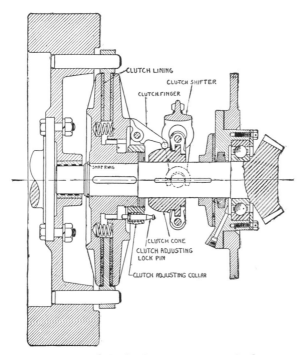

FIG. 23-5. *Twin-disk clutch construction and adjustment.*

oil pump carries oil from a small reservoir in the lower part of the housing to all parts of the clutch, including the metallic-faced plates. The oil aids in reducing wear and dissipating heat.

Figure 23-7 is a disassembled view of a plate-type clutch as built into the belt pulley of a two-cylinder, horizontal engine placed crosswise on the tractor frame. Two driving members—the main driving disk and a sliding driving disk—are attached to the crankshaft and must turn with it. The belt pulley with its attached spur gear is free to turn on and independently of the crankshaft. Also a facing disk and outer adjusting plate are attached to the belt pulley. Thus these three members become the driven parts of the clutch. Two heat-resistant, asbestos-composition clutch facing rings are placed between these driving and driven parts to give better frictional contact and to reduce wear. A hand-lever-operated, over-center type of mechanism built into the pulley provides engagement by compressing the clutch disks and facings together by means of three stud bolts attached to the outer adjustment plate. Periodic adjustment for wear can be made with these bolts.

Clutch troubles and adjustments. The modern tractor clutch, if given ordinary care and attention, will seldom fail to perform satisfactorily.

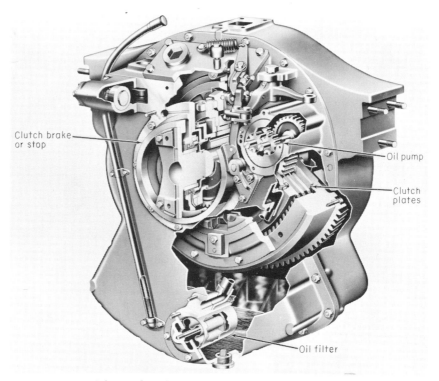

FIG. 23-6. *Special heavy-duty hand-lever–operated clutch.* (Courtesy of Caterpillar Tractor Company.)

Any abnormal or unusual action is nearly always due to one of the following causes:

1. Failure to keep the clutch fully engaged, due to riding the clutch pedal or permitting the hand lever to remain only partly in the engaged position.

2. Failure to keep the clutch adjusted to compensate for normal wear.

3. Permitting oil and grease to get on friction surfaces.

4. Failure to lubricate the throwout collar and bearings as directed.

Slippage is the most common clutch trouble and develops from one or more of the first three causes just named. It is immediately indicated and detected by the tendency of the engine to speed up, when the clutch is engaged and a load is applied, without apparently exerting any appreciable tractive or belt power. Naturally, if for any reason the clutch surfaces are not firmly pressed together, there will be some slippage and wear. If this condition exists for any length of time, it is apparent that undue wear, heat, and other effects will develop which will produce slippage even with the lever fully engaged. The precaution, therefore, is always to keep a clutch either completely disengaged or completely engaged. If it is desired to let the engine run with the tractor standing still, the best practice is to put the gears in neutral and engage the clutch. Leaving the gears engaged and holding the clutch disengaged

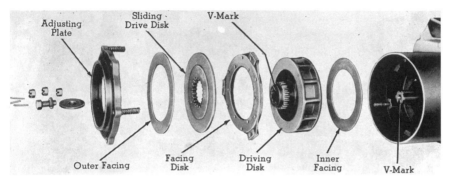

FIG. 23-7. *Belt pulley, hand-lever–operated plate-type clutch.* (Courtesy of Deere and Company.)

causes heating and wearing of the throwout collar and may wear the clutch facings.

A dragging clutch is one that does not completely disengage. It is indicated by failure of the tractor or pulley to stop and by clashing of the gears when shifting. A dragging clutch is usually caused by incorrect adjustment of the clutch or clutch lever, or both.

TRACTOR TRANSMISSIONS

The mechanism involved in transmitting the engine power to the drive wheels or tracks of a tractor ordinarily includes three distinct parts, namely, (1) the change-speed gears, (2) the differential, and (3) the final-drive mechanism. There are some exceptions to this, as will be pointed out later. Unlike the automobile, there is considerable variation in the construction, arrangement, and operation of these three units in the different makes of tractors. In general, a tractor transmission must serve the following purposes:

1. It must provide a means of self-propulsion and the proper speed reduction between the engine crankshaft and the traction members to give the required travel speeds.

2. It must provide for an equalization of the power transmission to the traction members on both gradual and short, quick turns.

3. It must provide a means of reversing the direction of travel.

Gear ratios and travel rates. As in automobiles, the different gear changes in tractors are designated as first, second, third, and so on. However, the fundamental reasons for having three or more speeds are not necessarily the same. In the case of an automobile, there is not nearly so great a speed-reduction ratio between the engine and the rear axle when it is in high gear as there is in a tractor. Therefore, if an attempt were made to start an automobile directly in high gear, either the engine would stall or the car would be subjected to too great a jerk or strain. Consequently, the machine is gradually brought to a certain speed by means of the low and intermediate gears and finally shifted into high without producing undue strain on the engine, gears, or other parts involved. In other words, the primary function of the low and intermediate gears in an automobile is to permit a gradual rather than a sudden speed acceleration. Incidentally, these low-speed gears also provide the gear reduction necessary under unfavorable road conditions, such as mud, sand, and hills.

In tractors, even in high gear, the engine-to-rear-axle speed ratio is rather high, and the machine travels at a very slow rate as compared to an automobile in high gear. Therefore, the machine will start off directly in high gear without first going through low and intermediate. In tractors the speed changes are provided primarily to handle different drawbar loads or to permit a certain field machine to be drawn along at the correct speed. In general, the low gear is for extremely heavy loads or for very slow field speeds. The third and fourth gears are probably the ones that are used the most for plowing, harrowing, and similar work, although lower speeds may be necessary to meet unusual conditions.

Most tractors have four to six speeds forward, and some have as many as eight to twelve depending upon the type of transmission. For wheel tractors, the travel speeds vary from 1.5 to 2.8 m.p.h. in the lowest range to 6.5 to 18.0 m.p.h. in the high range. For track-type tractors, the low range is 1.5 to 2.0 m.p.h. and the high range is 5.0 to 6.0 m.p.h. The high travel speed for wheel tractors permits only a limited pulling effort and is used primarily for pulling trailers, for faster traveling over highways, or in going to and from fields.

The principle involved in securing these different speeds is to bring into mesh with each other certain gears having different numbers of teeth, as shown in Fig. 23-8. For example, in a tractor, the ratio of the engine speed to the rear-axle speed may be 25:1 in high gear and 50:1 in an intermediate gear. This means that in the one case certain smaller gears in the change-gear set, known as driving gears, mesh with other driven gears having a greater number of teeth. In the second case, these

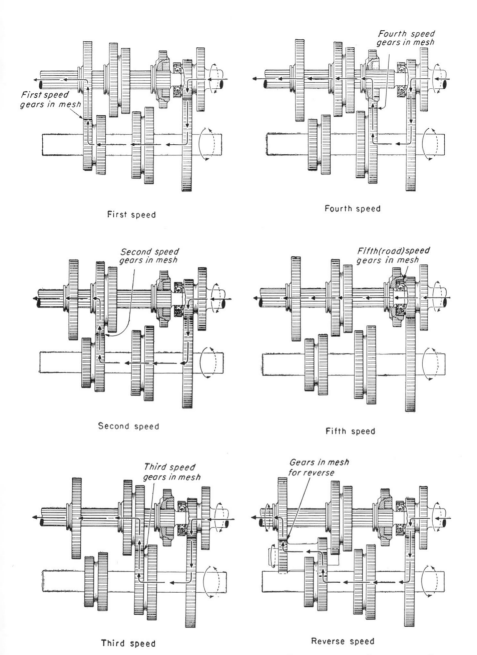

First speed

Fourth speed

Second speed

Fifth speed

Third speed

Reverse speed

FIG. 23-8. *Operation of a typical tractor five-speed transmission.* (Courtesy of International Harvester Company.)

FIG. 23-9. *Three-speed all-purpose tractor transmission.*

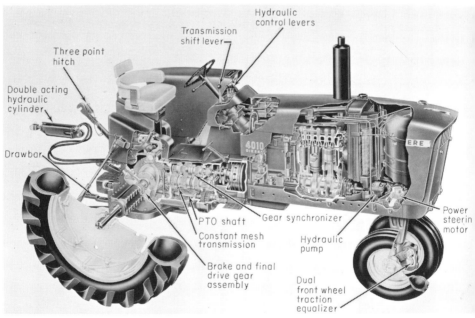

FIG. 23-10. *Deere eight-speed all-purpose tractor transmission.* (Courtesy of Deere and Company.)

same small driving gears are meshed with other driven gears having a still greater number of teeth. Consequently, the speed is reduced proportionately.

Transmission types. The change-speed gears, as well as all other transmission parts of tractors, are made of hardened steel and are completely enclosed and run in a bath of oil. The different speed changes are made by sliding certain gears into or out of mesh with other gears

FIG. 23-11. *Horizontal two-cylinder engine with four-speed transmission.* (Courtesy of Deere and Company.)

having different numbers of teeth. In order to slide the gears and at the same time make them turn with the shaft, the latter is splined; that is, it has a number of ribs running lengthwise and cut integral with it. The gears have corresponding grooves in the hub to receive these splines. The splines and grooves are carefully machined and just enough clearance is allowed to permit the gear to slide freely when lubricated. Such transmissions are known as the selective sliding-gear type. Figure 23-8 illustrates how the different speed changes are obtained and how the power is transmitted in a five-speed gear set.

Figures 23-9 and 23-10 illustrate representative transmission layouts. In each case the engine crankshaft is at right angles to the rear axle and a bevel gear and pinion are necessary at some point in the assembly. Figure 23-11 illustrates a transmission in which bevel gears are unnecessary, because the engine crankshaft is parallel to the rear axle.

Constant-mesh transmissions. A few tractors and most passenger cars, trucks, and other vehicles use helical-type gears (Fig. 23-12) which remain in constant mesh and therefore provide quiet operation. The speed changes are obtained by means of notched and splined collars or sleeves inserted on the main and countershafts between certain gears. In changing speeds, the shifting mechanism moves these collars into or out of mesh with matching notches on the gears but does not slide any gears.

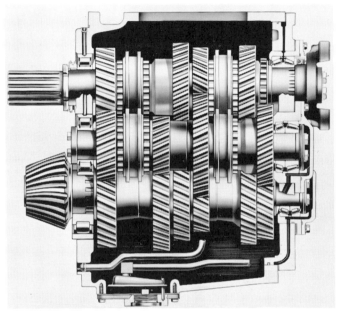

FIG. 23-12. *Constant-mesh transmission with helical gears and shifting collars.* (Courtesy of Caterpillar Tractor Company.)

Hence these collars, as they engage certain gears, provide a positive connection between those gears and their shafts to give the desired speed reduction or increase. Such transmissions when used in passenger cars have the shifting sleeves equipped with synchronizing clutches which bring the mating gears to the same speed before positive engagement occurs. These are known as synchromesh transmissions.

Reverse gear. In reversing the direction of travel of a tractor, since the engine cannot be reversed, it is necessary to interpose an additional gear, known as a reverse idler gear, in the change-gear set. By transmitting the power around through this gear, the direction of rotation of the countershaft, differential, and final-drive mechanism is reversed and the machine moves backward. The reverse gear is in constant mesh with some other gear and therefore turns at all times.

Differentials. A differential is a special arrangement of gears so constructed and located in the transmission system of an automotive machine that it will permit one driving member to rotate slower or faster than the other and at the same time propel its share of the load. For example, referring to Fig. 23-13, it is quite evident that, in making a turn, the outside wheel of an automobile or tractor must travel farther and therefore turn faster than the inside wheel. If some special device were not provided to permit this unequal travel and at the same time equalize the pull, it is obvious that slippage, excessive strain, and abnormal wear would result.

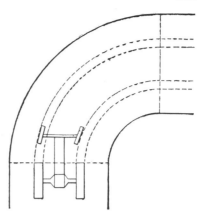

FIG. 23-13. *Sketch showing effect of turning on rear-wheel travel.*

Differential construction. Figure 23-14 shows the construction and important parts of a differential. The operating principles of the bevel-gear-type differential are best understood by referring to Fig. 23-15. The

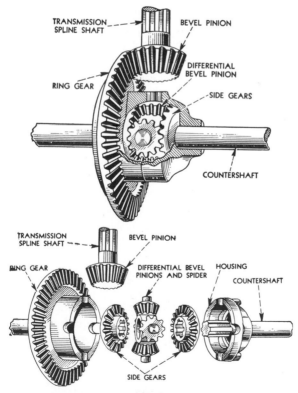

FIG. 23-14. *Construction and parts of a differential gear assembly.* (Courtesy of International Harvester Company.)

main drive pinion B meshes with and drives the large gear C. A differential housing E is bolted rigidly to one side of gear C. This housing may be solid or split and carries one or more studs F, upon each of which is mounted a differential pinion G, which is free to rotate on the stud.

The two halves of the axle or shaft to be driven, namely, K and K_1, are inserted, one from each side as shown, and bevel gears H and H_1 placed on the ends. These two gears and their respective shaft ends are splined or keyed in such a manner that they must turn together. At the

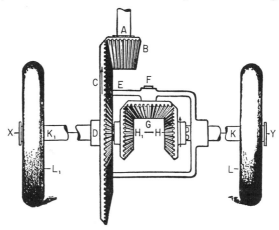

FIG. 23-15. *Differential construction and operation.*

same time, gears H and H_1 mesh with differential pinion G. Main drive gear C and its attached housing E are free to rotate as an independent unit about the shafts K and K_1.

Differential operation. 1. *First condition,* with wheels L and L_1 fastened to outer ends of shafts K and K_1, respectively, and entire mechanism raised up so that the wheels are clear and free to rotate: Power is received by the drive pinion B and in turn is transmitted to gear C, turning it in the direction indicated. This likewise rotates the housing E in the same direction. Since the wheels L and L_1, shafts K and K_1, and gears H and H_1 are free to move, they rotate in the same direction also; that is, the entire mechanism rotates as one unit. The differential pinion G does not turn on its stud F, because the bevel gears H and H_1 are turning at the same rate and, therefore, lock pinion G. Consequently, with this condition existing, that is, with an equal resistance applied to both wheels, the latter will turn at the same rate and the tractor will move straight ahead.

2. *Second condition,* with one wheel locked and the other clear and free to rotate: Suppose wheel L is resting on a rough, firm surface and

wheel L_1 is raised and is free to rotate. Power is again applied to large gear C from pinion B. This again rotates housing E as indicated and carries pinion G around with it. But wheel L and its shaft K are subjected to much greater resistance than wheel L_1 and its shaft K_1; therefore, L, K, and gear H remain stationary. Therefore pinion G, as it is carried around by the housing E, is also forced to turn on its stud F and, in so doing, causes gear H_1, shaft K_1, and wheel L_1 to rotate in the same direction as the drive gear and housing. Thus the pinion G, in making one revolution with the housing E, also makes one complete revolution on its stud by rolling on the stationary gear H. The axle gear H_1 is thus subjected to two rotative actions—one revolution due to its being in mesh with the differential pinion G, which has been bodily revolved about the axis XY, and the other due to the rotation of the pinion G on its stud as it is rolled once around the stationary axle gear H. The free wheel thus makes two complete forward revolutions while the drive gear and housing are making one revolution. This is the condition that causes one wheel of an automobile or tractor to spin while the other remains stationary when there is unequal resistance applied to them, as when one is in soft mud and the other on firm footing.

In a similar manner it will be observed that any difference in the rotation of the wheels is compensated for by the rotation of the differential pinion G on its stud F while also revolving with the entire housing about the axis XY. Any rotation of this differential pinion on its stud means that it rolls on one of the axle gears, and the amount of motion in rolling on one gear is transmitted to the other as additional turning and driving effort. Any retarded motion of one wheel results in accelerated motion of the other. The power and driving force are thus transmitted to the wheels in proportion to the distance each must travel.

Spur-gear differential. A spur-gear-type differential is used in a few cases but is not so common as the bevel type, probably because of difficulty in making it as compact. It does eliminate the spreading action or side thrust that is always present with bevel gearing.

As the name implies, a spur-gear differential uses spur-differential pinions and axle gears instead of bevel pinions and gears. Otherwise it works in exactly the same manner.

Referring to Fig. 23-16, the differential pinions are arranged in pairs and rotate freely on their respective spindles attached to the housing. The two paired pinions mesh with each other, and one in each pair meshes with one of the spur axle gears while the other meshes with the opposite axle gear. With equal resistance applied to both axle shafts and wheels, the entire assembly will rotate as a unit, but the pinions will remain stationary on their studs. On the other hand, if one wheel is held stationary, the spur pinions meshing with this axle gear will roll around on it, and therefore will be rotated on their studs. They, in turn, will drive the other set of pinions meshed with the other axle gear and the latter will be rotated. Therefore, the one axle gear and shaft will be

FIG. 23-16. *Spur-gear differential construction.*

rotated by the rotation of the entire housing and also by the pinions turning on their studs.

The main driving gears, regardless of the type of differential, may be of either the spur, bevel, or worm type. In fact, in automobiles and trucks the main differential gear, often called the ring gear, is usually a spiral spur gear. Some trucks also use a worm gear, while most tractors use a spur gear.

Differential location. In some tractors the differential is located on the rear axle, the same as in all automobiles, as shown by Fig. 23-17. In such cases both drive wheels are fastened to the axle halves, and the latter transmit the power to the wheels in addition to supporting the machine. This is known as live-axle construction.

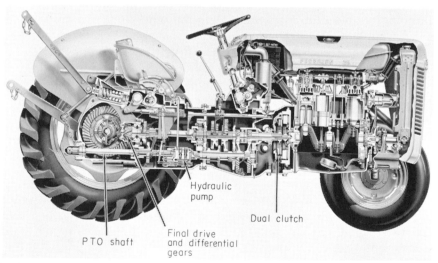

Hydraulic
pump

Dual clutch

PTO shaft

Final drive
and differential
gears

FIG. 23-17. *Cutaway view of a four-wheel tractor with dual-range six-speed transmission and hydraulic controls.* (Courtesy of Massey-Ferguson, Inc.)

In the transmission shown by Figs. 23-9 and 23-11, the differential is on a countershaft that carries two spur pinions, one on each side of the assembly. These pinions mesh directly with two larger spur gears on the inner ends of the two-piece axle. The wheels are attached to the outer ends of the axle shafts so that the latter transmit the power to the wheels. Thus, each wheel has its own driving gears and axle shaft and can rotate independently. This again is a live axle. Figure 23-20 illustrates this same type of differential location and power transmission, but roller chains and sprockets are used instead of gears.

Differential locks. As previously explained, one objection to the common bevel gear differential is that if the truck or tractor is moving forward in a straight line and either driving wheel encounters poor traction

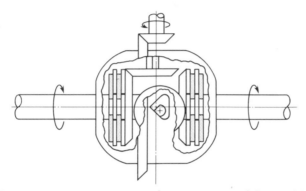

FIG. 23-18. *Automatic or unequal-torque type of differential lock.*

conditions such as a smooth wet surface or a mud hole, slippage occurs and that member turns faster than the wheel with good traction. Such a condition either reduces the travel rate of the vehicle or stops it entirely if resistance to the slipping wheel approaches zero. The basic solution for overcoming this difficulty is either to apply a braking action to the spinning wheel or to lock the differential in such a manner as to make both wheels turn together. Since tractors are equipped with independent drive-wheel brakes, it is possible to use them to lock partially and slow down the wheel which is slipping, thereby increasing the tractive effort of the other wheel and permitting movement of the entire machine. The use of the tractor brakes in this manner to overcome drive-wheel slippage depends on operator control, causes brake wear, wastes some engine power, and encourages engine stalling.

Differential locks, generally, are of two types. The first is one which is built into the differential assembly (Fig. 23-18) and functions automatically with variations in wheel traction, slippage, and turning radii. Geiger [1] states:

[1] M. L. Geiger, Value of Differential Locks for Farm Tractors, *Agr. Eng.*, Vol. 42, No. 3.

This type is sometimes called a torque bias or unequal torque differential. Driving torque causes locking by engagement of the friction clutch on each side through cam actuation. When one wheel spins, the cam action is reversed which releases the friction clutch at the slipping wheel and thus the greater portion of available torque is directed to the better traction wheel. The action is similar in a turn in that the outer wheel overruns and the inner wheel drives.

This type of automotive locking differential was not adapted to the common two-wheel-drive tractors because tractors must have the outside wheels driving during turns, individual wheel braking, and short turning radii. With this automotive locking differential, the driving is done by the inner rear wheel in turns, while the outside tractor wheel must drive to pull heavy loads in

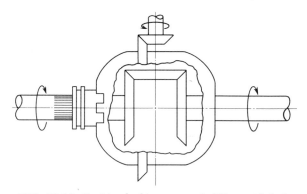

FIG. 23-19. *Positive-locking type of differential lock.*

turns. Individual wheel braking assists even a bare tractor in making sharp turns on loose soil surfaces. The desired turning radii of tractors for better maneuverability are very short compared to those of automobiles and trucks.

A second type of differential lock is the positive-locking type shown in Fig. 23-19 and described by Geiger [1] as follows:

One axle shaft is locked to the differential carrier through a sliding jaw clutch. This unit acts as a conventional differential when not engaged. Foot pedal actuation is normally used to engage the lock for emergency traction use only. Foot-pedal release returns the differential to conventional action. The foot-pedal engaging operation is somewhat equivalent to applying a brake, but no power is lost. Some differential locks are hand-operated and others have automatic control.

As a result of his investigations of differential locks for tractors Geiger [1] summarizes the situation as follows:

A differential lock may meet acceptance if the extra cost is reasonable. It is generally known to farmers that, in plowing, land wheels slip more than the

[1] M. L. Geiger, Value of Differential Locks for Farm Tractors, *Agr. Eng.*, Vol. 42, No. 3.

furrow wheels unless they have added weight. However, most farmers do not realize that the differences in slippage between the drive wheels are usually quite small.

One potential safety hazard with some differential-lock designs is the possibility of the operator failing to disengage the lock before reaching a turn.

Our results indicate that a differential lock is of little value in normal field operations, at least in most conditions in the United States. A little added weight on the land wheel is equivalent to the lock in equalizing wheel slippage in common field conditions. While compaction due to added weight should not be overlooked, it should be noted that the extra weight, in general, balances the weight distribution of the two drive wheels in plowing by bringing the land wheel weight up to the furrow wheel weight.

The other major deterrent to the differential lock is the essentially equivalent effect of braking for sustaining motion through intermittent areas of poor tractive conditions, providing sufficient engine power is available to offset the brake power loss. Brakes, of course, are already available as standard equipment for such use. The trend is to larger tractors which should have more reserve power available to meet this emergency.

Final drives. The illustrations accompanying this chapter show quite clearly the common types of final drives for tractors, that is, the means by which the power is transmitted finally to the rear axle and wheels. With the differential located on the rear axle, the final drive usually consists of a heavy bevel pinion on the countershaft meshing with a large bevel differential gear.

Figure 23-20 illustrates final drive by sprocket wheels and roller chain. This type of drive provides a limited amount of flexibility and thereby relieves the engine, clutch, and other parts of excessive shock under certain conditions. A chain final drive may also simplify the transmission construction by eliminating extra shafts, gears, and bearings, which would otherwise be required to give the proper speed reduction and carry the power back from the change-speed gears to the rear axle.

The principal objection to a chain drive is the tendency toward looseness due to wear and slight stretching. As will be noted, these drives are well enclosed and run in a bath of oil, so that once the chain is "broken in" it will wear very little and therefore slacken very slowly. Provision is made in most cases to take up the chains from time to time, as necessary. Of course, a small amount of slack should always be allowed. Otherwise the wear and power loss are apt to be greater than with the chain too loose.

Figure 23-21 shows a combined final drive gear and brake arrangement used on certain models of Deere and Ford tractors. It consists of a planetary gear set with the disk-braking assembly built into it. A complete unit is used to drive and brake each rear wheel, the individual units being located on each side of the differential gear. The planetary gear set provides some speed reduction between the transmission and the rear axles. The disk brakes, which are completely enclosed and operate in the transmission oil, are actuated by hydraulic pressure when the pedals are depressed.

Tractor brakes. Transmission brakes of some kind are essential on a tractor to control it on steep hills, to hold it stationary in doing belt work, and for making quick short turns. They are sometimes called dif-

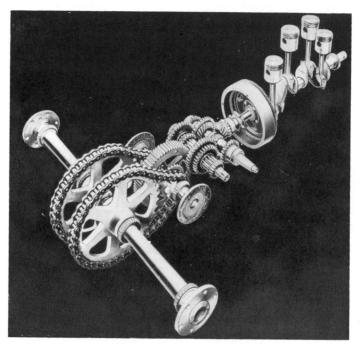

FIG. 23-20. *Transmission using roller chains for final drive.*

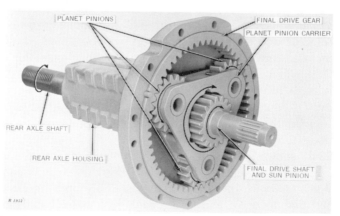

FIG. 23-21. *Planetary-type final drive gear and brake assembly.* (Courtesy of Deere and Company.)

ferential brakes because they are located on each side of the differential gear and shaft assembly. They are operated by individual foot levers which can be locked independently or interlocked, if necessary, to hold the tractor stationary.

Three types of brakes are used, namely, (1) contracting band, (2) expanding shoe (Fig. 23-22), and (3) self-energizing disk (Fig. 23-23).

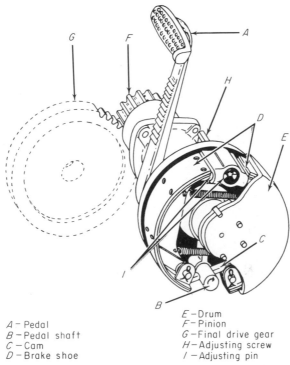

A – Pedal	E – Drum
B – Pedal shaft	F – Pinion
C – Cam	G – Final drive gear
D – Brake shoe	H – Adjusting screw
	I – Adjusting pin

FIG. 23-22. *Expanding-shoe type of differential brake.*

In all cases they are well enclosed and protected and provision is made for periodic adjustment. Linings are made of wear- and heat-resistant material and are replaceable.

One of the essentials of a row-crop tractor is the ability to make a short, quick turn with ease in row-crop operations in order to save time at the ends. These tractors, therefore, are provided with two foot-operated differential brakes, which permit holding one driver practically stationary and turning on it as a pivot.

Brake linings and clutch facings. The principal requirements for brake linings and clutch facings are (1) maintenance of the desired coefficient of friction over a wide range of operating conditions, (2) ability to withstand temperatures up to as high as 600 to 1000°F. without breakdown or physical injury, (3) resistance to glazing and scoring, and (4) wear resistance and long life.

In general, brake and clutch materials are classified as (1) those having an asbestos base and (2) those using powdered or sintered metals as the friction material. Asbestos brake linings are of two types, namely, woven and molded. In the manufacture of the woven facing, long-fiber asbestos, together with a small percentage of cotton, is twisted around fine brass wires to form threads. These threads are then woven into a band of proper width and saturated with synthetic drying resins, drying oils, and asphalt to bind the fibers together when compressed.

Molded lining and facing materials contain 50 per cent or more of short-fiber asbestos plus such wear-improving ingredients as particles of soft brass and powdered lead and zinc. The ingredients are molded under pressure by rolling and extrusion and impregnated with a binder such as graphite or ground soft rubber. Molded linings and facings are used more extensively than woven materials because of better resistance to high temperatures.

FIG. 23-23. *Self-energizing disk brake.* (Courtesy of International Harvester Company.)

Powdered and sintered metal linings and facings are made in two steps. First, the friction material such as a mixture of powdered bronze, graphite, tin, and other metals and certain nonmetallic materials is compressed under a pressure of 10 to 40 tons per sq. in. into sheets and wafers. This friction wafer is then bonded by heat-treatment in a special furnace to a copper-plated steel sheet or core. The core may be faced with the friction wafer on one or both sides. This type of brake material is more expensive, but it withstands relatively high temperatures, is not as much affected by water and oil, and requires less space than asbestos linings for the same amount of energy involved.

Some clutches and brakes operate in oil. This, in itself, reduces the coefficient of friction. Hence such devices require the best type of lining available such as a special grade of molded asbestos material or a powdered and sintered metal material. Also any oil-type clutch or brake requires a much higher pressure per unit of surface area.

The coefficients of sliding friction for dry brake linings and clutch facings are as follows:

Asbestos base, woven..................... 0.30–0.55
Asbestos base, molded.................... 0.20–0.47
Powdered metals........................ 0.20–0.60

For the same materials operating in oil, the coefficient would be 0.07 to 0.15.

Clutch facings and brake linings are attached to their supporting metal members by rivets or by bonding the friction element directly to the metal with synthetic resin or special cement. The bonding process is

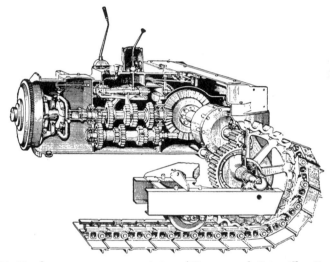

FIG. 23-24. *Track-type tractor transmission.* (Courtesy of Caterpillar Tractor Company.)

used more extensively because it eliminates rivet holes and possible contact of rivet heads with the metal clutch or brake member.

Track-type tractor transmissions. The transmissions for the track-type tractors are not unlike those in wheel machines except that the steering mechanism is incorporated in them. That is, the ordinary wheel tractor is propelled by the rear wheels and guided by means of the front wheels, whereas the conventional track-type tractor, having but two traction members, must be both propelled and guided through them.

Caterpillar transmission. Figure 23-24 shows the change-gear set for the Caterpillar tractor. The power is transmitted to a countershaft by means of bevel gears; thence, through two steering clutches located on this countershaft on each side of the bevel gear, to the spur-type final-drive gears; and thence to the sprocket. Steering is accomplished through the multiple-dry-disk steering clutches; that is, by means of hand levers, either clutch can be disengaged, which obviously cuts off the power to that particular track and causes the tractor to make a turn. Each clutch is equipped with a foot-operated brake which acts on the outside of the

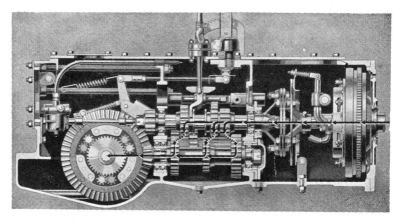

FIG. 23-25. *Track-type transmission with spur-gear differential.*

FIG. 23-26. *Differential gear and steering drums used on track-type tractor: 1 and 2, differential pinions; 3 and 4, external steering-drum pinions; 5 and 6, steering-drum gears; 7, main drive gear; 8 and 9, main drive and differential gears; 10, steering drums.*

clutch drum carrying the driven plates. If a quick, short turn is desired, not only is the clutch released but the brake for that particular clutch is actuated and the track movement virtually stopped on the one side. With all the power going to the other track, the machine obviously will turn very short. By pressing on both brakes at the same time, the machine can be stopped almost instantly. It should be noted that a differential is unnecessary in the Caterpillar transmission.

Oliver transmission. The Oliver transmission (Fig. 23-25) has the same general arrangement as the Caterpillar but uses a differential and brake for steering instead of special clutches. The spur-gear differential (Fig. 23-26) is located directly back of the change-speed gears in the center of the countershaft. A brake drum and band are placed on each side of the differential, as shown. The drum carries a spur gear that meshes with three spur pinions. The latter, in turn, are attached to the three differential spur pinions that mesh with the differential shaft gear on that particular side. Therefore, if the brake band is tightened on one side or the other, that particular differential gear and shaft will turn slower, the track will slow down, and the machine will turn in that direction. The tractor is steered by two hand levers that control the steering brakes.

SPECIAL TRANSMISSION TYPES

A number of wheel tractors are equipped with special transmissions which, in general, have two specific advantages. First, a greater number and range of travel speeds are available and, second, provision is made for shifting from the "low-range" to the "high-range" speeds, or vice versa, while the tractor is in motion and without disengaging the master clutch and coming to a dead stop. These advantages, in turn, permit a closer and more convenient adjustment and faster response of power, torque, and tractive ability of the tractor to the specific drawbar load conditions and requirements.

Farmall torque amplifier. This transmission is equipped with an additional clutch and gear-set unit which permits doubling the number of travel speeds of the ordinary sliding gear unit. The torque-amplifying unit (Fig. 23-27) consists of a planetary gear assembly and a hand-lever-operated disk clutch located between the main clutch and the regular transmission. In direct drive, the torque amplifier clutch is engaged and the power is transmitted directly by the planetary unit to the main transmission drive gear. If greater torque and a reduced travel speed are needed, the amplifier clutch is disengaged which results in the power being transmitted through the planetary pinions of the unit. These pinions are of such a size that they create a reduction in the speed of the main transmission gear and, consequently, a reduction in all travel speeds. This change in torque and travel speed can be made without releasing the master clutch or stopping the tractor.

Allis-Chalmers dual-range transmission. The Allis-Chalmers dual-range transmission (Fig. 23-28) uses a spur-gear reduction unit which is inserted between the main drive shaft and the power take-off drive shaft.

A special double-unit, over-center, hand-lever-operated disk clutch which runs in oil has three positions, namely, "low-range," "high-range," and "neutral." The change from one range to the other can be made by means of this clutch while the tractor is moving. The oil bath prevents excessive heating and wear of the plates during shifting.

Ford power-shift transmission. A special type of transmission (Fig. 23-29) has been developed for Ford tractors known as Select-O-Speed. It consists of four planetary gear units arranged one behind the other. The speed changes are obtained by three hydraulic clutches and three brakes on the first three planetary gear units. The fourth unit at the

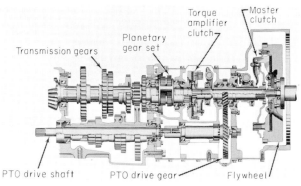

FIG. 23-27. *International Farmall torque amplifier or dual-range transmission.* (Courtesy of International Harvester Company.)

rear is a constant reduction. Of the four planetary sets, the middle two are controlled to give five forward and one reverse speed. The front set gives either overdrive or direct, making a total of ten forward and two reverse speeds. The brakes and clutches are actuated hydraulically by a control-valve assembly, the valves being controlled by a selector indicator and a lever (Fig. 23-30). Also a neutral and a parking position are provided. A constantly driven pump in the forward end of the transmission provides hydraulic pressure for all control functions and for lubrication. Shifting from one speed to another can be done quickly without stopping because the gears are in constant mesh. An additional foot-pedal-operated control is provided to maneuver the tractor slowly for hitching and unhitching and for starting loads slowly.

Deere Syncro-Range transmission. The transmission used in some models of Deere tractors has eight forward and three reverse speeds for each of three throttle positions or engine speeds. As noted in Fig. 23-10, the helical gears remain in constant mesh and speed changes are made by sliding collars located between the gears. Referring to Fig. 23-31, the shift quadrant has four stations plus a "park" and a "tow" position. Three of the stations have two forward and a reverse speed each, while

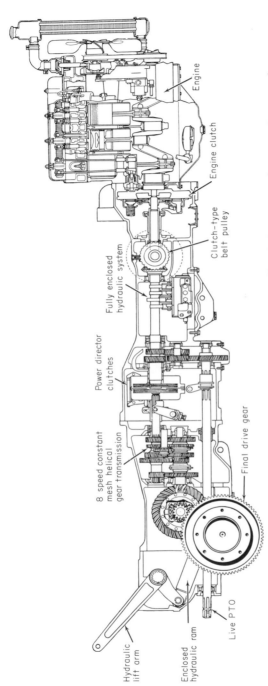

FIG. 23-28. *Allis-Chalmers dual-range transmission.* (Courtesy of Allis-Chalmers Manufacturing Company.)

Engine

Engine clutch

Clutch-type
belt pulley

Fully enclosed
hydraulic system

Power director
clutches

8 speed constant
mesh helical
gear transmission

Final drive gear

Hydraulic
lift arm

Enclosed
hydraulic ram

Live PTO

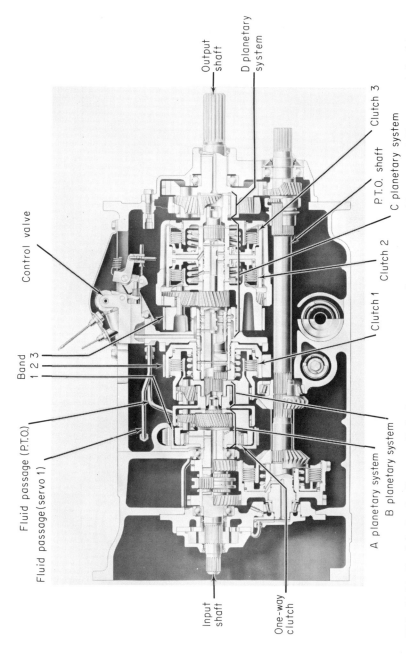

Input shaft

One-way clutch

A planetary system
B planetary system

Clutch 1
Clutch 2

P.T.O. shaft
C planetary system

Clutch 3

D planetary system

Output shaft

Band
1 2 3

Control valve

Fluid passage (P.T.O.)

Fluid passage (servo 1)

FIG. 23-29. *Ford hydraulically controlled planetary-type, ten-speed transmission.* (Courtesy of Tractor and Implement Division, Ford Motor Company.)

the fourth station has two forward speeds only. To operate the tractor, the lever is first shifted to one of the stations, depending upon the speed desired. Then, within this station, it is possible to shift from one forward speed to the other while the tractor is in motion. To shift from one station to another, the clutch pedal is depressed and the tractor stopped, and then the lever is shifted to neutral and to the new station and the desired gear.

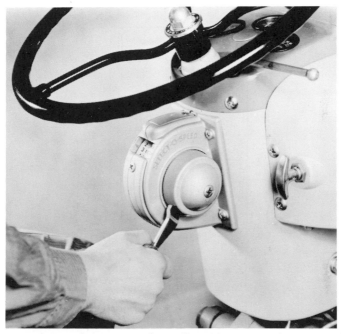

FIG. 23-30. *Ford transmission gear-selector lever.* (Courtesy of Tractor and Implement Division, Ford Motor Company.)

Hydraulic transmission devices. The utilization of the energy of a fluid in motion or under pressure for the purpose of transmitting power in automotive vehicles and tractors is now widely practiced. The principal advantages are: (1) manual gear shifting is either eliminated or simplified; (2) additional torque multiplication is automatically applied to any gear ratio to meet varying load demands; (3) the engine can run at an efficient speed under heavy load conditions; (4) engine stalling is prevented; and (5) smoother vehicle performance over a wide range of engine and travel speeds is obtained. The two general types of hydraulic drives are (1) the fluid coupling or drive and (2) the torque converter. The fluid coupling (also called *fluid drive, fluid flywheel,* or *fluid clutch*) consists of a driving member or impeller with radial vanes, a driven member or runner with similar vanes, and a cover which is welded to the driving member to form a housing. The entire assembly is mounted on the engine crankshaft in place of the conventional flywheel and is about three-fourths filled with a special oil. The driven shaft is made oil-tight with a special spring-loaded sealing ring. When the crankshaft

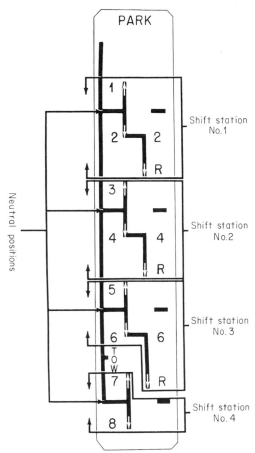

FIG. 23-31. *Deere Syncro-Range transmission shift lever and quadrant.* (Courtesy of Deere and Company.)

rotates, the oil is thrown by centrifugal force from the center to the out-side edge of the impeller between the vanes. This increases the velocity of the oil and its energy. It then enters the runner vanes at the outside and flows toward the center, imparting rotation to the runner. The oil circulates as long as the impeller and runner rotate at different speeds, but when they rotate at the same speed, circulation stops. A fluid coupling does not increase the applied torque but merely transmits all torque exerted on it when the runner speed approximates the impeller speed. Since the amount of slip is determined by the torque required by the driven member, the slip is 100 per cent when the vehicle is stationary but drops quickly as the vehicle gathers speed. Under certain conditions the slip may be 1 per cent or less. Advantages claimed for a fluid coupling are that (1) it provides a cushion effect between the engine and transmission and thus eliminates sudden jerks and strains, and (2) it helps to control and eliminate vibration. Figure 23-32 shows a fluid coupling with conventional plate clutch to permit shifting of gears.

The torque converter is a hydraulic device similar to the fluid coupling in that the power is transmitted entirely by hydraulic means. However, it differs in construction and operation from the fluid coupling in such a way that the engine torque is actually multiplied several times under certain conditions. The term *torque converter* is, therefore, a misnomer, and *torque multiplier* would seem more appropriate.

The mechanism consists of four basic parts, namely, (1) the pump rotor driven by the engine, (2) the turbine or driven member connected to the transmission, (3) the stators or reactors, and (4) the housing or hydraulic chamber. Referring to Fig. 23-33,

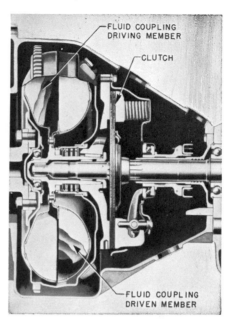

FIG. 23-32. *Fluid-coupling–type flywheel with plate clutch.* (Courtesy of Chrysler Corporation.)

the pump, driven by the engine, throws the fluid outward and gives it kinetic energy. As the fluid strikes the turbine blades, it tends to induce rotation of the latter. If the load on the output shaft is too great, little or no rotation will result; the fluid will rebound from these blades, and its direction of flow will be reversed. But only a small portion of the fluid energy is lost, and because of the shape of the hydraulic chamber, the fluid is forced to flow through a set of reactor blades attached to the inner wall of the chamber. This reverses the direction of motion again; that is, the first set of reactor blades causes the fluid to rebound again. This time, instead of being forced outward, it is forced downward through a second set of turbine blades, where it again attempts to rotate the output shaft in the same direction as the engine is turning. In passing through the second set of turbine blades, more of the energy is utilized and the direction is again reversed. Again some energy is spent, and the fluid is forced inward toward the center of the chamber through a second set of reactor blades and finally to the third and last set of turbine blades on the output shaft. Here the remaining energy in the fluid is spent, and it is conducted by this third set of turbine blades in toward the center of the centrifugal pump, where it started its cycle.

If the load on the output shaft is small, the blades will be rotated easily and the greater part of the energy in the fluid will be spent at the first set of blades with no reversal of the fluid direction taking place. As

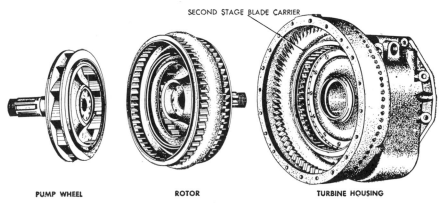

SECOND STAGE BLADE CARRIER

PUMP WHEEL   ROTOR   TURBINE HOUSING

FIG. 23-33. *Principal parts of a hydrokinetic torque converter.* (Courtesy of GMC Truck and Coach Division, General Motors Corporation.)

the fluid is forced to flow through the remainder of the blades, there would be no further push exerted on the output shaft. Multiplication of input torque depends upon the number of times the direction of oil flow is reversed by the driven rotor blades before its energy is spent and upon the completeness of reversal. Reversal of flow is complete only when the turbine or rotor blades are stationary. If the rotor blades move with the oil, the torque decreases accordingly. Therefore, the multipli-. cation of torque is at its maximum when the driven rotor is stationary, or when starting a motionless vehicle. It is at a minimum when the rotating speed of the driven shaft is approximately the same as that of the driving rotor, or when the vehicle is fully in motion. Maximum multiplication of torque is approximately 4.8:1.

Throughout the cycle of operation it must be remembered that power or energy cannot be increased. Consequently, if the torque is increased, the speed is correspondingly reduced. The natural losses incurred in circulating the fluid, due to the internal friction of the fluid itself and the friction of the reactor blades, also contribute to the loss in efficiency of the unit. These losses, however, are more than offset by the fact that an automatic torque ratio between the engine and drive members is maintained throughout the speed range of the vehicle with the engine at a constant throttle setting.

From the foregoing, it will be noted that maximum torque at the output shaft is obtained when the vehicle is stationary and the torque decreases as the vehicle speed increases. The efficiency of the unit increases to a point of slightly over 80 per cent, when the output shaft speed reaches a point of one-half to two-thirds of engine speed, and then efficiency drops off. Hence, if vehicle speeds of greater ranges are

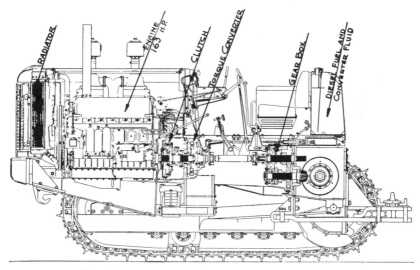

FIG. 23-34. *Track-type tractor equipped with torque-converter drive.* (Courtesy of Allis-Chalmers Manufacturing Company.)

desired, a selective transmission must be incorporated or a sacrifice of efficiency and overheating will result. Even during normal operation, a means must be provided for cooling the fluid as well as an expansion tank to accommodate its volumetric increase due to expansion.

Heat generated within the converter is directly proportional to its loss in efficiency; since it is operated normally above 70 per cent efficiency, cooling radiators capable of dissipating 30 per cent of the maximum engine horsepower must be provided. Circulation of fluid through the radiator is obtained by utilizing the pressure differential across the converter pump. This unit does not operate well when cold, because the thickened fluid does not circulate readily. For this reason a very thin fluid is used, ranging from an S.A.E. 10 engine oil to a straight diesel fuel.

Tractor torque converters. Figure 23-34 illustrates the application of the hydraulic torque converter to a tractor transmission. A conventional sliding gear transmission provides the necessary range of travel speeds

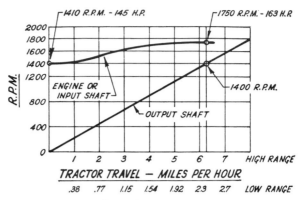

FIG. 23-35. *Curves showing relationship of engine speed and travel speed with torque-converter transmission.* (Courtesy of Allis-Chalmers Manufacturing Company.)

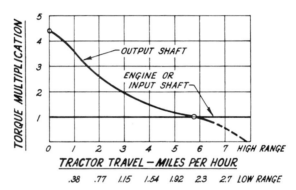

FIG. 23-36. *Curve showing relationship of engine speed and output torque with torque-converter transmission.* (Courtesy of Allis-Chalmers Manufacturing Company.)

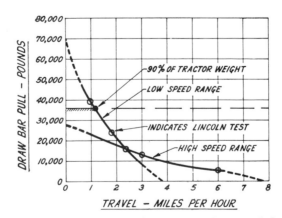

FIG. 23-37. *Curves showing relationship between travel rate and drawbar pull with torque-converter transmission.* (Courtesy of Allis-Chalmers Manufacturing Company.)

and torque variation. The torque converter serves to multiply the torque applied to the rear wheels regardless of the selected travel speed but, at the same time, prevents engine overload and stalling. A plate clutch is used to disconnect the power when shifting gears.

The performance characteristics of such a tractor, as reported by Frudden,[1] are shown by Figs. 23-35 to 23-37. Figure 23-35 shows the relationship between tractor travel rate and engine speed. As the load is started with zero tractor speed, the engine settles at 1,410 r.p.m., where it develops 145 hp. As the output shaft picks up speed and the travel speed increases, the engine speed also increases until, at a travel rate of 6½ m.p.h., the engine runs at 1,750 r.p.m. and delivers 163 hp. Figure 23-36 shows the relationship between engine speed and output torque and that they are equal at 5¾ m.p.h. Figure 23-37 shows the relationship between travel rate and drawbar pull. It will be noted that in low gear a theoretical drawbar pull of 70,000 lb. is indicated. However, owing to slippage, the actual maximum pull is limited to about 90 per cent of the tractor weight, or 36,000 lb.

Automatic transmissions. An automatic transmission is one which is so constructed that manual shifting of gears to obtain the different travel speeds is eliminated and the progressive gear changes are performed by mechanical means within the unit itself. A fluid coupling or torque converter unit is a part of the complete assembly. The speed changes are brought about by the hydraulic pressure of a special oil maintained by a pump. This pressure, by means of control valves, actuates planetary gear sets, which in turn create the necessary speed changes. A selector lever permits shifting to reverse, low-gear, and parking positions. The use of automatic transmissions is confined largely to automobiles.

Planetary gear unit. The preceding discussion of special transmissions has shown that in most instances a planetary gear set is utilized in some manner to obtain certain speed and torque changes. For this reason, a knowledge of the basic construction and operation of the planetary gear set is important. Referring to Fig. 23-38, a planetary gear set consists of four basic parts: a central sun gear, two or more planet gears, a planet-gear carrier, and a large outer (internal) gear.

All gears are in constant mesh with each other and the planet gears turn free on their spindles. By incorporating a clutch and a brake in the assembly, it can serve as a clutch, a direct coupling, a reduction gear, or as a reversing gear. Referring to Fig. 23-38, these conditions and the method of producing them are as follows:

1. *Forward drive and major torque multiplication.* If the internal gear is held stationary while the sun gear is driven clockwise, the planet gears

[1] *Agr. Eng.*, Vol. 30, No. 9.

are rotated counterclockwise around their own axes. Since they are also meshed with the stationary internal gear, they must "walk" clockwise around the sun gear and thereby rotate their planet carrier in a clockwise direction at a much lower rotational speed than the sun gear and with correspondingly higher torque.

2. *Forward drive and minor torque multiplication.* If the sun gear is held stationary while the internal gear is driven clockwise, a similar

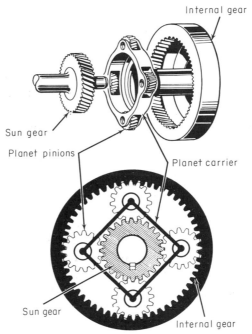

FIG. 23-38. *Construction of a planetary gear assembly.* (Courtesy of Texaco.)

action but of lesser effect occurs. In this case the internal gear drives the planets clockwise and forces them to "walk" clockwise around the stationary sun gear, carrying their planet carrier clockwise at a lower speed with higher torque than the internal gear.

3. *Direct-drive coupling.* If any two of the three major assemblies of a planetary gear set are locked together in some manner, the entire set is locked and rotates as a solid unit or coupling which merely transmits speed and torque without changing either.

4. *Neutral or idling position.* If power is applied to any one of the three planetary gear major assemblies, and neither of the other two is restrained, no torque is transmitted and the elements merely rotate or "idle" in their neutral position.

5. *Reverse.* If power is applied to the sun gear in a clockwise direction and the planetary carrier is restrained, then the planets must rotate

counterclockwise and drive the internal gear in a counterclockwise or reverse direction from the input sun gear.

REFERENCES

BARGER, E. L., W. M. CARLETON, E. G. McKIBBEN, and ROY BAINER, "Tractors and Their Power Units," John Wiley & Sons, Inc., New York, 1952.

CROUSE, W. H., "Automotive Transmissions and Power Trains," McGraw-Hill Book Company, Inc., New York, 1959.

Development of the Hydra-matic Automatic Transmission, *Gen. Motors Eng. J.*, Vol. 1, No. 7.

EGER, G. W., and C. A. RAMSEL, Power Shift Transmission for Track-type Tractors, *Agr. Eng.*, Vol. 41, No. 12.

ERWIN, R. E., and C. T. O'HARROW, Tractor Transmission Responds to Fingertip Control, *Agr. Eng.*, Vol. 40, No. 4.

FERGUSON, H. A., New Farmall Torque Amplifier, *Agr. Eng.*, Vol. 35, No. 10.

Fluid Couplings and Torque Converters for Industrial Equipment, *Lubrication*, February, 1950.

FRUDDEN, C. E., Applications of Torque Converters in Farm Machines, *Agr. Eng.*, Vol. 30, No. 9.

GEIGER, LYNNE, Value of Differential Locks for Farm Tractors, *Agr. Eng.*, Vol. 42, No. 3.

HELDT, P. M., "Torque Converters or Transmission," 5th ed., Chilton Company, Philadelphia, 1956.

MOSES, BEN D., and KENNETH R. FROST, "Farm Power," John Wiley & Sons, Inc., New York, 1952.

Operating Principles of Buick's Twin-turbine Dynaflow Torque Converter, *Gen. Motors Eng. J.*, Vol. 1, No. 8.

SIMPSON, H. W., Evolution in Tractor Transmissions, *Agr. Eng.*, Vol. 40, No. 6.

The Hydra-matic 1939 through 1956, *Lubrication*, February, 1956.

PROBLEMS AND QUESTIONS

1. Explain the construction and operation of (*a*) multiple-disk clutch, (*b*) single-plate, foot-operated clutch, and (*c*) hand-lever-operated clutch.

2. What are the important characteristics of a suitable clutch lining material?

3. Explain the expression "over-center" clutch and just how this type is adjusted for wear.

4. What is meant by "riding" a clutch, and why is this practice objectionable?

5. How is a slipping clutch detected, and what are the common causes?

6. In general, what are the lubrication needs of a clutch, and what are the effects of excessive lubrication?

7. Check and list the travel speeds of a number of different makes and sizes of tractors, and explain the specific need for this number and their use.

8. Compute the crankshaft-rear-axle speed ratio required to give travel speeds of 2, 4.5, and 15 m.p.h. for a tractor having an engine speed of 2,000 r.p.m. and rear wheels that are 46 in. in diameter. Compute the same if the rear wheels are 60 in. in diameter.

9. Referring to Fig. 23-22, assume that the bevel pinion has 12 teeth, the

bevel gear 40 teeth, the final drive pinion 14 teeth, the final drive gear 50 teeth, the track sprocket has an effective radius of 13 in., and the speed reduction in the transmission is 2.5 to 1. What is the speed of the engine if the tractor travel rate is 4 m.p.h.?

10. What is meant by a constant-mesh transmission, and how does it differ in construction and operation from a conventional tractor transmission?

11. Examine the transmissions shown or described in this chapter, and list three distinct designs used by which travel speed can be changed while the tractor is moving.

12. Explain why it is undesirable to make a short turn with a wheel tractor in a high gear with a high engine speed.

13. In what part of a tractor transmission would you expect to find the brakes?

14. What are the essential parts of a brake, and what specific care and attention do brakes require?

15. Distinguish between the terms fluid flywheel, torque converter, and automatic transmission.

24

Traction Devices—Steering Mechanisms—Power-transmission Accessories

Modern tractors are designed not only to perform efficiently but to supply power in a multiplicity of ways. Likewise much attention has been given to design features which provide ease of operation and handling and simple and quick adjustment of the field machine or equipment being driven. A consideration of recent changes and developments with respect to traction devices, steering, power take-off operation, and hydraulic mechanisms is essential to a full understanding of farm tractor design and application.

Steel wheels. The ordinary wheel-type tractor is equipped with two rear-drive wheels and two front steering wheels. Some wide-tread, all-purpose tractors have two rear-drive wheels and only one front steering wheel. Although there may be two front wheels, they are so close to each other that they are not unlike a single, wide wheel.

For many years, all wheel tractors used steel wheels with lugs. However, low-pressure, pneumatic, rubber tires are now used almost exclusively on all types of farm tractors. Steel-wheel tractors are still preferred to a limited extent by rice growers because of the very adverse traction conditions often encountered in the production of this crop. Figure 24-1 shows a steel drive wheel with lugs, and Fig. 24-2 shows a steel front wheel with guide band.

Traction devices and efficiency. The proper working of a tractor under certain conditions often depends upon its means of securing traction and upon the use of the correct equipment. In general, two types of tractors are available according to the method of obtaining traction: (1) the wheel type, and (2) the track type.

Considerable investigation has been made in connection with the factors involved in the effective and efficient operation of tractor wheels, wheel equipment, and other traction devices.

The power applied to any traction device, either round-wheel or track, is consumed largely in about four ways, namely, (1) by rolling resistance, (2) by wheel slippage, (3) by the action of the lugs on the soil, and (4) by the tractor-drawbar resistance. Obviously the most efficient device is one in which the first three factors named are low, so that the net power available at the drawbar is as high as possible. In other words, the problem of securing efficient traction is dependent upon the reduc-

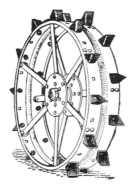

FIG. 24-1. *Conventional-type steel-rim tractor wheel with spade lugs.*

FIG. 24-2. *Front-wheel skid ring or guide band.*

tion of these apparent power losses. Rolling resistance varies with the soil type and conditions and the weight upon the tractor. A certain amount of weight is essential for traction, but too much weight produces a high rolling resistance and therefore may reduce the net power output of the wheel. The second factor, wheel slippage, is likewise apt to prove excessive under certain conditions and result in low tractive efficiency.

The most important factors affecting the efficiency of a tractor wheel and its equipment are (1) wheel diameter, (2) wheel width, (3) weight on wheel, (4) type of wheel lug or tread surface, (5) speed of travel, (6) soil type and condition, (7) grades, and (8) height of hitch. These factors likewise apply to track-type tractors.

The great variation in soil types and conditions is perhaps the most outstanding handicap encountered in the solution of the problem of tractor traction. It seems quite impractical to attempt to provide a distinct type of equipment for every condition, but it would be desirable to have one type of equipment that is adapted to as many conditions as possible. Some of these are:

1. Unplowed grain or corn stubble having a firm surface.

2. Turf or sod which, in addition to being firm, is matted with roots, which assist traction.

3. Plowed land or soil having a similar condition of tilth.

4. Very loose soil such as sand.

5. Firm but sticky soil.

6. Slippery surface, but firm underneath.

7. Hard, firm surfaces, such as highways, pavements, etc.

8. Tall weeds or high cover crops.

9. Terraces, checks, levees, ridges, and ruts.

RUBBER TIRES FOR TRACTORS

The first tractors to be equipped with solid or pneumatic rubber tires were those used for industrial purposes around factories, airports, and the like and for highway maintenance, the reason being that satisfactory traction was secured and that jarring, vibration, and damage were reduced even though the machine traveled relatively fast over the packed gravel, pavement, or similar hard surface. About 1931, investigations were begun concerning the possibility of using low-pressure pneumatic tires for agricultural tractors. Extremely favorable results were immediately observed, and a number of advantages in favor of rubber tires over steel wheels and lugs were disclosed.

Tire construction—size—mounting. Tractor tires are classified as "front-wheel" and "rear-wheel." Front-wheel tires (Fig. 24-18) usually have one or more concentric tread ribs to provide easy steering and to control skidding. The number of plies varies from four to six, depending upon the size of the tractor and the type of service. The size is designated by the tire cross-sectional diameter and the rim diameter. Some common sizes are 4.00-12, 4.00-15, 5.00-15, 5.50-16, 6.00-16, 6.50-16, and 7.50-16.

Rear tires have special tread designs to provide maximum traction under all conditions combined with smooth rolling action and good earth-shedding characteristics. Figure 24-3 shows the different kinds of rear-tire treads. The number of plies varies from four to eight, the section diameter varies from 6 to 18 in., and the rim diameter from 24 to 38 in. Some common sizes are 8-24, 9-24, 9-36, 10-24, 10-28, 11-38, 12-28, 12.4-36, 13.6-38, 14-34, 15-34, and 18-26. Rims are usually of the drop-center type with either a deep or a shallow well.

Inflation pressures. Proper inflation pressure is extremely important for tractor ties. Pressures recommended are as follows:

	Air pressure, lb.
Front tires—all sizes	
Four-ply tires	20–28
Six-ply tires	20–36
Rear tires—all sizes	12–16
Increase in furrow-wheel tire when plowing	4

When special heavy wheels are used, or heavy implements such as corn pickers, bedders, etc., are carried on the tractor, inflation pressure must be increased.

Tests made by Sauvé and McKibben [1] show that low inflation pressures give somewhat better traction, especially in loose soils, than higher pressures. Results of these tests are shown in Figs. 24-4 and 24-5.

FIG. 24-3. *Types of rear-wheel treads.* (A) *Heavy-duty deep tread;* (B) *standard-type farm tread;* (C) *cane-field special tread;* (D) *general-purpose and industrial tread.* (Courtesy of Goodyear Tire and Rubber Company.)

Weights for rubber tires. Since the wheels and tires alone are relatively light and hence do not provide sufficient traction under most conditions, it is necessary to add weight in some manner. This may be done by attaching special iron or concrete weights to the wheels or by partially filling the inner tube with water or some other suitable liquid. The amount of additional weight needed is determined largely by the size and power of the tractor and the traction conditions. For small tractors, 100 to 200 lb. per wheel is usually sufficient. For larger tractors, as much as 400 to 600 lb. per wheel may be needed to obtain the maximum drawbar pull. In general, only sufficient weight should be added to obtain good traction without undue slippage. As little weight as possible should be used in harrowing, planting, drilling, and cultivating land, in order to reduce soil packing.

Figure 24-7 shows the effect upon drawbar pull of adding wheel

[1] *Mich. State Univ. Agr. Expt. Sta. Quart. Bull.*, Vol. 27, No. 1.

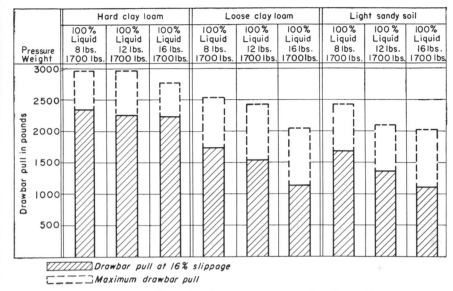

FIG. 24-4. *Effect of inflation pressure on drawbar pull.*

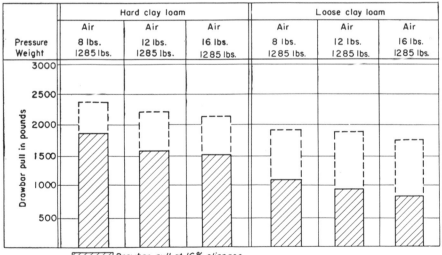

FIG. 24-5. *Effect of inflation pressure on drawbar pull.*

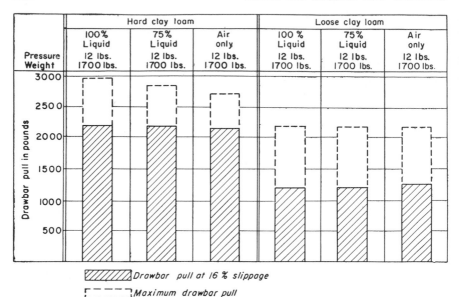

Drawbar pull at 16 % slippage

Maximum drawbar pull

FIG. 24-6. *Effect of different methods of weighting tires on drawbar pull.*

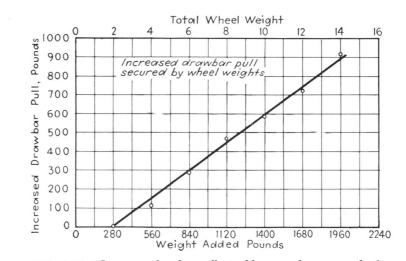

FIG. 24-7. *Effect upon drawbar pull of adding weight to rear wheels.*

weights. Investigations show that the increased drawbar pull will be approximately 50 per cent of the weight added to the wheels.

Weighting rubber-tired tractor wheels by partly filling the inner tube with water or some other suitable liquid is now common practice and seems to be preferable to using external weights for the following reasons:

1. Liquids are usually easy to obtain and inexpensive.

2. Better cushioning and shock-absorbing effects are obtained, thus improving riding qualities.

3. The weight is always located in the lower portion of the tire and directly over the tread, thus providing the most effective traction possible.

The quantity of liquid to use depends upon the tire size and the extra weight desired. As a rule, for smaller tires, a quantity of liquid is used equal to one wheel weight (150 lb.); for medium-size tires, an amount equal to two wheel weights; and for large tires, an amount equal to three wheel weights.

In colder climates, where freezing may give trouble, a calcium chloride solution may be substituted for water, although no harm is done by water's freezing inside a tire if the tractor is kept out of service and the wheels are jacked up. Water is placed in a tractor tire by one of four methods, namely, (1) by line pressure, (2) by gravity, (3) by a hand force pump, or (4) by a pressure tank.

PNEUMATIC TIRES VS. STEEL WHEELS

Numerous investigations relative to the comparative performance of pneumatic tires and steel wheels for farm tractors have been made by various experiment stations. Some of the important problems studied were:

1. Traction effects and efficiency as influenced by
   a. Traction surface and soil condition
   b. Inflation pressure
   c. Weight on wheels
   d. Travel speed
   e. Tire size
   f. Chains and special traction devices
2. Drawbar horsepower
3. Fuel consumption
4. Adaptability to various field operations
5. Ease of handling and riding qualities
6. Tractor wear

Rolling resistance. According to Davidson [1] et al.,

Rolling resistance is the drawbar pull or its equivalent required to move the tractor over a given surface. The tractor in field work passes over soft traction surfaces. The wheels or tracks, in sustaining the weight of the tractor, sink into the surface. Therefore the tractor is virtually climbing an incline as it moves forward. In addition, rolling resistance includes resistance due to friction in traction members and losses incurred in obtaining adhesion.

[1] *Iowa State Coll. Agr. Expt. Sta. Research Bull.* 189.

Table 24-1. Comparative Rolling Resistance of Steel Wheels and Pneumatic Tires on Sod and on Plowed Ground [1]

Wheel	Tractive surface	Speed, m.p.h.	Force required to pull tractor, lb.	Horse-power
Steel............	Sod	2.16	827	5.24
Steel............	Sod	3.05	911	7.64
Steel............	Sod	4.21	878	10.81
Rubber-tired.....	Sod	3.14	273	2.53
Rubber-tired.....	Sod	4.44	265	3.45
Steel............	Plowed ground	2.14	1,042	6.46
Steel............	Plowed ground	2.67	1,150	9.08
Steel............	Plowed ground	3.56	1,102	11.54
Rubber-tired.....	Plowed ground	2.24	557	3.66
Rubber-tired.....	Plowed ground	2.95	592	5.13
Rubber-tired.....	Plowed ground	3.72	739	6.93

[1] *Ohio Agr. Expt. Sta. Research Bull. 556.*

Table 24-1 shows the comparative rolling resistance of steel wheels and pneumatic tires for both sod and plowed ground. Relative to this, McCuen and Silver state:

A tractor, when equipped with rubber tires, has much less rolling resistance than when equipped with steel wheels and spade lugs. This is true both on sod and on plowed ground. Furthermore, the difference in rolling resistance between the two types of wheels is greater on sod than it is on plowed ground, and the rolling resistance of a rubber-tired tractor on plowed ground is less than that of the steel-wheel tractor on sod.

Tractor tractive efficiency. The tractive efficiency of a tractor wheel or track may be defined as the ratio of its work output to the work applied to it at the axle. The principal factor affecting tractive efficiency is slippage or travel reduction which is expressed as follows:

Travel reduction (per cent)

$$= 100 - \frac{\text{distance traveled per wheel revolution without drawbar load}}{\text{distance traveled per wheel revolution with drawbar load}}$$

In order to determine the relative traction efficiency of steel wheels and pneumatic tires, Smith and Hurlbut [1] made some tests of a standard four-wheel tractor weighing 4,545 lb. with steel wheels and 5,000 lb.

[1] *Univ. Nebraska Agr. Expt. Sta. Bull. 291.*

with rubber tires and weights. Figure 24-8 shows the results of these tests with respect to drawbar pull as affected by speed. The conclusions of Smith and Hurlbut were:

1. Under favorable operating conditions, pneumatic-tired wheels transform a greater proportion of the engine horsepower into drawbar horsepower than do steel wheels and spade lugs.

2. Under favorable conditions, steel wheels and spade lugs attain a greater drawbar pull in low gear than can be attained with rubber tires.

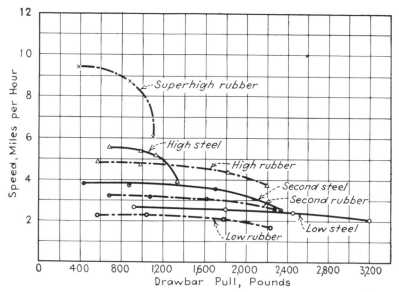

FIG. 24-8. *The relation of speed to drawbar pull for steel wheels and rubber tires.*

3. There are two ways of increasing the drawbar horsepower of a tractor, namely, by increasing the drawbar pull and by increasing the speed of travel. The drawbar pull of pneumatic tires is limited by traction in the first three gears. The drawbar pull of a steel-wheeled tractor is usually limited by engine horsepower in any gear.

4. The maximum drawbar horsepower of a rubber-tired tractor in various gears covers a much wider range of values than that of a steel-wheel-and-lug tractor. Horsepower values for rubber tires at high speeds exceed any derived for steel wheels and lugs. At low speeds, the horsepower for rubber tires is less than for steel wheels and lugs.

5. Maximum economy was secured for the rubber-tired tractor when the drawbar pull was slightly more than 50 per cent of the static weight of the rear of the tractor.

6. Maximum drawbar horsepower values were secured for the rubber-tired tractor when the travel reduction was about 16 per cent. No such point is found for steel wheels and lugs. The percentage of travel reduction is less for steel wheels and lugs than for rubber tires and decreases as speed increases.

Figure 24-9 shows the results of studies of tractor tires made by Reed et al.[1] with respect to their tractive efficiency on concrete and with different soil conditions and types.

Life of tractor tires. The life of pneumatic tractor tires will depend on such factors as (1) abrasive wear, (2) chipping, (3) punctures and blowouts, (4) chemical decomposition, and (5) general care given.

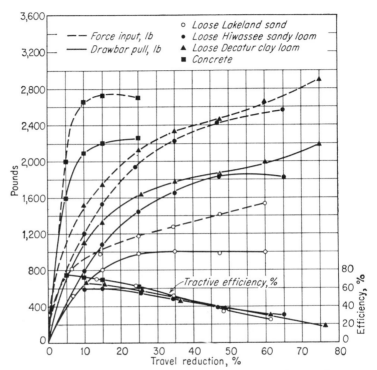

FIG. 24-9. *Performance of 11-38 tractor tires on various surfaces.*

Abrasive wear is dependent upon the soil surface condition and the speed of travel. It seems logical to assume that the travel speed will have much less effect on tractor tires than on automobile and truck tires. Truck tires are usually operated on hard surfaces at high speeds. The abrasive action due to these high speeds has a wearing tendency that is almost entirely absent in slow-speed operation, particularly on the soft surfaces where a tractor operates. A high-grade truck tire, operating in heavy-duty work and on pavements, frequently goes 20,000 miles before being discarded. A tractor tire used 800 hr. per year at a speed of 3 m.p.h.

[1] I. F. Reed, C. A. Reaves, and J. W. Shields, Comparative Performance of Farm Tractor Tires Weighted with Liquid and Wheel Weights, *Agr. Eng.*, Vol. 34, No. 6.

would cover 2,400 miles per year. Assuming it would give the same total mileage as the truck tire, its life would be about eight years.

McKibben and Davidson [1] report that Iowa farmers estimated the average life of tractor tires to be about eight years. Figure 24-10 shows the results of this survey and the variation in estimated life. Figure 24-11 shows the average life of tractor tires as indicated by a survey made by the U.S. Department of Agriculture.[2]

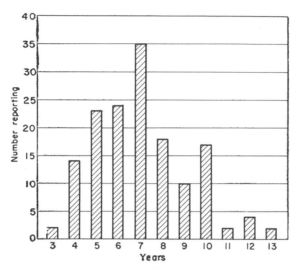

FIG. 24-10. *Estimated life of tractor tires.*

Track mechanisms. The traction mechanism of a track-type tractor (Fig. 24-12) consists of (1) frame, (2) drive sprocket, (3) front idler, (4) track rollers, and (5) track. The track frames are built of structural steel. The sprocket and front idler drive and support the track. The track rollers on the underside of the track frame act as supports between the machine and that part of the track in contact with the ground. In fact, these rollers might be considered as small wheels rolling and conveying the tractor over a stationary track.

The track itself is built up of forged-steel shoes bolted to forged-steel heat-treated links, with alloy-steel heat-treated pins (see Fig. 24-13).

Since any track mechanism must have so many wearing points, which are continually exposed to dirt and grit, three fundamentally important considerations must be observed by the manufacturer, namely, (1) the parts themselves must be made of high-grade materials that have been carefully heat-treated and hardened; (2) any important bearings, such

[1] *Iowa State Coll. Agr. Expt. Sta. Bull.* 382.
[2] *Farm Implement News,* Vol. 71, No. 13.

as track rollers, front idlers, and so on, must be well enclosed and properly lubricated; and (3) there must be some provision for taking up the slack and maintaining the proper track tension.

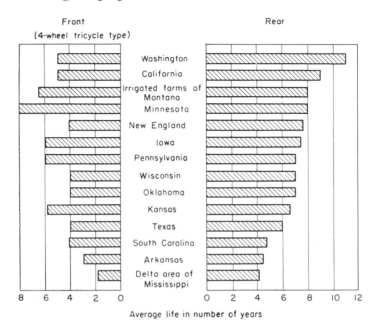

FIG. 24-11. *Estimated life of tractor tires for different geographical areas.* (Courtesy of Farm Implement News.)

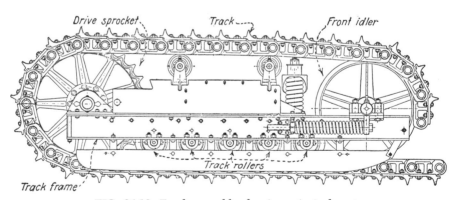

FIG. 24-12. *Track assembly showing principal parts.*

Wheels versus tracks. The over-all drawbar efficiency of a tractor is the relationship of the power supplied at the drawbar and the power generated by the engine under a given set of conditions. That is,

$$\text{Drawbar efficiency (per cent)} = \frac{\text{drawbar hp.}}{\text{b.hp.}} \times 100$$

The comparative drawbar efficiency of track-type and wheel-type tractors is clearly disclosed by an analysis of tests made by the University of Nebraska.[1] For example, the maximum horsepower tests of 25 current-model, wheel-type machines show an average efficiency of 88.1 per cent. Similar tests of 12 current-model, track-type tractors show an average efficiency of 84.9 per cent. The average slippage in these same tests was 5.67 per cent for the wheel-type tractors and 2.95 per cent for the track-type machines. The higher drawbar efficiency of the wheel-type machines in spite of their greater slippage loss can be attributed largely to the power consumed by the track mechanism and the heavy tracks as

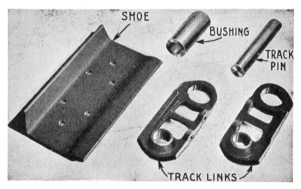

FIG. 24-13. *Track construction and parts.*

they are rotated and move the machine. In other words, the rolling resistance of wheel tractors is considerably less than that of the track types.

The outstanding advantage of the track type is, no doubt, its ability to secure traction under conditions that will not permit the wheel type to operate with any degree of success. Not only can the track tractor usually secure good footing under most adverse conditions, but there is likely to be less loss from slippage under average operating conditions.

Front axles. Front-axle construction for wheel tractors depends upon the tractor type. Figure 24-16 shows the axle and steering linkage for a four-wheel tractor, and Figs. 24-15 and 24-18 show the front axle and steering mechanism for a tricycle-type tractor. All front wheels are equipped with roller bearings and a convenient means of wear adjustment. Lubrication is either by packing the bearing with grease or by periodic application of the lubricant with a grease gun. Figure 24-19 shows a device for equalizing the traction of dual front wheels when traveling on ridges or over uneven ground.

Steering mechanisms. The operator of wheel-type tractors controls the directional movement of the machine by means of an assembly con-

[1] Official reports of Nebraska tractor tests.

sisting of (1) a steering wheel, (2) a steering gear, and (3) a suitable linkage to the front wheels. The steering gear is the most important part of the entire assembly because it must transmit the rotary movement of the steering wheel to the linkage at a relatively slow speed and with as little operator effort as possible. Figures 24-14 and 24-15 show representative types of steering gears and Fig. 24-16 shows the complete steering assembly for a typical wheel-type tractor. These gears are al-

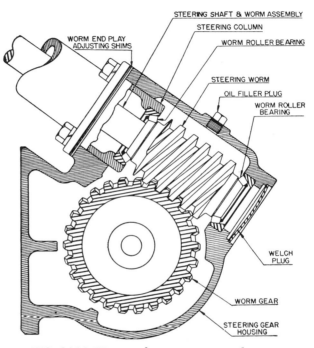

FIG. 24-14. *Worm-and-gear steering mechanism.*

ways enclosed in a dirtproof housing and operate in oil or grease. Most have a simple and convenient adjustment for wear.

Power steering. The medium and larger sizes of wheel tractors, when equipped with the standard type of steering mechanism previously described, require considerable effort on the part of the operator in steering them, particularly in loose soil or rough ground conditions or when the tractor is stationary or moving slowly. Hence most of these tractors are equipped with a power-actuated steering mechanism (Fig. 24-17). The necessary assembly is usually a part of the hydraulic system of the tractor and includes (1) the pump, (2) the steering motor actuated by hydraulic pressure from the pump, (3) a steering spindle, (4) the control valves actuated by the operator through the steering wheel, and (5) the connecting oil lines. Obviously, the engine must be running in order to operate the pump which forces the oil through the lines to the steering unit. The oil pressure reacts on a rotor or vane which, in turn, rotates the steering spindle and thereby moves the wheels. The operator turns the steering wheel in the usual manner, but, in doing so, actuates valves which control the oil flow and the pressure from the pump and applied to the steering rotor and spindle. Hence the operator effort is greatly reduced, and the engine actually supplies the energy needed for steering.

Another slightly different power-steering mechanism involves the use of an ordinary hydraulic ram cylinder and piston assembly connected externally in the steering linkage such as between the drag link and the steering arm. Thus the steering-wheel movement controls the oil flow to the ram piston which, in turn, moves the drag link and steers the tractor.

Power-steering mechanisms are equipped with an oil-pressure relief device to prevent damage if the normal turning movement of the wheels is restricted in any manner. Furthermore, in case of failure of the oil pump and pressure, the tractor can be steered manually in the usual manner. Other advantages of power steering are elimination of steering shock and wheel shimmy.

FIG. 24-15. *Worm-and-sector type. of steering mechanism for an all-purpose tractor.*

Wheel-tread adjustment. Row-crop or all-purpose tractors must be provided with some convenient means of adjusting the wheel tread to adapt them to different machines and row spacings. In general, for plowing, the wheels must be relatively close together, while for cultivating or planting two or four rows they must be set rather far apart.

Standard four-wheel tractors must have a means of adjusting both the front-wheel and the rear-wheel tread, while tricycle-type tractors require only a rear-wheel adjustment. The front-wheel adjustment is usually taken care of by shortening or lengthening the axle on each side by a telescoping arrangement or by bolts and a series of holes.

Rear-wheel treads are changed (1) by sliding the wheel hub inward or outward on the axle; (2) by having an offset hub, or dished wheel, and reversing the wheel on the axle; (3) by shifting the rim and tire inward or outward by means of rim lugs or spacers; or (4) by a combination of

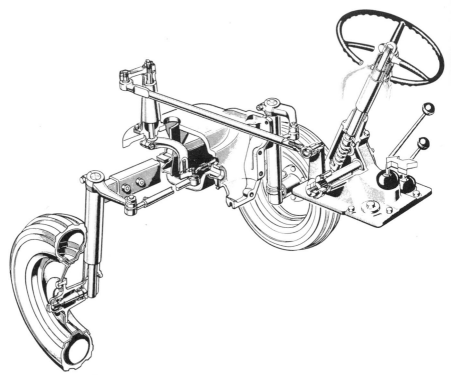

FIG. 24-16. *Axle construction and steering mechanism for a four-wheel tractor.* (Courtesy of Massey-Ferguson, Inc.)

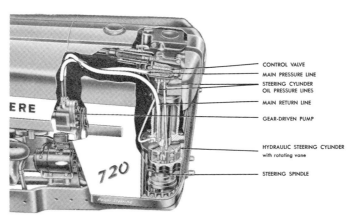

CONTROL VALVE
MAIN PRESSURE LINE
STEERING CYLINDER
OIL PRESSURE LINES
MAIN RETURN LINE
GEAR-DRIVEN PUMP
HYDRAULIC STEERING CYLINDER
with rotating vane
STEERING SPINDLE

FIG. 24-17. *Tractor steering mechanism using hydraulic power.* (Courtesy of Deere and Company.)

402

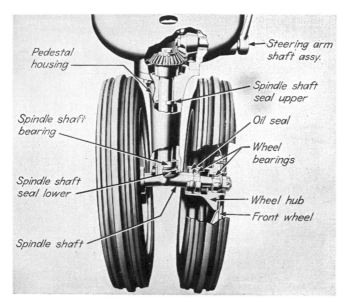

FIG. 24-18. *Dual front-wheel mounting for row-crop tractor.* (Courtesy of Allis-Chalmers Manufacturing Company.)

FIG. 24-19. *Special device for equalizing traction of dual front wheels.* (Courtesy of Deere and Company.)

these methods. Figure 24-20 shows a tread adjustment from 48 to 76 in. by 4-in. intervals by using methods 2 and 3. Figure 24-21 shows the long

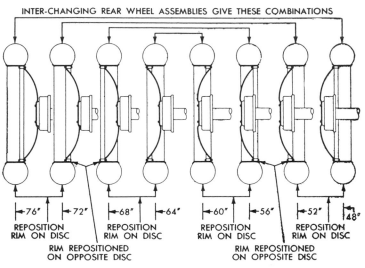

INTER-CHANGING REAR WHEEL ASSEMBLIES GIVE THESE COMBINATIONS

|←76″| |←72″| |←68″| |←64″| |←60″| |←56″| |←52″| |←48″|

REPOSITION RIM ON DISC   REPOSITION RIM ON DISC   REPOSITION RIM ON DISC   REPOSITION RIM ON DISC

RIM REPOSITIONED ON OPPOSITE DISC   RIM REPOSITIONED ON OPPOSITE DISC

FIG. 24-20. *Method of spacing rear wheels.*

axle with adjustable hub and dished wheel. Figure 24-22 shows a special type of quick tread adjustment involving the use of spiral rim cleats and special locking devices. The power of the tractor itself is used to shift the wheels.

Belt pulley. The belt pulley on wheel-type tractors is usually located on the right-hand side and to the rear of the engine. If the engine is placed crosswise of the tractor frame, the pulley is located on the crankshaft and driven direct. If the engine is placed lengthwise, the pulley must be driven through a special bevel gear. Some wheel tractors and most track-type tractors have the pulley on the rear just above the drawbar.

Pulley and belt speeds. There is considerable variation in the size and speed of tractor belt pulleys. As a consequence, manufacturers of belt-driven farm machines must supply a number of different sizes of pulleys for their machines so that they can be operated at the correct speed by any tractor. Inconvenience and difficulty in this respect could be overcome if all tractor manufacturers would adopt one belt speed as a standard.

FIG. 24-21. *Extension-axle method of wheel-tread adjustment.*

The belt speed for a given pulley is equal to the product of its circumference and revolutions per minute. That is, given a pulley 16 in. in diameter operating at 600 r.p.m., the belt speed is equal to

$$\frac{16 \times 3.1416 \times 600}{12} = 2{,}513.3 \text{ ft. per min.}$$

The American Society of Agricultural Engineers and the Society of Automotive Engineers have established the following standards:

1. The standard belt speed for farm tractors shall be 3,100 ft. per min., plus or minus 100 ft. per min.

2. The minimum width of tractor-belt pulleys shall be such as to provide for the use of a belt 6 in. wide.

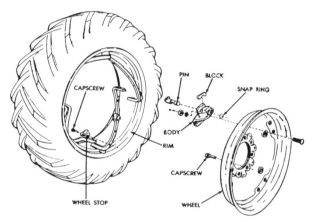

FIG. 24-22. *Wheel-tread adjustment by means of spiral guides and engine power.* (Courtesy of Allis-Chalmers Manufacturing Company.)

Belt speed depends on both pulley diameter and speed. The tractor maker, therefore, would not necessarily be restricted to any given pulley speed or size. On the other hand, the use of a single standard belt speed for all tractors would mean that manufacturers of belt-driven machines would need to supply but one size of pulley for a given machine. Tractor belt speeds usually range from 2,300 to 3,500 ft. per min.

In any case, in doing belt work, the transmission gears are kept in neutral and the pulley controlled, as a rule, by means of the main clutch. A few tractors have a special pulley clutch so that the pulley can be kept stationary without stopping the engine or holding the main clutch disengaged. In such cases the pulley can also be held stationary when the tractor is doing field or road work.

Power take-off. The early type of power take-off consisted essentially of a shaft driven by a special gear from the transmission and projecting from the rear of the housing so that it could be connected conveniently to any machine. It received its power through the master clutch; therefore when it was in operation, the tractor had to be moving or, for stationary operation, the gears shifted to neutral. This construction proved inconvenient and usually necessitated overworking the master clutch. Most current types of power take-off are of the independently driven type, as shown by Figs. 23-28 and 24-23. In each case, the power is transmitted to the shaft independently of the transmission gears and a special clutch is provided for starting and stopping the power shaft independent of the master clutch. The independent power take-off offers the following advantages: (1) the driven machine can be started and stopped without shifting gears; (2) the full power of the engine is available, if necessary,

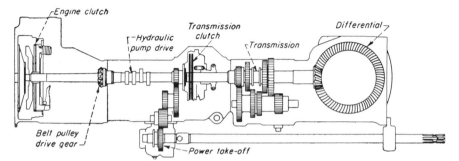

FIG. 24-23. *Direct-driven power take-off.* (Courtesy of Allis-Chalmers Manufacturing Company.)

to operate a machine; (3) the speed can be closely controlled by the engine speed; and (4) the use and wear of the master transmission clutch is reduced.

Immediately upon introduction of the power take-off, it was recognized that certain standard specifications involving both the tractor and the driven machine were essential in order to permit any machine driven by power take-off to be operated successfully by any make of tractor. The most important of these specifications is the speed of the power take-off shaft. A speed of 540 r.p.m. was adopted and has been accepted for many years. However, as more machines driven by power take-off have been introduced and this means of utilizing tractor power has been expanded, this one speed has not proved entirely adequate under all conditions. Hence revised specifications for power take-off recommend a shaft speed of 1,000 r.p.m. as well as the slower speed of 540 r.p.m. The higher speed permits the transmission of more power without any increase in the size of the shaft. For further information concerning power take-off, the reader is referred to the Appendix.

REFERENCES

A Comparative Study of Pneumatic Tires and Steel Wheels on Farm Tractors, *Univ. Nebraska Agr. Expt. Sta. Bull.* 291.

BARGER, E. L., W. M. CARLETON, E. G. McKIBBEN, and ROY BAINER, "Tractors and Their Power Units," John Wiley & Sons, Inc., New York, 1952.

FORREST, P. J., J. M. HOOPER, R. W. SOHL, and G. F. MULLIN, Effects of Improper Inflation Pressures on Farm Tractor Tires, Agr. Eng., Vol. 35, No. 12.

HANSEN, MERLIN, Loads Imposed on Power-take-off Shafts by Farm Implements, Agr. Eng., Vol. 33, No. 2.

Life, Service and Cost of Service of Pneumatic Tractor Tires, Iowa State Coll Agr. Expt. Sta. Bull. 382.

LINCOLN, C. W., Hydraulic Power Steering, Agr. Eng., Vol. 38, No. 1.

REED, I. F., and M. O. BERRY, Equipment and Procedures for Farm Tractor Tire Studies under Controlled Conditions, Agr. Eng., Vol. 30, No. 2.

SOHL, R. W., Tractor Tire Testing Equipment, Agr. Eng., Vol. 30, No. 9.

Studies on the Use of Liquid in Tractor Tires, Mich. State Univ. Agr. Expt. Sta. Quart. Bull., Vol. 27, No. 1.

Traction Efficiency of the Farm Tractor, Iowa State Coll. Agr. Expt. Sta. Bull. 189.

PROBLEMS AND QUESTIONS

1. What is meant by the traction efficiency of a tractor and what are the factors affecting it?

2. Why is it necessary to add weight to tractor drive wheels, and what are the usual specifications concerning the amount needed?

3. A certain tractor has a drawbar pull of 2,000 lb. without wheel weights. If 400 lb. is added to each wheel, what pull could be expected without excessive slippage?

4. Explain the meaning of drawbar efficiency, and compare wheel and track-type tractors in this respect.

5. Enumerate all the measurements or specifications needed to compute the soil surface pressure in pounds per square inch for (a) a wheel tractor and (b) a track-type tractor. Compute this information on any tractors available.

6. A tractor has a belt speed of 3,100 ft. per min. at normal engine speed. A feed mill has a recommended speed of 2,100 r.p.m. What size of pulley is needed on the mill?

25

Tractor Hitches and Stability—
Hydraulic Controls—Field Operation

Originally, all tractor-powered field operations were performed by trailing machines attached to the drawbar of the tractor at one fixed point. With the introduction of (1) certain row-crop field tools, (2) the power take-off driving mechanism, and (3) hydraulic lifting and control mechanisms there was a transition from plain drawbar-operated machines to integrally mounted or more directly connected tools. These developments have necessitated distinct changes in tractor design and operation, which, in turn, have provided greater versatility, convenience and ease in control and operation, and better maneuverability, performance efficiency, and weight distribution.

Trailing and mounted machines. In general, tractor-operated field machines are (1) pulled behind it by a simple flexible hitch to a drawbar, (2) mounted or directly attached to it at the rear, front, or sides, or (3) operated by a combination of these methods. Examples of trailing implements are moldboard and disk plows, disk and other types of harrows, grain drills, grain combines, hay rakes, and balers. Most tools used in row-crop production such as bedders and listers, planters, cultivators, corn pickers and cotton strippers, and sprayers are mounted on the tractor and thereby become more or less integral with it.

A number of basic factors must be recognized in designing any tractor to pull and operate all types of field machines under the many and varying conditions encountered. These are (1) weight and weight distribution, (2) attachment of driven machine in such a manner as to obtain the most effective performance with a minimum power loss, (3) reasonable operating ease and operator safety assurance, and (4) elimination of excessive or abnormal wear and strains on both the tractor and the driven machine.

Some knowledge of the mechanics of a tractor is basic to a clear understanding of hitching principles and design and tool attachment and operation.

Principles of mechanics. A knowledge of mechanical principles is essential to a clear understanding of any analysis of the mechanics of a

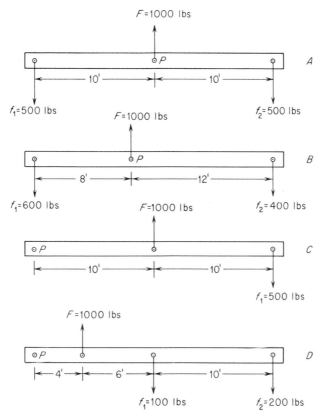

FIG. 25-1. *Elementary mechanics as applied to parallel force reactions.*

tractor and the reactions involved, particularly when it supplies power at the drawbar. Referring to Fig. 25-1A, a force F of 1,000 lb. applied at the center P of the bar is balanced by two forces of 500 lb. each and equidistant from P. Likewise, the moments (force times its distance from center of rotation) are balanced; that is,

$$500 \times 10 = 500 \times 10$$

or we may say that the moments about P are zero. In Fig. 25-1B the force F is counterbalanced by two unequal opposing forces. The moments with respect to P are likewise balanced; that is,

$$600 \times 8 = 400 \times 12$$

Figure 25-1C represents another slightly different but balanced arrangement with respect to the fixed point P; that is, taking moments with respect to P,

$$1,000 \times 10 = 500 \ (10 + 10)$$

Figure 25-1D represents a more complex arrangement having an unbalanced system of moments which results in clockwise rotation about P; that is,

$$100 \times 20 + 200 \times 20 = 5,000 \ \text{ft.-lb.}$$

and $$1,000 \times 4 = \underline{4,000} \ \text{ft.-lb.}$$

Net unbalanced moment $= 1,000$ ft.-lb.

Center of gravity—basic tractor mechanics. A number of factors enter into the effective drawbar performance of a tractor. Some of these are (1) total weight, (2) center of gravity and weight distribution, (3)

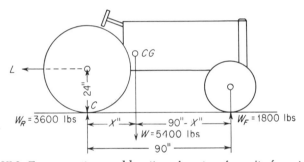

FIG. 25-2. *Force reactions and location of center of gravity for a tractor.*

traction member size and type, (4) drawbar and hitch design and location, (5) traction surface condition, (6) surface grade, (7) travel speed, and others.

The analyses which follow are based only upon the more common and simpler conditions encountered in tractor operation as follows: (1) wheel type and rear-wheel drive, (2) uniform travel in one direction on a smooth, level surface, (3) drawbar load L reacting horizontally and attached midway between drive wheels parallel to direction of travel, (4) supporting soil reaction on front and rear wheels applied vertically under centers of axles, and (5) horizontal soil reaction parallel to direction of travel and tangent to low point of wheel rim. These conditions are shown in Fig. 25-2.

The center of gravity of an object such as a tractor is that point from which it might be suspended or supported and still have it remain at rest in its normal position with respect to a level surface. In simple words, it is some point within the body of the machine where its entire weight might be considered as being concentrated.

The location of the center of gravity of a tractor determines its weight distribution longitudinally with respect to the front and rear wheels, as well as transversely and vertically. In general, the center of gravity for standard rear-wheel-drive tractors is located forward of the rear axle a distance equal to about one-third of the wheel base. In track-type tractors it is located ahead of the mid-point of the tracks in order to provide uniform and maximum track pressure and soil contact.

The approximate center of gravity of a wheel tractor can be located by measuring its wheel base and weighing the loads supported by the front and rear wheels and adding these loads to get the total weight. The center of gravity is then computed by moments about the point C, as shown in Fig. 25-2. By computation

$$5,400x = 1,800 \times 90$$

$$x = 30 \text{ in.}$$

Drawbar pull and weight transfer. Tractor stability and steering, as well as maximum traction and minimum slippage, are greatly dependent upon the drawbar design and location and the correct attachment of the implement to the tractor. Referring to Fig. 25-2, it is assumed that a load L attached directly behind the rear axle exerts a certain force in a horizontal plane. This load is counteracted by the force created by the rear wheels in contact with the ground or other surface at C. Furthermore, the moment of this force about C reacts against the moment of W_F with respect to C; that is,

$$24 \times L = 1,800 \times 90$$

or $$L = 6,750 \text{ lb.}$$

Hence, any load greater than 6,750 lb., applied as indicated, would lift the front end of the tractor off the ground and upset it. On the other hand, if L is less than 6,750 lb., some weight will remain on the front end. For example, if L is 1,200 lb. then

$$1,200 \times 24 = F \times 90$$

or $$F = 320 \text{ lb.}$$

This means that a force of 320 lb. acts against W_F, reducing it to $1,800 - 320$, or 1,480 lb., and that some additional weight is transferred to the rear wheels to provide better traction. It will also be noted that attaching the hitch and load L below the rear axle reduces the weight transfer and the tendency of the tractor to rear up, while attaching it above the axle increases weight transfer but reduces front end stability.

Rolling resistance and soil reaction. Thus far, we have considered the conditions existing with the tractor as a stationary body. Since, in actual practice, it is moving and rolling along a more or less level and possibly flexible surface, certain other factors must be considered which slightly alter the previous theoretical analysis. The principal factor involved is the resistance of the wheels as they roll and carry their load along. Figure 25-3 illustrates the conditions existing with a steel wheel and lugs on a somewhat loose soil surface; that is, the point of maximum resistance R is at C_1 rather than at C directly below the wheel center. However, studies [1] made of rubber-tired tractors show that on firm, level ground

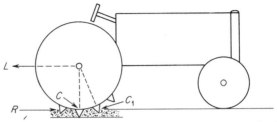

FIG. 25-3. *Effect of rolling resistance and soil reaction on wheel traction.*

where lug penetration is negligible and wheel traction is at a maximum, the dynamic reaction of the soil is through a point directly below the rear axle and at the ground surface rather than somewhat forward of this point. Under less firm or loose soil conditions, the tires sink into the soil, increasing the rolling resistance and decreasing drawbar pull. Under such conditions, the point of drive-wheel reaction with the soil shifts forward of the rear axle center to a slight degree.

Horizontal reactions and stability. The performance and stability characteristics of a wheel tractor with respect to the forces acting laterally or crosswise are dependent mainly upon (1) the tractive surface whether level or sloping, (2) the hitch relationship between the load pulled and the drawbar, and (3) certain tractor design factors such as wheel diameter and spacing and location of center of gravity.

Figure 25-4 shows how lateral stability is affected by land slope, wheel height, rear-wheel tread, and the location of the center of gravity. The tractor will not tip sideways as long as the vertical projection from the center of gravity falls at some point between the wheels, as indicated. In general, for a given cross grade, the best stability is obtained with small wheels spaced far apart and with a low center of gravity. The machines pulled by the tractor and their attachment to it also affect this stability.

[1] Worthington, *Agr. Eng.*, Vol. 30, Nos. 3 and 4.

Drawbars, offset hitches, and side draft. Figure 25-5 shows a desirable and typical drawbar arrangement. The assembly consists of (1) two side members attached rigidly to the rear-axle housing and somewhat below the rear axle itself, (2) a crossbar with clevis holes, and (3) a flexible swinging drawbar attached underneath and forward of the axle housing. The pulled machine may be attached either directly to

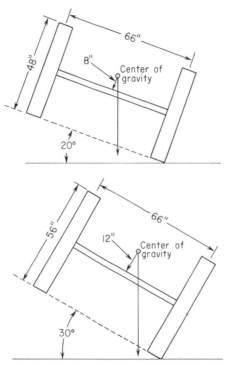

FIG. 25-4. *Effect of surface slope and wheel height on lateral stability.*

the crossbar or to the drawbar. Good drawbar design includes (1) a range of adjustability both horizontally and vertically to meet all drawbar applications, (2) proper location to give maximum drawbar power effectiveness, and (3) maximum operator safety under all conditions.

A good understanding of certain mechanical principles is important in attaching trailing machines to tractors to obtain satisfactory performance as well as safety. Referring to Fig. 25-6, the true line of pull of an ordinary tractor passes through a point in the hitch midway between the rear wheels and is parallel to the direction of travel. The true line of draft of any drawbar-operated implement passes through that point on the implement to which one can hitch and make it move squarely

forward in the direction of travel. In other words, the true line of draft
of an implement is a line parallel to the direction of travel and passing
through its center of resistance. In all drawbar work the object should be

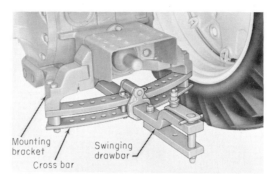

FIG. 25-5. *A typical tractor drawbar assembly.* (Courtesy of Deere and Company.)

to make the true line of pull of the tractor and the true line of draft of the
implement coincide as far as possible. If they do not, more or less side
draft results.

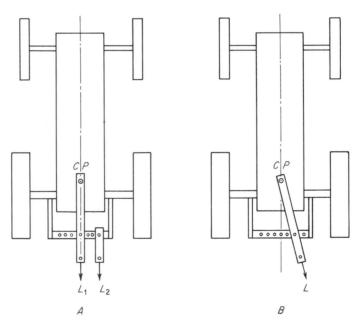

FIG. 25-6. *Typical load reactions for tractor drawbars.*

In a tractor with two drive wheels connected by the usual differential,
the pull exerted by the wheels is approximately equal. Friction in the
differential gears is all that permits one wheel to pull slightly more than

the other. For all practical purposes a point *CP* (Fig. 25-6) may be called the center of pull, being on a longitudinal axis slightly ahead of and midway between the wheel centers. Side draft exists if the pull is not straight back from *CP*. For example, in Fig. 25-6A the load L_2 is attached to the right of the center hole of the drawbar. This offset reaction has a tendency to pull the front end of the tractor sideways and to the right. Hitching to the left of the center hole would pull the front end to the left. This reaction, commonly called side draft, can be counteracted only through the steering of the tractor and may be great enough to make steering and control difficult. Another condition (Fig. 25-6B), in which the load *L* is pulled at an angle, also creates a similar side-draft effect. The swinging hitch bar (Figs. 25-5 and 25-7) offers the advantage of permitting a wide machine such as a disk harrow or a grain drill to trail in the proper manner in making short turns and thus reduces side draft and makes a better corner.

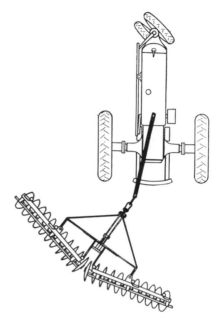

Side draft is encountered largely with trailing plows and, to some extent, with some harvesting machines. In these cases the path of the tractor with respect to the implement is somewhat restricted, for example, by

FIG. 25-7. *Use of swinging drawbar with disk harrow.*

the edge of the furrow wall or by standing grain or hay. Plows give more trouble in this respect because of their heavy draft and narrow swath. Side draft in tractor plowing is affected by a number of factors such as (1) whether the tractor runs in the furrow or entirely on the unplowed land, (2) width and tread of drive wheels, (3) type of plow, and (4) width of cut and number of plow bottoms.

In plowing, all the small and medium sizes of wheel tractors are operated with the right-hand wheels in the furrow. This simplifies steering and eliminates the use of a special guiding device. Some large-size wheel tractors and all track-type machines operate on the unplowed land.

Referring to Fig. 25-8, the center of resistance of a single moldboard bottom is located one-fourth of the width of the bottom to the right of the shin and about where the share joins the moldboard. For plows having two or more bottoms, the center of resistance of the entire unit is midway on a line connecting the points of resistance of all bottoms as shown by Fig. 25-8 and in Table 25-1. Assuming that one wheel of the tractor runs in the furrow, the spacing of the drive wheels (inside to inside of tires) required to eliminate all side draft is twice the distance from the furrow wall to the center of resistance of the plow, as shown in Table 25-1.

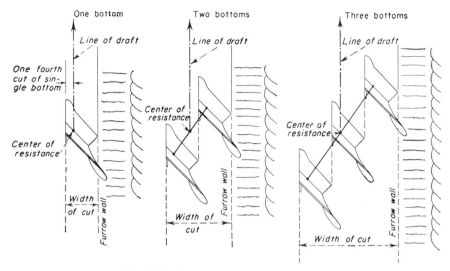

FIG. 25-8. *Location of center of resistance.*

Table 25-1. Centers of Resistance and Tractor-wheel Spacing for Moldboard Plows

Number of bottoms	Size of bottom, in.					
	12		14		16	
	A^1	B^2	A	B	A	B
1	9	18	11	22	12	24
2	15	30	18	36	20	40
3	21	42	25	50	28	56
4	27	54	32	64	36	72
5	33	66	39	78	44	88

[1] A = distance in inches from furrow wall to true line of draft of plow and tractor.

[2] B = distance in inches between inside edges of drive wheels to give least side draft.

Frequently it is difficult to adjust the spacing of tractor wheels to eliminate all side draft. This is particularly true when a wide-tread tractor is used with a one- or a two-bottom plow or a narrow-tread tractor is used with a four- or a five-bottom plow. In such cases it is recommended that any offset between the line of draft of the plow and the center line of hitch of the tractor be divided between the tractor and the plow.

GENERAL RULES FOR TRACTOR HITCHES AND STABILITY

1. A long, low-mounted drawbar is preferable to a short, high one from a safety standpoint as well as better draft and traction.

2. A low center of gravity and a wide tread consistent with the desired crop clearance is preferred to a high center of gravity and a narrow tread.

3. The location of the center of gravity along a longitudinal axis should be such as to provide only sufficient weight on the front wheels to give satisfactory steering and control under normal hitch and drawbar pull conditions.

4. The longitudinal stability of a tractor is reduced when the drive wheels dig in or drop into a ditch. Placing a timber crosswise in front of the wheels is particularly hazardous and may cause overturning.

5. Sudden engagement of the clutch of a tractor pulling a heavy load under good traction conditions may lift the front end or cause overturning.

Integral or mounted machines. All manufacturers now provide an almost complete line of integral or mounted implements for their tractors. This includes plows, harrows, planters, cultivators, crop-harvesting machines, earth-moving equipment, and others. Integral machines are used almost exclusively on the small and medium-sized tractors. Trailing machines—particularly plows and harrows and multiple units—are still used with the large tractors. A second and coincidental development which has given major impetus to the use of integral tools is the use of hydraulic mechanisms for their operation and control.

Integral implements have the following advantages:

1. Greater maneuverability. The entire unit is compact, and ease in backing and making short turns readily adapts the outfit to small irregular fields and adverse working conditions.

2. Attachment and control are relatively easy and, in most cases, can be accomplished from the tractor seat.

3. The problem of transportation about the farm or over hard-surfaced highways is simplified because the machine is not in contact with the surface and its weight is carried entirely by the tractor.

4. The initial cost and weight of integral machines is usually less because of the elimination of transport and gauge wheels, control levers, and other parts.

5. The additional weight carried by the tractor when integral machines are used improves traction and steering control.

6. There is better visibility of machine operation and performance.

Trailing-type machines when compared with integral tools have the following advantages:

1. They are universally adaptable to all makes and models of tractors, whereas most integral tools are adapted to but one make of tractor.

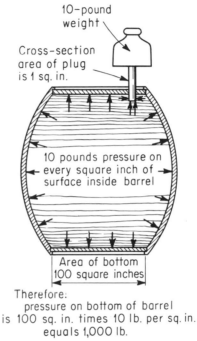

FIG. 25-9. *The pressure reaction of a liquid in a closed container.*

2. Attachment to the drawbar by a clevis and pin is simpler.

3. The full power of the tractor can be utilized by using multiple machine units or multiple operation machines, thus reducing time and labor costs.

4. Trailing implements when once adjusted are not thrown out of adjustment when detached from the tractor.

Integral hitch types. The method of attaching and controlling mounted machines depends largely upon the kind of machine and the field operation involved. Pull-behind machines such as plows, listers, harrows, and some planters and cultivators use the three-point hook-up (Fig. 25-12). Most row-crop machines, including planters, cultivators, corn pickers, and cotton strippers, are attached directly or indirectly to the tractor frame on the side or in front or both. In either case, operator control, including raising and lowering and depth control, is performed hydraulically in various ways.

Hydraulic-control principles. The basic principle upon which all hydraulic-control mechanisms operate is known as Pascal's law. It states that the pressure applied to an enclosed fluid is transmitted equally in all directions. This is illustrated by Fig. 25-9. Figure 25-10, the hydraulic press, illustrates further the application of this principle; that is, a small pressure reacting against a surface of limited area can be multiplied many times by being applied to another surface of greater area. In fact, the pressures vary directly as the areas involved, or

$$P_2 = P_1 \frac{a_2}{a_1}$$

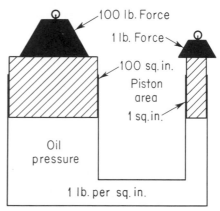

FIG. 25-10. *The effects and relationship of pressure and area for a liquid in a closed container.*

Also, the work done by the small piston is equal to the work done by the large piston; that is, $P_1d_1 = P_2d_2$ and the distances through which the pistons move vary inversely as their areas.

Figure 25-11 shows the essential parts and principles of operation of a simple hydraulic-control device as used on tractors. It consists of (1) an oil reservoir, (2) a pump to provide circulation and pressure, (3) a hydraulic or ram cylinder and piston, (4) a control valve and lever, and (5) the necessary oil lines. The piston rod may be connected directly to a suitable lifting linkage to raise and lower the implement, or it may be connected to a crank and a rock shaft on the tractor, which in turn supplies the lifting action. Although the gear pump, as illustrated, is most commonly used, some systems use either a piston or a vane-type pump. Pressures vary from 500 to 2,500 lb. per sq. in. Pressures higher than this require a multiple-cylinder piston pump.

Types of hydraulic controls

A. Rear-mounted and trailing machines
  1. Three-point hitch.
    a. Implement raised hydraulically but depth controlled by machine weight, gauge wheels, hitch adjustment, or other implement adjustments or characteristics.
    b. Implement lifted hydraulically and depth controlled by manual control lever or by load reaction or both.

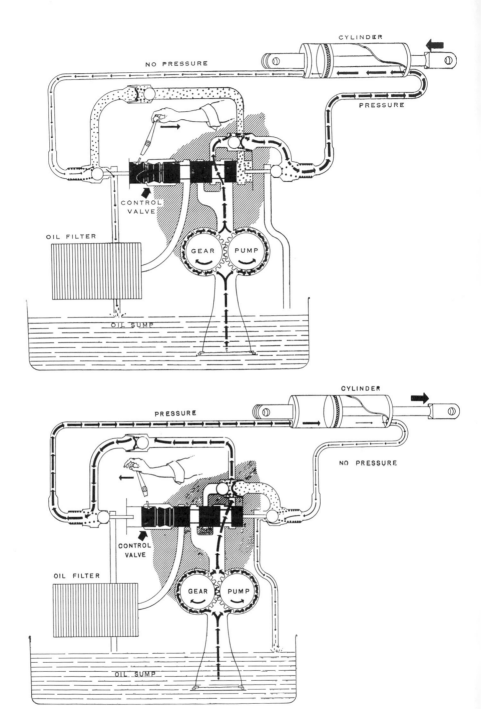

FIG. 25-11. *Make-up and operation of a hydraulic lift system for a tractor.* (Courtesy of J. I. Case Company.)

2. Drawbar or similar special hitch for trailing implements.

    a. Machine setting and adjustment controlled by remote hydraulic cylinders and flexible oil lines.

B. Side- and front-mounted machines.

1. Implement position and depth controlled by linkage connection to hydraulically operated rock shaft.

2. Implement lowered and raised and otherwise controlled by one or more hydraulic cylinders connected to lift pump by flexible oil lines.

3. Combination of rock shaft and independent hydraulic cylinders.

Three-point hitches. Figures 25-12 and 25-13 show typical three-point hitch mechanisms consisting of two side-draft links and an upper center link. The implement is equipped with suitable attachment members, and

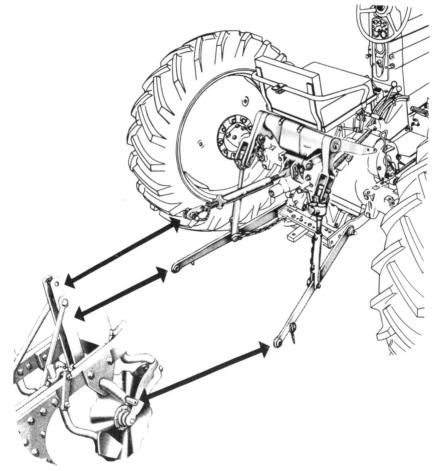

FIG. 25-12. *Typical three-point hitch mechanism.* (Courtesy of Deere and Company.)

provision is made to permit easy and quick attachment. Adjustments on both the side and upper links permit proper setting of the implement to give the most effective performance. A special drawbar attached to the side-draft links readily adapts the device to ordinary trailing machines.

Normally, the raising and lowering of the implement and its depth setting is controlled by a hand lever connected to very sensitive valves

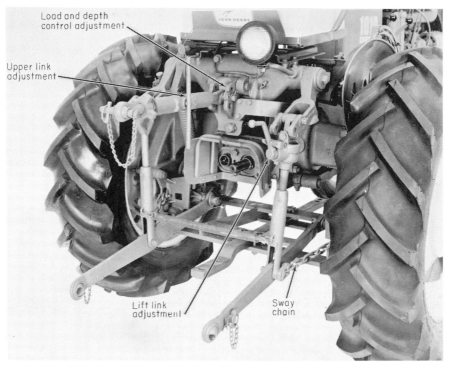

Load and depth control adjustment

Upper link adjustment

Lift link adjustment

Sway chain

FIG. 25-13. *Universal-type three-point hitch.* (Courtesy of Deere and Company.)

in the oil circuits. However, some three-point hitches are so designed that the draft or load reaction automatically adjusts the draft of the implement to the soil and traction conditions. This is particularly applicable to plows operating in a field in which soil conditions vary considerably. All these automatic-load and depth-control devices function in much the same manner, that is, by means of the varying force and pressure reaction in the upper hitch link. This link is connected indirectly through a very heavy coil spring to a sensitive valve in the hydraulic circuit. For example, referring to Fig. 25-14, when the plow encounters a heavy or hard soil condition, a forward pressure is exerted on the upper link, which, in turn, reacts against the spring and actuates a valve in the hydraulic circuit causing the mechanism to lift the implement slightly and relieve the load. When the hard spot is passed, the force on the spring decreases and the plow returns to its normal depth setting. Usually a number of spring-pressure settings are provided to vary the spring and valve-control sensitivity according to the type of implement and the soil conditions. A means is also provided to lock out the automatic depth-control device so that the implement will remain at some set working depth without regard to field conditions. Figure 25-15 shows

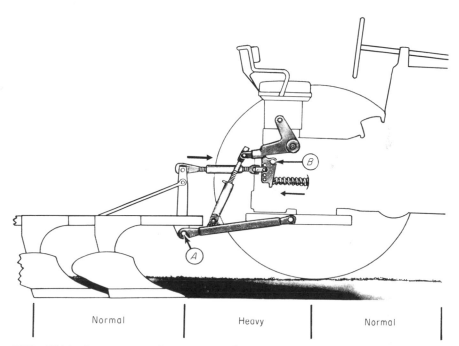

Normal   Heavy   Normal

FIG. 25-14. *Operation of the automatic load and depth control for a hydraulic mechanism.*

another load- and depth-control mechanism which utilizes a cam-and-lever arrangement and an external hydraulic cylinder to effect the proper depth, draft, and traction relationships. A hand lever *F* enables the operator to adjust the setting quickly to the existing conditions.

Hydraulic controls for side- and front-mounted tools. Side- and front-mounted machines such as cultivators, planters, and loaders are controlled hydraulically either (1) directly by a linkage to the rock shaft or (2) by remote cylinders (Fig. 25-16). Remote-lift cylinders are connected to the pressure pump and control mechanism by heavy-duty flexible hose lines with convenient leakproof push-pull couplings. Lift cylinders may be either single or double acting. Single-acting cylinders produce only a lifting action and depend upon the weight of the implement or load and oil-flow rate for the downward movement. Double-acting cylinders

provide positive action in either direction and must have two oil lines
and connections. Hydraulic cylinders may be equipped with stroke-limit-
ing stops to limit the piston travel and working depth of the implement.

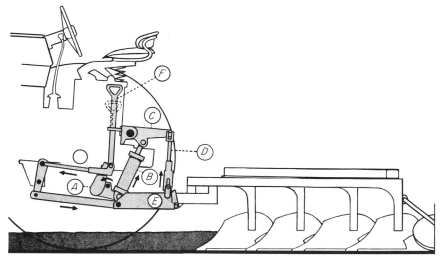

FIG. 25-15. *Hydraulic load- and depth-control mechanism with manual adjustment.*
(Courtesy of International Harvester Company.)

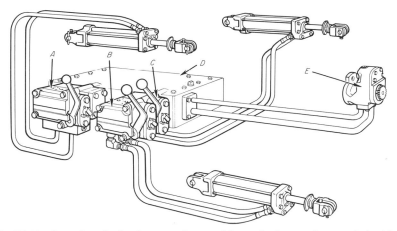

FIG. 25-16. *Complete hydraulic-control assembly with three valves and double-lift
cylinders.* (Courtesy of International Harvester Company.)

These stops are either a simple mechanical device on the cylinder or a
piston-actuated valve which controls the oil flow.

   Delayed and selective action lifts. Mounted-type tractor cultivators
usually consist of three separate units, namely, two side gang units and
a rear unit. Figure 25-16 shows a three-cylinder arrangement with pump

and control valves which permits delaying the lifting of the rear gang so that it cultivates to the end of the row and even with the other gangs. In other cases, it is possible to lift one side unit independently of the other. This is particularly desirable in small, hilly, irregular, or terraced fields.

Trailing implement control. Certain drawbar-pulled trailing implements such as plows, disk harrows, and grain drills utilize remote hydraulic cylinders to raise and lower or adjust them to operating conditions, as shown by Fig. 25-17. Other machines such as grain combines

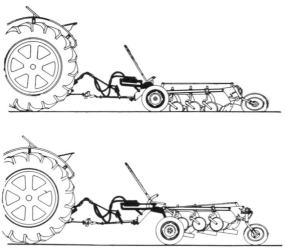

FIG. 25-17. *Hydraulic control of a trailing plow.*

and cotton pickers utilize hydraulic cylinders for controlling certain machine parts such as the header on combines and the picking drum on cotton pickers.

Special hydraulic systems. Some late models of tractors which have hydraulic-powered brakes and steering as well as hydraulic implement controls are equipped with a hydraulic system which is specially designed to supply the power for these different operations in the most effective, efficient, and convenient manner. Such a system is shown in Fig. 25-18 and consists of a main pump, power steering, power brakes, hydraulically operated rockshaft, one or two selective control valves to operate remote hydraulic cylinders, a transmission pump, and an oil cooler. These components are connected together and supplied with oil from a common reservoir—the transmission case. The same oil which operates the hydraulic mechanisms lubricates the transmission and differential gears. A small, gear-type pump in the transmission assures adequate circulation of oil to the transmission parts. It also changes and cools the main pump and routes the oil to the cooler to maintain proper oil temperature.

This system is known as a closed-center, constant-pressure system because no oil is pumped unless there is a demand for it from one of the hydraulic mechanisms, and, when the operating valves which control the hydraulic mechanisms are in the neutral position, there is no flow of oil through these valves. It is a constant-pressure system for the reason that, with the engine and pump running, a constant pressure of 2,300 lb. per

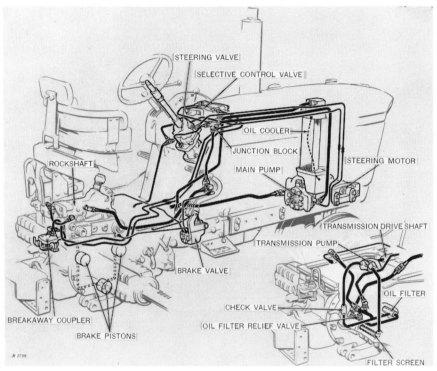

FIG. 25-18. *Complete closed-center hydraulic system.* (Courtesy of Deere and Company.)

sq. in. is maintained in the system. The open-center system pumps oil constantly through the hydraulic-mechanism operating valves and returns it to the reservoir.

According to Lehmann and Richey,[1] the closed-center hydraulic system has certain advantages and disadvantages as follows:

The advantages are:

1. Simpler valving and circuits in the case of multiple uses. Any number of cylinders can be operated from the single system simply by tapping a control valve into the pressure line. No provision is necessary for bypass oil other than the unloading valve at the pump.

[1] C. B. Richey and H. A. Lehmann, A Tractor Closed-center Hydraulic System, *Report,* Tractor and Implement Division, Ford Motor Company.

2. Simpler feathering control and instant response without waiting for pressure build-up. The pump is not required to withstand rapid pressure fluctuations, as in feathering or draft control with an open-center system.

3. Lower peak power requirement than in an open-center system. An open-center system operates only at the pressure required, but at its peak pressure, power requirement will exceed that required by a small pump with an accumulator for power storage.

The disadvantages are:

1. All oil is pumped at high pressures although only a small proportion of the usage may require this pressure. Oil is throttled for low-pressure usage, thus wasting some energy which goes into heat build-up. On the other hand, bypass horsepower is appreciable with the open-center system, particularly where several valves are used. In the latter case power loss and heat build-up could equal or exceed that with a closed-center system.

2. Valves must seal against the full pressure at all times to avoid wasting energy, thus requiring poppet or ball check valves, and balancing for reasonable actuating effort is more difficult than with spool valves.

3. Either a variable-displacement pump or a fixed-displacement pump with an unload valve and accumulator is required, compared with only a fixed-displacement pump in an open-center system.

Care, lubrication, and servicing of hydraulic transmissions and implement controls. Hydraulic-type tractor transmissions and hydraulic mechanisms for controlling and operating various machines and attachments powered by the tractor will perform properly, provided certain precautions are observed and followed. These are (1) use the exact type and viscosity of oil recommended by the manufacturer; (2) maintain the correct oil level at all times; (3) avoid mixing of oils of dissimilar characteristics; (4) drain the system and refill with the specified lubricant and service the filter according to instructions; (5) avoid getting dust, grit, or foreign material in the system or on the oil line connections; and (6) check frequently for leaks.

There is considerable variation in the lubricant types and service recommendations for hydraulic transmissions and hydraulic-control mechanisms with respect to the different makes, types, and sizes of tractors. Hence it is most important that the specific instructions for any tractor be observed.

REFERENCES

BAINER, ROY, R. A. KEPNER, and E. L. BARGER, "Principles of Farm Machinery," John Wiley & Sons, Inc., New York, 1955.

BARGER, E. L., W. M. CARLETON, E. G. McKIBBEN, and ROY BAINER, "Tractors and Their Power Units," John Wiley & Sons, Inc., New York, 1952.

CLYDE, A. W., Mechanics of Plow and Tractor Hitches, *Agr. Eng.*, Vol. 15, No. 11.

CLYDE, A. W., Mounted Plows and Their Effects on the Tractor, *Agr. Eng.*, Vol. 21, No. 5.

CLYDE, A. W., Pitfalls in Applying the Science of Mechanics to Tractors and Implements, *Agr. Eng.*, Vol. 35, No. 2.

HEITSHU, D. C., The Kinematics of Tractor Hitches, *Agr. Eng.*, Vol. 33, No. 6.

JOHANNSEN, B. B., Tractor Hitches and Hydraulic Systems, *Agr. Eng.*, Vol. 35, No. 11.

TANQUARY, E. W., and A. W. CLYDE, New Principle in Tractor Hitch Design, *Agr. Eng.*, Vol. 38, No. 2.

WORTHINGTON, W. H., Evaluation of Factors Affecting the Operating Stability of Wheel Tractors, *Agr. Eng.*, Vol. 30, Nos. 3 and 4.

WORTHINGTON, W. H., and J. WALDO SEIPLE, Hydraulic Capacity Requirements for Control of Farm Implements, *Agr. Eng.*, Vol. 33, No. 5.

PROBLEMS AND QUESTIONS

1. Referring to Fig. 25-1D, compute the force F which is required for equilibrium if f_1 and f_2 are 850 lb. and 400 lb., respectively.

2. A tractor has a wheel base of 88 in. and weighs 6,400 lb. The static weight on the front wheels is 2,100 lb. Calculate the location of the center of gravity longitudinally with respect to the rear axle.

3. Referring to the tractor in Prob. 2, compute the drawbar load L which would be required to upset the tractor if the drawbar is attached below the rear axle and 16 in. vertically above point C.

4. What particular specifications with respect to stability should be considered in selecting a tractor to be used on extremely hilly land?

5. A track-type tractor has an over-all track width of 54 in. How much hitch offset on the drawbar, if any, is necessary if the tractor pulls four 14-in. moldboard plow bottoms and the desired minimum distance from the right-hand track to the furrow wall is 10 in.?

6. What force will be supported by the large piston (Fig. 25-10) if the pressure is 20 lb. per sq. in. and its area is reduced one-half?

7. Referring to Fig. 25-11, if the pump pressure is 300 lb. per sq. in., the cylinder is 3 in. in diameter, the piston stroke is 15 in., and the rate of oil flow is 300 cu. in. per min., what is the total force exerted by the piston, the work done by it in one stroke, and the time in seconds required to complete a stroke?

8. What are the advantages of integral or mounted machines?

9. Name some common examples of machines which can be operated satisfactorily when pulled from the tractor drawbar.

10. Explain the meaning of automatic draft control as applied to the three-point hitch, and describe the construction and operation of such a mechanism.

11. Explain the meaning of delayed and selective action lifts, and give their application and advantages.

26

Tractor Power Rating—Nebraska Tractor Tests

The present-day farm tractor is designed to deliver power in three distinct ways, namely, (1) by a pulley and belt, (2) by pulling effort at the drawbar, and (3) by means of a power take-off.

Power rating. As a rule, tractor sizes are designated according to the power capable of being generated at the pulley and at the drawbar. Obviously, the maximum power that can be generated by the power take-off will be practically the same as the belt power. However, when a tractor is operating a machine through the power take-off, the machine is usually being pulled. Therefore, only a certain fraction of the engine power is available at each point.

The usual practice of tractor manufacturers is to designate their various sizes by numbers or letters such as Model 520, D-12, and so on rather than by the actual power output. The specific available belt and drawbar power of any model is included in the detailed specifications.

Because of their crude construction and excessive weight, early tractors seldom delivered more than one-half the engine power at the drawbar. With the adoption of higher grade, lighter weight materials, enclosed transmissions running in oil, antifriction bearings, and precision workmanship, this power loss has been greatly reduced until at the present time it is not uncommon for a tractor to deliver 90 per cent of its belt power at the drawbar.

Tractor rating code. The American Society of Agricultural Engineers and the Society of Automotive Engineers have adopted a standard procedure for testing tractors.

Tractor horsepower testing. The belt horsepower of a tractor can be conveniently tested with an electric dynamometer or other type of dynamometer, as described in Chap. 5. The drawbar power is determined by placing a drawbar dynamometer in the hitch between the tractor and the load to be pulled, as explained in Chap. 5.

NEBRASKA TRACTOR LAW AND TESTS

A law known as the "Nebraska tractor law," which was enacted in that state and put into effect in 1919, has been of far-reaching effect, particularly in the design, construction, and operation of the farm tractor. The provisions of the law, the tests involved, and the results are outlined in detail in the discussion that follows.

Purpose of the law. The Nebraska tractor law, as stated in the Revised Statutes of Nebraska, 1943, Chapter 75, Article 9, Sections 75-901 to 75-911, inclusive, as amended in 1949, was enacted to encourage the manufacture and sale of improved tractors and to contribute to a more successful use of the tractor for farming.

It was thought that the best method of accomplishing these objects would be to require a tractor of each model sold in the state to be tested at the University of Nebraska and to have the results of these tests made public.

Provisions of the law. Stated briefly, the provisions of the law are:

1. That a stock tractor of each model sold in the state shall be tested and passed upon by a board of three engineers under state university management.

2. That each company, dealer, or individual offering a tractor for sale in Nebraska shall have a permit issued by the state railway commission. The permit for any model of tractor shall be issued after a stock tractor of that model has been tested at the University and the performance of the tractor compared with the claims made for it by the manufacturer.

3. That a service station with full supply of replacement parts for each model of tractor shall be maintained within the confines of the state and within reasonable shipping distance of customers.

It is understood that the tractor presented for testing shall be a stock model and shall not be equipped with any special appliance or apparatus not regularly supplied to the trade as outlined in the Nebraska tractor law. However, such things as mufflers, precleaners, starters, lights, generators, hydraulic pumps, power take-offs, and any other accessories that consume power and are purchased by users in the state shall be on the tractor at time of test.

Preliminary Procedure and Tests Prior to 1959

A representative of the manufacturer should be present during the test. His duties include unloading the tractor, installing wheel equipment or other accessories, operating the tractor during the "limber-up" run, making such adjustments as he may deem necessary before the test, and making repairs when necessary during the test. In addition to these duties, the manufacturer's representative makes all decisions involving permissible choices or company policy relative to the current test which are not covered in the application for test.

Before any tests are made, the lubricating oil is drained from the crankcase and is replaced with new oil. This new oil is selected by the manufacturer's representative from the brands generally available in Nebraska. It is of the viscosity specified in the application for test and is purchased by the tractor-testing laboratory in sealed containers. The oil specified shall have the same viscosity as the seasonal grade oil recommended for the first year's use. The oil is weighed and the weight per gallon at 60°F. is determined. All figures in the test report showing consumption of oil, fuel, or water in gallons are based on the amounts used in pounds and the weight per gallon at 60°F.

The fuel used is the lowest grade recommended by the manufacturer for use in the tractor being tested. For instance, if the application for test states that the tractor will operate on gasoline, tractor fuel, and distillate, distillate or tractor fuel will be used. The gasoline used is of the lowest commercial grade available, and in no case is a premium fuel used in an official test except in those cases where it is specified by the manufacturer as being essential to the successful operation of the engine.

Test A. The first test is made on the drawbar and is known as the *limber-up test.* The principal object of this test is to take out the stiffness likely to be found in a new machine and give the manufacturer an opportunity to check the condition of the tractor and ascertain if all the parts are working normally. The tractor is operated at approximately one-third rated load for 4 hr., two-thirds rated load for 4 hr., and full rated load for 4 hr. A reasonable amount of additional time is granted if desired. Each one of the forward gears is used for some portion of this test. The manufacturer's representative is responsible for the operation of the tractor during this test and may make such adjustments as he believes necessary, provided they do not conflict with the specifications in the application for test.

Adjustments that are permissible include setting the valve tappet clearance and the gap of the breaker points or spark-plug points, adjusting the clutch, and making other adjustments of a similar nature. This provision does not permit the installation of new parts or accessories without having them mentioned in the official report of the test.

Belt Tests

Test B, 100 per cent maximum belt test. The engine is run at full load until it is thoroughly warmed up and has reached a condition of constant operating temperature. All adjustments are made to secure maximum output from the engine at rated speed. Rated crankshaft speed is that number of revolutions per minute recommended by the manufacturer for normal operation. The governor is set to hold the throttle valve to the extreme open position, the spark is set to give the best results, the manifold heat control, if present, is set at the most favorable position, and the carburetor is carefully adjusted to that point at which an additional amount of fuel gives no increase but less fuel decreases the power output at the rated speed of the engine. After uniform operating conditions are reached, this test, known as the 100 *per cent maximum test,* is continued for 2 hr. The object of this test is to check or establish belt-horsepower ratings.

Test C, operating maximum belt test. In case the manufacturer wishes to use a carburetor adjustment leaner than the 100 per cent setting, a series of trial runs of 20 to 30 min. at leaner settings are made and the manufacturer's representative is permitted to choose from these an "operating setting." This operating setting of the carburetor is the setting recommended by the manufacturer as being the most practical for general use, and it is used throughout the remainder of the test with the exception of the 100 per cent maximum drawbar test in rated gear (to determine the drawbar rating), when the adjustment used is the 100 per cent maximum power setting as obtained on the belt.

The first run on this operating setting is a 1-hr. maximum power test known as the *operating maximum belt test*. The object of this test is to determine the maximum power developed and the fuel consumption at the carburetor setting that is practical for field operations. The radiator cover or shutters, manifold heat control, and spark are set at the most favorable positions, the engine is run until operating conditions have become stabilized, and then readings are taken at 10-min. intervals over a 1-hr. period.

In case the tractor has a fixed-jet carburetor, or the manufacturer does not wish to use a leaner mixture with an adjustable-jet carburetor, or the tractor has a diesel engine, the operating setting is the same as the 100 per cent setting and Tests B and C are the same.

Test D, rated-load belt test. The next belt test is of 1 hr. duration and is known as the *rated-load belt test*. The object of this test is to determine whether the tractor will carry its rated load on the belt and to secure a record of fuel consumption and other operating data. The carburetor remains set at the operating setting. The tractor is given, as nearly as possible, its rated load, and the governor is adjusted to maintain rated engine speed. Rated load is determined in one of two ways. If the tractor is rated by the manufacturer, sufficient load is applied to develop rated horsepower at rated engine speed. In case the manufacturer either does not specify the rating of the tractor or elects to accept the "calculated" rating, then rated load becomes 85 per cent of the corrected maximum as calculated from the results of the 100 per cent maximum belt test.

Test E, varying-load belt test. The last run on the belt is known as the *varying-load test*. The carburetor setting, governor setting, and ignition timing are the same as in the rated-load test. The object of this test is to show fuel consumption and governor control of the engine speed when the load varies. It is composed of six 20-min. runs made in the following order: The first is rated-load, which is the same load as the 1-hr. rated-load test just completed; in fact, if conditions are favorable, the rated- and varying-load tests are continuous and the last 20 min. of the rated-load run are used for the first 20 min. of the varying-load test. This is followed by 20 min. at no load. The minimum load is applied and the power developed is approximately one horsepower. The next load applied is one-half the rated-load torque, and this is followed by a maximum-horsepower test in which enough load is applied on the dynamometer to pull the engine far enough under rated speed to ensure an extreme throttle opening. The last two runs are made at one-fourth and three-fourths rated-load torque, respectively.

During the varying-load test the amount of heat applied to the intake manifold may be changed according to the load if an easily controlled manual adjustment, such as a lever operating from the driver's seat, is provided. An effort is made to maintain the recommended temperature of the cooling medium when possible, by regulating the amount of covering on the radiator in those cases where an adjustable cover is provided. These adjustments, it is believed, require no more attention than may reasonably be expected from a careful operator.

Drawbar Testing Equipment and Procedure

Drawbar pull is determined by means of a hydraulic cylinder inserted in the hitch between the tractor and the load. The drawbar pull exerted on a piston in this hydraulic cylinder creates a pressure in the cylinder. This pressure is carried through flexible metal tubing to the draft-recording instrument. The essential mechanism of this draft-recording unit is an engine-pressure indicator which has been so modified and calibrated that it leaves on a chart a continuous record of the drawbar pull of the tractor. From this chart, showing the pull in pounds, and from stop-watch readings showing the time of travel over a measured course 500 ft. long, the drawbar horsepower developed is calculated.

In determining slippage, the number of revolutions made by the drive wheels while the tractor is driven with no drawbar load over a 500-ft. distance is accurately determined. Rotary switches having 10 contact points are attached to each drive wheel and are connected to magnetic counters which record to one-tenth of one revolution the number of revolutions made over the 500-ft. distance. The difference between the actual number of revolutions recorded by the counter and the no-load count, divided by the former and the result multiplied by 100, is the per cent of slippage. When speaking of rubber-tire tests, some prefer to use the term *travel reduction*.

The engine speed is calculated by multiplying the wheel count by the gear ratio and dividing by the time.

In determining the drawbar horsepower of a tractor, it is necessary to provide a source of load that may be readily varied. The two principal loading units now used are built around a Massey-Harris 55 tractor and an Oliver Standard 88 HC tractor. The load is obtained by placing the loading unit in gear and operating its engine against compression without fuel or ignition. The load may be increased or decreased by closing or opening valves which have been installed on the exhaust manifolds of the engines. If a light load is desired, the tractor may be placed in gear, the fuel and ignition turned on, and the throttle set to give such assistance as will result in the desired load.

The instrument car, designed and built at the tractor-testing laboratory, was placed in service in 1940. It provides protection for the recording instruments and the operator from the weather and dust. Some of the instruments included in the car are the draft-recording instrument, two temperature indicators showing tractor cooling-medium temperature and air temperature, the wheel counters, and an engine-speed indicator. Two small gear pumps, mounted in the car and driven by the rear wheels through two transmissions, provide a small amount of drawbar load.

For all drawbar tests except Test H, at least two suitable drawbar runs are obtained over a measured distance of 500 ft. on the testing course. A suitable run is one in which the operating temperatures are normal, the load is relatively constant, and the average engine speed is at or very close to that specified by the manufacturer. Very seldom is a pull used in which the variation from rated speed is more than 1 per cent, and in each test in each gear an attempt is made to obtain an average number of revolutions per minute that does not deviate from rated speed more than one-half of 1 per cent.

Drawbar Tests

All tests of tractors with rubber tires are made on a concrete test course. All track-type tractors are tested on an earthen course which is maintained by grading, sprinkling, and rolling so that it remains nearly the same for each test.

FIG. 26-1. *Testing a tractor for drawbar power at University of Nebraska.*

Test F, 100 per cent maximum drawbar test. The first drawbar test is a maximum horsepower test using the "100 per cent" carburetor setting as found on the belt. The 100 per cent maximum test is made in one gear only—that gear designated by the manufacturer as most suitable for plowing or ordinary farm work. This is commonly known as *rated gear.* The results of this test are used to determine the "calculated" drawbar rating. The observed 100 per cent maximum drawbar horsepower is corrected to standard conditions and multiplied by 0.75. The result is the "calculated" rating.

Test G, operating maximum drawbar test. Operating maximum drawbar tests are made in the forward gears, using the operating carburetor setting selected and used on the operating belt tests. The object of these tests is to determine the maximum horsepower the tractor will develop in each forward gear with engine running at rated speed under the prevailing temperature and barometric conditions.

In the lower gears the traction developed by tractors equipped with rubber tires and added weights, and occasionally steel wheels, is not usually sufficient to transmit maximum engine horsepower. To determine the maximum horsepower in such gears, a series of runs is made in each gear, starting with the throttle partly closed so that the governor controls the engine speed and with sufficient load applied to produce a drive-wheel slippage of 5 to 6 per cent. Other runs are made with increased load, but with the throttle opened wider to give rated engine speed, which increases slippage. This balancing of throttle opening, engine speed, load, and slippage is carried to the point where either the engine is developing maximum power or the slippage is so great that the horsepower is appreciably reduced. Usually no results are used when the slippage exceeds 16 per cent. The horsepower is calculated for each of the 500-ft. runs. The runs producing the largest amount of power, and at the same time keeping within 1 per cent of rated engine speed, are averaged and recorded as the operating maximum drawbar horsepower in that gear.

Test H, rated-load drawbar test. The next run made on the drawbar is the rated-load test. The duration of the test is 10 hr. actual running time, as nearly continuous as possible, with constant load. A record is made of the time and reason for each stop, and also of any adjustments or repairs made on the tractor. The objects of this test are to determine whether the tractor can pull its rated load continuously and to secure a record of fuel consumption on drawbar work. The governor is adjusted to give rated speed of the engine with the tractor pulling rated load. The gear used is that recommended for plowing or ordinary farm work, which is known as rated gear. The carburetor remains at the operating setting. Rated load is determined in one of two ways. If the tractor is rated by the manufacturer, sufficient load is applied to develop rated horsepower at rated engine speed in rated gear. In case the manufacturer either does not specify the rating of the tractor or elects to accept the "calculated" rating, then rated load becomes 75 per cent of the corrected maximum as calculated from the results of the 100 per cent maximum drawbar test in rated gear.

Once each hour during the rated-load drawbar tests a chart is taken of the drawbar pull by means of the graphic recording drawbar dynamometer, and observations are made of the time required to travel 500 ft., the revolutions of the drive wheels over this same measured course, and the temperature of the air and cooling medium. From the chart and observations, calculations are made for the drawbar pull in pounds, the rate of travel in feet per minute and miles per hour, the drawbar horsepower, the engine revolutions per minute, and the drive-wheel slippage in percentage. The testing operator maintains the load as nearly constant as possible and, by following the progress of the test, applies such a load as will be sufficient to develop horsepower equal to or slightly in excess of rated horsepower.

Test J is made in rated gear only, using the operating carburetor setting. The principal object of Test J is to show the effect of the removal of added weight on the performance of the tractor. In Test J, the wheel and the tire equipment used is the same as in Tests F, G, and H except that all added weight, either liquid, cast iron, or any other form, is removed. Test J may be compared directly with the rated-gear run in Test G.

Test K is made in rated gear only, using the operating carburetor setting. The principal object of Test K is to show the effect of using smaller tires and wheels on the performance of the tractor. In Test K the smallest wheels and tires furnished as optional equipment by the manufacturer are used. This test can be compared with Test J. All added weight, either liquid, cast iron, or any other form, is removed.

Final Inspection

At the conclusion of the drawbar tests the lubricating oil is drained from the crankcase and weighed, the specific gravity at 60°F. is determined, and the number of gallons drained is calculated. A record is kept throughout the test of all oil added or drained. The test report and columns 9 and 10 of the summary sheet show the total number of gallons of new oil put in the crankcase and the gallons of used oil drained.

At this time the tractor is inspected. The manufacturer's representative, when so directed by the engineer in charge, disassembles any part of the tractor or its accessories in order to facilitate inspection. Particular attention is centered on such specifications as clearance volume, valve and port dimensions, bore and stroke, transmission, differential and belt-pulley reduction ratios, and the condition of such parts as valve heads and seats, spark plugs, magneto or distributor breaker points, pistons, bearings, and fuel, oil, and water connections.

Calculation of Horsepower Rating

Stipulations in the Nebraska tractor law require continued use of the same method of determining belt and drawbar ratings as was formerly embodied in the A.S.A.E. and S.A.E. code. These ratings are somewhat less than the maximum horsepower output of the tractor in order that the operator may be sure of having a certain amount of reserve for emergencies. The belt horsepower rating is 85 per cent of the maximum corrected horsepower obtained by correcting the observed horsepower in Test B to standard conditions (60°F. and 29.92 in. Hg).

The drawbar horsepower rating is 75 per cent of the maximum corrected horsepower obtained by correcting the observed horsepower in Test F to standard conditions (60°F. and 29.92 in. Hg).

A formula is used for making corrections for differences in air temperature and atmospheric pressure so that direct comparisons of maximum drawbar horsepower can be made. The formula used is as follows:

$$\text{hp}_c = \text{hp}_o \frac{P_s}{P_o} \sqrt{\frac{T_o}{T}}$$

where hp_c = corrected horsepower
  hp_o = observed horsepower
  P_o = observed barometric pressure, in. Hg
  P_s = standard barometric pressure, in. Hg
  T_o = observed absolute temperature, °F.
  T_s = standard absolute temperature, °F.

TESTING PROCEDURE AND REPORTS AFTER 1958

Effective with the 1959 testing season, the testing procedure was changed in some respects and is as follows:

General Conditions

The manufacturer selects the tractor that is tested. An official representative of the company is present during the test to see that the tractor gives its optimum performance.

Each tractor is a production model equipped with the common power-consuming accessories. These accessories can be disconnected only when it is convenient to do so in practice. Additional weight can be added as ballast if the manufacturer regularly supplies it for sale. The static tire loads and the inflation pressures must conform to recommendations in the tire standards published by the Tire and Rim Association.

Preparation for Performance Runs

The engine crankcase is drained and refilled with a measured amount of new oil conforming to specifications in the operator's manual. The fuel used and the maintenance operations must also conform to the published information delivered with the tractor. The tractor is operated in each gear with light to heavy loads during the limber-up period of 12 hours and is equipped with approximately the amount of added ballast that is used during maximum drawbar tests. The tire tread-bar height must be at least 65 per cent of new tread height prior to the maximum power run.

Belt or Power Take-off Performance

Power outlet performance runs are made by connecting either the belt pulley or the power take-off to a dynamometer. During a preliminary power outlet run the manufacturer's representative may make final adjustments for the fuel, ignition, and governor control settings. The manually operated governor control lever is set to provide the high-idle speed specified by the manufacturer for maximum power. No adjustments or settings are changed during all subsequent runs.

Maximum power and fuel-consumption test. Maximum power is obtained by setting the manually operated governor control lever in maximum position or by the specified setting of the diesel fuel pump and the rated engine speed specified by the manufacturer.

Standard power take-off speed. Whenever the power take-off speed during the maximum power run differs from the speeds set forth in the A.S.A.E. and S.A.E. standards, an additional run is made at either 540 or 1,000 r.p.m. of the power take-off.

Varying power and fuel consumption. Twenty-minute tests are made at six different horsepower levels to show corresponding fuel consumption and governor performance. They are 85 per cent of the dynamometer torque at maximum power, minimum dynamometer torque, maximum power, and one-fourth, one-half, and three-fourths of the 85 per cent torque. The average results of these tests indicate the average fuel consumption of a tractor under the varying loads encountered in field operations.

Drawbar Performance

All engine adjustments are the same as those used in the belt or power take-off tests. If the manufacturer specifies a different rated crankshaft speed for drawbar operations, then the position of the manually operated governor control is changed to provide the high-idle speed specified by the manufacturer in the operating instructions.

Maximum available power. The tractor is operated with a drawbar pull such that the manufacturer's selected travel speed is maintained over the straight 500-foot sections of the test course. Power output during this run may differ somewhat from that obtained in the maximum power run because of load changes around the two 180-degree turns of the test course.

Seventy-five per cent of pull at maximum power. The tractor is operated for 10 hours at 75 per cent of the drawbar pull obtained during the maximum power test.

Fifty per cent of pull at maximum power. The tractor is operated for 2 hours at 50 per cent of the drawbar pull obtained during the maximum power test.

Maximum power with ballast. Maximum drawbar power is determined at the manufacturer's specified engine speed in each gear of the tractor within certain limits as follows: (1) slippage of the drive wheels may not exceed 15 per cent for pneumatic tires on the concrete test course or 7 per cent for steel cleats on the well-packed earthen test course; (2) ground speeds may not exceed 15 miles per hour; (3) safe stability limits of the tractor may not be exceeded; (4) static tire loads and inflation pressures must conform to published standards. The drawbar load is increased until the manufacturer's specified engine speed is obtained with either wide-open throttle or the specified setting of the diesel pump. Travel speed, drawbar pull, and other data are recorded over two 500-foot straight, level portions of the test course.

Maximum power without ballast. All added ballast is removed from the tractor. The maximum drawbar power is determined by the same procedure used in obtaining maximum power with ballast. The travel speed is the same as that used in the 10-hour run.

Varying power and travel speed with ballast. Travel speeds corresponding to drawbar pulls beyond the maximum power range are obtained to show the lugging ability of the tractor. The run starts with the pull at maximum power. Then additional drawbar pull is applied at 10 per cent intervals to cause decreasing speeds. The test is ended by one of three conditions, namely, when (1) maximum pull is attained, (2) the maximum slippage limit is reached, or (3) some other operating limit is reached.

Test Report

The following is a representative test report as prepared and issued upon completion of a test:

Nebraska Tractor Test 766—Oliver 1800 Gasoline

Department of Agricultural Engineering

Dates of Test: October 3 to October 11, 1960. Manufacturer: The Oliver Corporation, Charles City, Iowa. Manufacturer's power rating: not rated.

Fuel, Oil, and Time

Fuel: regular gasoline. Octane No.: motor 84. Research: 92 (rating taken from oil company's typical inspection data). Specific gravity converted to 60°/60° 0.7475. Weight per gallon 6.223 lb. Oil S.A.E. 10W. A.P.I. service classification MS, DG. To motor 1.644 gal. Drained from motor 1.248 gal. Transmission and final-drive lubricant S.A.E. 10W-30 engine oil with Oliver special oil additive. Total time engine was operated 45 hr.

Engine

Make: Oliver gasoline. Type: 5 cylinder vertical. Serial No. 115662. Crankshaft mounted lengthwise. Rated r.p.m. 2,000. Bore and stroke 3¾ by 4 in. Compression ratio 8.5 to 1. Displacement 265 cu. in. Carburetor size 1¼ in. Ignition system battery. Cranking system 12-volt electric. Lubrication pressure. Air cleaner oil washed wire mesh. Oil filter replaceable pleated paper element. Fuel filter screen in sediment bowl. Muffler was used. Cooling medium temperature control thermostat.

Chassis

Type: tricycle. Serial No. 90526-886. Tread width: rear 68 to 89½ in.; front: 9¼ to 14½ in. Wheel base 103 in. Center of gravity (without operator or ballast, with minimum tread, with fuel tank filled and tractor serviced for operation). Horizontal distance forward from center line of rear wheels 30.9 in. Vertical distance above roadway 35.5 in. Horizontal distance from center of rear wheel tread 0 in. to the right/left. Hydraulic-control system direct engine drive. Transmission: selective gear fixed ratio. Advertised speeds, m.p.h.: first 1.59, second 3.07, third 4.29, fourth 5.31, fifth 8.27, sixth 14.30; reverse 1.80 and 4.84. Clutch: single plate operated by foot pedal. Brakes: double disk operated by foot pedals which can be locked. Steering: power assisted. Turning radius (on concrete surface with brake applied) right 115 in., left 115 in.; (on concrete surface without brake) right 124 in., left 124 in. Turning space diameter (on concrete surface with brake applied) right 237 in., left 237 in.; (on concrete surface without brake) right 256 in., left 256 in. Belt pulley 1,053 r.p.m. at 2,000 engine r.p.m. diam. 11⁵⁄₁₆ in. face 8¾ in. Belt speed 3,100 f.p.m. Power take-off 1,000 r.p.m. at 2,000 engine r.p.m.

Repairs and Adjustments

No repairs or adjustments.

Remarks

All test results were determined from observed data obtained in accordance with the S.A.E. and A.S.A.E. test code.

We, the undersigned, certify that this is a true and correct report of official Tractor Test 766.

L. F. LARSEN, Engineer-in-Charge

L. W. Hurlbut, Chairman
G. W. Steinbruegge
J. J. Sulek
Board of Tractor Test Engineers

Power Take-off Performance

Hp.	Crank-shaft speed, r.p.m.	Fuel consumption		Hp.-hr. per gal.	Temp., °F.			Barom-eter, in. Hg
		Gal. per hr.	Lb. per hp.-hr.		Cool-ing med.	Air wet bulb	Air dry bulb	

Maximum Power and Fuel Consumption
Rated Engine Speed—2 hr.

Hp.	Crank-shaft speed, r.p.m.	Gal. per hr.	Lb. per hp.-hr.	Hp.-hr. per gal.	Cooling med.	Air wet bulb	Air dry bulb	Barometer, in. Hg
73.92	2,000	5.608	0.472	13.18	133	60	75	29.048

Varying Power and Fuel Consumption—2 hr.

Hp.	Crank-shaft speed, r.p.m.	Gal. per hr.	Lb. per hp.-hr.	Hp.-hr. per gal.	Cooling med.	Air wet bulb	Air dry bulb	Barometer, in. Hg
64.34	2,048	4.975	0.481	12.93	130	60	75	. . . .
0.00	2,181	1.649	. . . .	. . . .	120	58	72	. . . .
32.69	2,082	3.418	0.651	9.56	122	58	74	. . . .
73.78	2,000	5.616	0.474	13.14	130	60	75	. . . .
16.59	2,114	2.589	0.971	6.41	125	59	74	. . . .
48.71	2,067	4.127	0.527	11.80	128	60	75	. . . .
Avg. 39.35	2,082	3.729	0.590	10.55	126	59	74	29.028

Drawbar Performance

Hp.	Draw-bar pull, lb.	Speed, m.p.h.	Crank-shaft speed, r.p.m.	Slip of driv-ers, %	Fuel consumption		Hp.-hr. per gal.	Temp., °F.			Ba-rom-eter, in. Hg.
					Gal. per hr.	Lb. per hp.-hr.		Cool-ing me-di-um	Air wet bulb	Air dry bulb	
Varying Drawbar Power and Fuel Consumption with Ballast Maximum available power—2 hr.—4th gear											
61.66	4,427	5.22	2,000	4.33	5.267	0.532	11.71	132	58	68	28.730
75% of pull at maximum power—10 hr.—4th gear											
50.32	3,485	5.41	2,060	3.51	4.580	0.566	10.99	129	54	63	28.789
50% of pull at maximum power—2 hr.—4th gear											
33.68	2,275	5.55	2,080	2.15	3.725	0.688	9.04	130	58	65	28.770
Maximum Power with Ballast											
40.77	10,619	1.44	2,067	14.99	1st gear............		131	58	70	28.920
61.55	8,115	2.84	1,999	9.78	2d gear.............		134	58	70	28.920
62.58	5,703	4.11	2,000	6.73	3d gear.............		138	58	70	28.920
63.71	4,626	5.16	1,998	5.12	4th gear............		136	58	70	28.920
63.03	2,860	8.26	2,006	2.93	5th gear............		135	57	67	28.900
55.98	1,452	14.46	2,005	1.71	6th gear............		133	57	67	28.900
Maximum Power without Ballast											
63.12	4,605	5.14	2,004	7.06	4th gear............		134	69	77	28.930

Varying Drawbar Pull and Travel Speed with Ballast—4th Gear

Pounds pull.....	4,650	4,700	4,800	4,850	4,900	4,950	4,750
Horsepower.....	63.7	58.9	52.5	46.6	40.5	34.3	26.6
Miles per hour...	5.2	4.7	4.1	3.6	3.1	2.6	2.1

Tires, Ballast, and Weight

	With ballast	Without ballast
Rear tires:		
No., size, ply, and p.s.i . . .	Two 18.4-34; 8; 20	Two 18.4-34; 8; 16
Ballast:		
Liquid	745 lb. each	None
Cast iron	1,950 lb. each	None
Front tires:		
No., size, ply, and p.s.i . . .	Two 7.50-15; 6; 36	Two 7.50-15; 6; 28
Ballast:		
Liquid	None	None
Cast iron	268 lb. each	None
Height of drawbar	21 in.	22 in.
Static weight:		
Rear	11,280 lb.	5,890 lb.
Front	2,880 lb.	2,345 lb.
Total weight with operator	14,335 lb.	8,410 lb.

REFERENCES

Farm Equipment Red Book, 45th ed., Technical Publications, Inc., Kansas City, Mo., 1961.

HURLBUT, L. W., L. F. LARSEN, G. W. STEINBRUEGGE, and J. J. SULEK, The Nebraska Tractor Tests, *Agr. Eng.*, Vol. 41, No. 4.

Nebraska Tractor Tests, *Univ. Nebraska Agr. Expt. Sta. Bulls.* 388, 392, and 397.

SMITH, C. W., and L. F. LARSEN, Method of Drawbar Testing at the Nebraska Tractor Testing Laboratory, *Agr. Eng.*, Vol. 30, No. 9.

PROBLEMS AND QUESTIONS

1. State the reasons for the passage of the Nebraska Tractor Law, name its basic provisions, and explain why other states do not have a similar law.

2. Using the formula given in the test procedure, compute the corrected maximum belt and drawbar horsepower as well as the recommended rated belt and drawbar power for the Oliver tractor, Test Report 766.

3. Using the data showing fuel consumption at different belt power loads in Test Report 766, prepare a curve showing the relationship of thermal efficiency and belt power at different loads.

4. Tabulate the maximum belt and drawbar horsepower test results for ten representative wheel tractors and compare them with respect to drawbar efficiency.

5. Repeat Question 4, using five representative track-type tractors.

6. Referring to the test reports for the tractors used in Question 4, com-

pute the drawbar-horsepower–weight ratio (maximum available power with ballast) for these tractors and compare them.

7. Repeat Question 6, using the test reports for the five track-type tractors used in Question 5.

8. What consideration is given to wheel ballast and tire sizes in testing a tractor at the University of Nebraska?

27

Engine and Tractor Servicing and Maintenance

The life and service given by an internal-combustion engine or tractor are dependent largely upon the care and treatment accorded it by the operator. Farm power equipment is made of high-grade materials, fine precision and workmanship are used in its manufacture, and its design in every respect is being constantly improved and refined.

No attempt will be made here to outline any definite procedure or set of rules that, if followed, will ensure the satisfactory performance of any machine under all conditions. All tractor manufacturers now supply with their machines a well-prepared set of operating and service instructions. The first thing a tractor operator should do is become thoroughly familiar with the machine by studying the instruction book carefully. Second, he should follow these instructions in adjusting, repairing, and operating the machine.

ENGINE TROUBLES

A large part of all tractor troubles is confined to the engine. As a rule, certain conditions are essential in order to start an engine and have it operate normally. These are:

1. Each cylinder should have reasonable compression.
2. A correct fuel mixture must be supplied to each cylinder.
3. The ignition system must function properly and ignite the fuel mixture at the right time.
4. The valves must be correctly timed.
5. The moving parts must be properly lubricated.
6. The cooling system must maintain the usual operating temperature.

In short, there are six general classes of troubles, namely, (1) compression, (2) fuel and carburetion, (3) ignition, (4) timing, (5) lubrication, and (6) cooling.

Again there are (1) starting troubles and (2) running troubles. An engine may start hard or fail to start at all, or it may start readily but run only a short time and stop.

Causes of poor compression. Any engine must have reasonable compression in order to start readily and operate efficiently. Compression depends largely upon the care and attention given an engine and the period of service since its initial operation or last overhaul. Some of the common causes of poor compression are:

1. Badly worn piston, piston rings, or cylinder.
2. Poorly fitted piston or rings.
3. Scored or damaged cylinder walls.
4. Leaks around cylinder head or spark plug.
5. Worn, damaged, stuck, or poorly adjusted valves, or weak or broken valve spring.
6. Carbon or other foreign matter under valves.
7. Poor piston and cylinder lubrication.

Fuel and carburetor troubles. The fuel-supply and carburetion system of an engine probably ranks next to the ignition system as a source of trouble, both in starting and in operating. Most of the more common troubles are listed below but no attempt is made to include every possible trouble or to suggest a diagnosis and remedy for each one. Some of the usual troubles are:

1. Fuel flow cut off or restricted, due to closed valve, clogged fuel line or strainer, low fuel supply, stuck carburetor float and valve.
2. Excessive fuel flow, due to stuck float and valve, dirt under valve, punctured or waterlogged float.
3. Fuel mixture too lean or too rich, due to improperly adjusted carburetor.
4. Water in the fuel or carburetor.
5. Air cleaner loose, leaking, or in need of servicing.
6. Intake manifold leaking or obstructing mixture flow.

Ignition troubles. The generation and production of a good electric spark in the combustion chamber at the correct time in the cycle depends upon the almost perfect functioning of a number of more or less delicate parts and devices, even in the simplest electric system. A particle of metal, a bit of moisture, or a single loose connection may disrupt the ignition system entirely, which would mean considerable delay and loss of time.

Ignition troubles are usually indicated by the engine failing to fire when cranked, or by its suddenly going "dead" while apparently running smoothly. However, certain ignition troubles, such as loose connections or parts which intermittently open and close the circuit as a result of vibration and jars, cause the engine to fire irregularly or unevenly.

The troubles as listed below are divided into two groups depending on whether the source of ignition is a battery or a magneto.

A. Battery ignition troubles:
1. Open switch
2. Battery weak or discharged
3. One or more weak cells in a battery
4. Loose or corroded connections
5. Broken wire
6. Short circuit due to bare wire, moisture on coils, spark plugs, or connections
7. Coil winding short-circuited or burned out
8. Breaker points rough, wet, oily, poorly adjusted, or sticking
9. Spark plug fouled and short-circuited by carbon
10. Spark plug damp or wet on outside
11. Spark-plug insulator cracked or broken
12. Spark-plug points too close or too far apart
13. Spark out of time
14. System not wired up correctly
B. Magneto ignition troubles:
1. Brushes dirty or broken
2. Armature dragging because of worn bearings
3. Breaker points rough, dirty, oily, or improperly adjusted
4. Movable breaker point stuck and does not work freely
5. Winding short-circuited
6. Cracked or broken insulation
7. Magneto grounded
8. Magneto not in time with engine
9. Magnet poles incorrectly arranged—like poles should be on same side
10. Magnets weak
11. Distributor gear or breaker point opening not in time with armature

Timing troubles. Timing troubles involve the correct opening and closing of the valves and occurrence of the spark with relation to the piston travel. Incorrect timing seldom prevents the engine from starting and running reasonably well, but it often reduces the power output and causes overheating and high fuel consumption. Some of the common timing troubles are:
1. Cam gear improperly timed with crankshaft gear.
2. Valve clearance improperly adjusted.
3. Ignition-timing mechanism such as breaker points or distributor poorly adjusted or improperly connected.

Overheating. Overheating of an engine may be caused by the following:

1. Late spark.
2. Late exhaust opening.
3. Too rich or too lean fuel mixture.
4. Engine poorly lubricated.
5. Cooling system not functioning properly—water low, fan belt broken or loose, water pump not working, excessive scale deposits in water jacket, or water passages clogged.
6. Excessive carbon deposits.
7. Piston, piston rings, and bearings tight.

Lack of power. Some of the usual causes of lack of power are:

1. Improperly adjusted carburetor
2. Valves out of time
3. Spark coming too early or too late
4. Engine stiff or poorly lubricated
5. Poor compression
6. Engine running too hot

Knocking and pounding. In general, knocks are caused by preignition of the fuel mixture or by loose parts. The former is readily distinguished from the latter by the characteristic "ping." Preignition and detonation knocks are caused by:

1. Spark advanced too far
2. Engine overheated
3. Excessive carbon deposits
4. Incorrect fuel mixture
5. Use of low-octane fuel

The usual engine knocks may be due to:

1. Loose or worn bearings
2. Loose or worn piston pins
3. Worn timing gear
4. Excessive valve clearance
5. Badly worn pistons

STARTING TROUBLES

Engine fails to start. When an engine fails to start or show any signs of firing, check it as follows:

1. See that there is fuel in the tank and that it is turned on and flowing to the carburetor. Starting troubles are often caused by low-grade fuels, water in the fuel or carburetor, or a fuel that has stood in the tank long enough to permit the more volatile portions to evaporate. Fresh fuel should be used for starting in cold weather.

2. See that a fuel mixture is being drawn into the cylinder but not

in such quantities as to flood the engine. Too much fuel in the cylinder is just as troublesome as too little.

3. See that the switch is closed and the ignition system is producing a good spark at the correct time.

4. See that there is reasonable compression.

5. See that the valves are properly timed.

Engine hard to start. Difficult starting and slow pickup in an engine may be due to one or more of a number of conditions, some of which are:

1. Poor compression.

2. Poor grade of fuel or water in the fuel, carburetor, or cylinder.

3. Carburetor improperly adjusted so that fuel mixture is too lean or too rich.

4. Weak spark or ignition system poorly timed.

5. Valves poorly timed.

6. Engine stiff, due to tight bearings and pistons, cold weather, poor lubrication, or overheating.

Engine starts easily but stops immediately. If an engine starts readily but runs only a few minutes at the most, check up the following:

1. The fuel flow from the tank to the carburetor may be slow or irregular due to a clogged fuel line or strainer, stuck float and valve, or a low fuel level in the tank.

2. There may be water in the fuel.

3. There may be a loose connection or a broken wire in the ignition system.

4. The engine may be poorly cooled or lubricated and, therefore, heat up rapidly.

Tractor maintenance—workshop and tools. Tractor maintenance in general may be appropriately broken down into (1) operator or owner maintenance and (2) dealer service. Owner maintenance includes those regular or periodic adjustments and operations—daily, weekly, or monthly—necessary to keep the machine operating in a normal manner without excessive wear and breakage. Dealer service includes those operations involving disassembly, replacement, and reconditioning of major parts or units. Modern tractor construction is such that special tools and equipment as well as skilled mechanics are needed for these major repair operations, and the average tractor owner cannot afford to make the needed investment in such tools unless he is using a large number of units.

In this day of intensive farm mechanization, a convenient, well-planned, and well-equipped shop is a worth-while investment. The proper size and type of construction for a suitable shop depends largely on the size of the farm and amount of equipment utilized. For a small farm having a limited amount of machinery and building investment, the shop may perhaps consist merely of a small room about 12 by 14 ft., attached to the garage or some other outbuilding. For a medium-size farm utilizing one or more large tractors and other machinery, the shop should be about 16 by 24 ft. and should have a door large enough for a truck or tractor to enter. Very large farms having a large quantity of machinery should have a relatively large shop equipped with numerous power tools as well as hand tools.

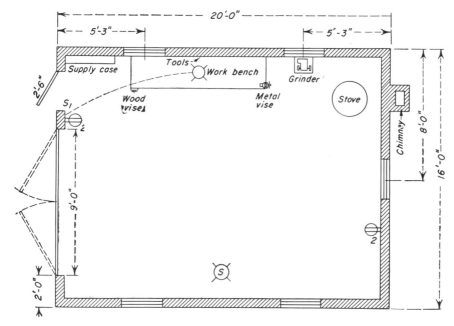

FIG. 27-1. *Floor plan for a practical farm repair shop and garage.*

Frequently it is desirable to combine the shop with the garage (Fig. 27-1). In that way sufficient space can be kept open for parking the family car and additional space provided in front and to one side for workbenches and tools. Then, when a tractor is to be repaired, it can be driven into the space usually occupied by the car and worked on during bad weather.

In general, a good farm repair shop should have:
1. Floor space large enough for repairing farm machinery.
2. Entrance door large enough to admit machinery.
3. Workbench, metal vise, anvil, drill, and emery wheel.
4. Hand tools to do any ordinary repair or construction work.
5. Welding outfit—either electric or gas.
6. Electricity, with several wall-outlet sockets.
7. Ample light, both natural and artificial.

8. Storage space for hand tools, machinery parts, lumber, iron, oil, wire, belts, and portable equipment.

9. Storage facilities for necessary bolts, screws, nails, rivets, washers, cotter pins, and the like.

The selection of shop tools depends to a large extent upon the kinds and types of jobs that occur about the farm. Furthermore, the size of the farm and amount of equipment used are important factors.

In general this tool equipment can be classified according to its use, such as woodworking tools, metalworking and blacksmith tools, tractor- and machine-repair tools, power tools, and so on. The tools listed below represent those which are most common and which should prove most useful in a shop on an average general crop and livestock farm.

Woodworking tools
  1 hand saw
  1 rip saw
  1 nail hammer
  1 steel square
  1 try square
  1 carpenter's level
  1 folding rule
  1 steel tape
  1 jack plane
  1 block plane
  1 ratchet brace
  1 set wood bits
  1 set wood chisels
  4 screw drivers (assorted sizes)
  1 ax
  1 hand ax
  1 divider
  1 wood mallet
  1 plumb bob
  1 draw knife
  1 pliers
  1 oil stone
Blacksmith and metalworking tools
  1 ball peen hammer
  1 heavy blacksmith hammer
  1 set cold chisels (assorted sizes and types)
  1 set punches (assorted sizes)
  6 files—flat and round (assorted sizes)
  1 tin snips

1 post or electric drill
1 set twist drills ($\frac{1}{16}$ to $\frac{1}{2}$ in.)
1 hack saw
1 tap and die set ($\frac{1}{4}$ to $\frac{1}{2}$ in.)
1 blowtorch
1 soldering copper
1 hand or electric bench grinder
3 pipe wrenches (10, 14, and 18 in.)
Tractor and machinery repair tools
  1 pliers
  1 long-nose pliers
  1 locking pliers
  1 socket-wrench set ($\frac{7}{16}$ to $1\frac{1}{2}$ in.)
  1 set box-end wrenches ($\frac{3}{8}$ to $\frac{3}{4}$ in.)
  1 set open-end adjustable wrenches (6, 8, and 10 in.)
  1 set open-end wrenches
  1 speed counter
  1 extension cord and lamp
Optional tools
  1 forge
  2 forge tongs
  1 anvil
  1 pipe vise
  1 pipe stock and die set
  1 portable electric drill with stand
  1 electric bench saw
  1 oxygen-acetylene welding outfit
  1 electric arc welder

The suggested lists are primarily to assist the individual in making a suitable selection. If electricity is available, such equipment as an elec-

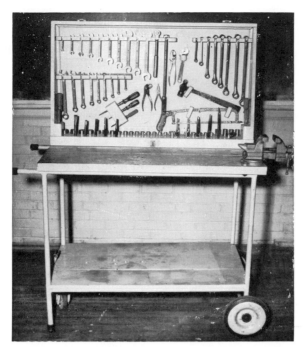

FIG. 27-2. *Portable tool cabinet and workbench.*

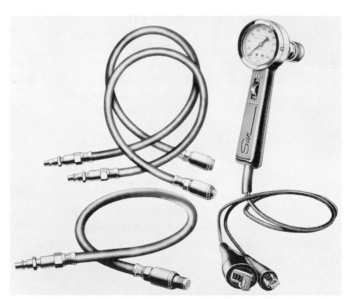

FIG. 27-3. *Gauge and adapters for testing compression pressure.* (Courtesy of Sun Electric Corporation.)

tric bench grinder, portable drill, power saw, and similar tools will be found extremely useful and will speed up most repair operations.

Suitable cabinets (Fig. 27-2) should be provided for all tools and some plan worked out whereby each item has its place and all tools are systematically arranged so that they can be readily located and put away. When not in use, all tools should be kept clean and dry.

Special engine testing and tune-up equipment. Various types of checking and testing equipment are available and extremely useful in determining the condition of an engine and for making precision adjustments which are important in order to obtain the best performance. This equipment is useful and almost indispensable in commercial automotive and tractor repair shops. Although many tractor owners cannot afford or have only limited need for most of the more expensive items of engine testing equipment, there are some devices which are relatively inexpensive and can be used to advantage in servicing and tuning up automobile, truck, and tractor engines. Four such instruments are (1) the compression testing gauge, (2) the vacuum and fuel-pump pressure gauge, (3) the ignition timing light, and (4) the battery cell tester.

The compression gauge (Fig. 27-3) is used by removing the spark plugs and testing each cylinder for compression as the engine is cranked by the battery with wide-open throttle. Low compression in a cylinder may indicate numerous things such as (1) worn cylinder, piston, and piston rings, (2) leaky or bad valves, (3) incorrect valve clearance, (4) weak valve springs, or (5) a bad cylinder head gasket.

FIG. 27-4. *Vacuum and fuel-pump pressure gauge.* (Courtesy of Sun Electric Corporation.)

The vacuum gauge (Fig. 27-4) can be used to detect (1) leaky or bad valves, (2) worn cylinder, piston, and piston rings, (3) manifold leak, (4) worn intake valve guides, (5) weak valve springs, (6) incorrect valve clearance, (7) incorrect spark timing, and (8) incorrect carburetor adjustment.

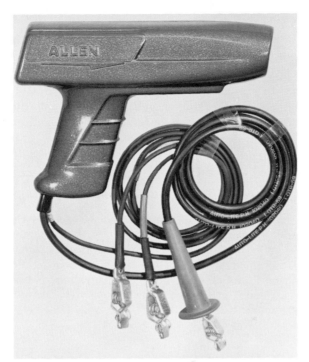

FIG. 27-5. *Ignition timing light.* (Courtesy of Allen Electric and Equipment Company.)

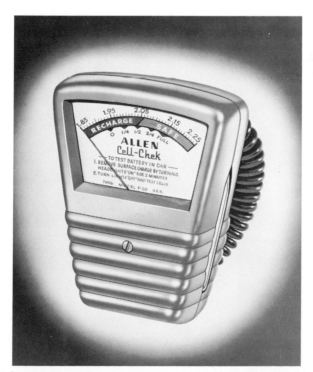

FIG. 27-6. *Voltmeter for testing battery cells.* (Courtesy of Allen Electric and Equipment Company.)

The timing light (Fig. 27-5) is used specifically for obtaining the proper timing of the ignition system and spark. It is difficult to adjust the spark of present-day high-speed engines without this device.

The battery tester (Fig. 27-6) is an inexpensive and simple and reliable instrument for checking the charged or output condition of the automotive storage battery. It will indicate instantly the condition of each individual cell of a battery.

Complete directions and instructions for the use of all these instruments are supplied with them.

REFERENCES

CROUSE, W. H., "Automotive Mechanics," 4th ed., McGraw-Hill Book Company, Inc., New York, 1960.

Instruments for Automotive Engine Tune-up, *Lubrication*, August, 1949.

JOHNSON, ELMER J., and ALVIN H. HOLLENBERG, "Servicing and Maintaining Farm Tractors," McGraw-Hill Book Company, Inc., New York, 1950.

TOBOLDT, W. K., and TED PURVIS, "New Automotive Encyclopedia," Goodheart-Willcox, Inc., Chicago, 1956.

PROBLEMS AND QUESTIONS

1. Differentiate clearly between "on the farm" tractor maintenance service and dealer repair service.

2. Make a list of the essential service and shop tools needed for a general crop and livestock farm equipped with two tractors and other mechanical equipment.

3. Name the common engine troubles which can be detected with (a) a vacuum gauge and (b) a compression gauge.

28

Economics of Tractor Utilization

The farm tractor has come to be recognized as a major source of power in both American and foreign agriculture. Mechanical power is now being applied successfully to practically all the operations involved in the production of the major field crops as well as fruits, vegetables, and similar farm commodities.

There is a vast amount of information available concerning the subject of farm power and its utilization under the great variety of existing agricultural conditions. Yet, because of the rapid changes in tractor design and equipment and in crop-production methods, much of this information is more or less obsolete. It is not the purpose of the author to present the detailed results of all the published material on the subject of tractor economics but merely to give such information as will be of general application and answer the more common questions along this line. For the assistance of the reader who desires to make a more complete and intensive study of the subject, a carefully selected list of authoritative references will be found at the end of this chapter.

ECONOMICS OF THE TRACTOR

Factors determining kind of power to use. The principal factors to be considered in choosing the most suitable kind of power for a given farm setup are:

1. Size of the farm
2. Topography of the land
3. Crops and kind of farm
4. Soil characteristics
5. Size of fields

The smallest size of farm on which a tractor can be used profitably cannot be stated definitely because other factors, such as crops raised, size of fields, and so on, also enter into the problem. Before the introduction of the cultivating type of tractor, farms devoted largely to row crops were dependent upon animal power for planting and cultivation. Consequently, the size of the farm on which a tractor could be used profitably was seldom less than 80 acres, and some investigations showed that farms considerably larger than this could be operated about as profitably with horses alone. Now that small tractors are available that will successfully perform all operations in row-crop production and thereby eliminate the need of a single horse or mule, it seems reasonable to say that the size of farm on which a tractor can be used with profit might be as low as 10 to 20 acres.

The topography of the land is of minor consideration except in extreme cases. A tractor will not operate satisfactorily on steep hillsides because of the tendency to slip and slide downhill. In going directly up the hill most of the power may be consumed in propelling the tractor without a load. Land that is terraced to control soil erosion can usually be handled satisfactorily with tractors.

The particular crops to be grown on a given farm and the acreage of each must be considered along with the other factors mentioned. However, the introduction of the all-purpose tractor has removed certain limitations in the utilization of mechanical power for producing a number of crops and greatly simplified the problem from this standpoint.

The size of fields is no longer an important factor in economical tractor operation. It is true that for most operations larger fields mean somewhat less loss of time and more efficient results, but the smaller tractors are now capable of being handled easily in small or irregular fields containing as few as 5 to 10 acres.

In selecting the proper kind of power for a farm, one should consider carefully the numerous jobs, both tractive and stationary, that are likely to develop. If a tractor of a certain type is well suited to handling the majority of these jobs, it should prove a profitable investment. In other words, the greater the amount of time the machine is kept busy, the lower the cost per horsepower-hour of power developed. The possibility of doing a certain amount of custom work for neighbors, provided it is done at a profit, often solves the problem of whether to buy a tractor or not. Frequently certain special tractor jobs develop, such as clearing land, dragging roads, moving buildings, operating snowplows, and the like, which assist in reducing the annual power cost.

Choice of type and size. As a rule the acreage and kind of crops raised determine the type of tractor best adapted to a given farm. If such row crops as corn, cotton, or grain sorghums are grown either alone or with wheat, oats, hay, and similar broadcast crops, the all-purpose tractor can probably be utilized to best advantage and with greater efficiency. This type is particularly well adapted to dairy and general grain and livestock farms because of the variety of power jobs which arise. For wheat, rice, or all-grain farming the ordinary general-purpose tractor of the wheel or track type is most suitable.

The choice of the correct size of tractor is important, particularly if the farm setup justifies the use of an all-purpose tractor. In general, for small farms or for large farms made up of small fields, the small or two-row size will prove most satisfactory. On the other hand, for large farms having large fields, a larger tractor capable of handling a three- to five-bottom plow and four-row planters and cultivators will be likely to prove more economical.

If the particular setup requires a standard-type four-wheel or track-type tractor, then a choice must be made among sizes ranging from a machine rated at 15 hp. at the drawbar and capable of handling a two-bottom plow to machines rated as high as 60 to 70 hp. at the drawbar and capable of pulling as many as eight plow bottoms. Certain heavy tractive jobs for which large tractors are frequently used are subsoiling, land clearing and drainage, terracing, road construction and grading, and heavy hauling.

Make of tractor. In selecting a tractor, construction and design should be observed closely. This is important from the standpoint of durability, service, accessibility, and adaptability to the kinds of work to be done. Parts requiring frequent adjustment should be accessible, and lubrication should be simplified but positive. Convenience and safety in operation are especially desirable. This includes ease of steering, control levers that are readily manipulated, good rear-wheel fenders, a well-located belt pulley to facilitate lining up, a convenient and properly protected power take-off, and suitable hydraulic control equipment.

The past reputation and future stability of the manufacturer and the character and dependability of the local dealer are factors of prime importance in selecting the most suitable make of tractor. The tractor business is highly competitive and necessitates constant alertness and persistent effort on the part of the manufacturer to place upon the market a reliable machine at a reasonable price. He must ever be on the lookout for weaknesses in design and possibilities of improvement in construction and operation. He knows that his best salesman is the satisfied customer.

The success of a tractor often lies with the local dealer. The successful tractor dealer must have a thorough knowledge of the merits, adaptability, construction, and operation of the machines that he sells. Furthermore, he must be able to provide his customers with prompt, reliable, and competent service. This includes a well-equipped shop, trained mechanics, and a good stock of staple repair parts.

TRACTOR POWER COSTS

Factors affecting power costs. The cost of the use of a tractor or of any other kind of mechanical power-generating device is dependent upon a number of factors, as follows: (1) probable life in hours, days, or years, (2) annual use in hours or days, (3) interest on investment, (4) housing, (5) insurance, (6) taxes, (7) fuel consumption, (8) lubricants, and (9) repairs. Specifically, for a tractor these items may be classified as follows:

1. Fixed or overhead costs
   a. Depreciation
   b. Interest on investment
   c. Housing
   d. Insurance
   e. Taxes
2. Operating costs
   a. Fuel
   b. Lubricants
   c. Repairs

The fixed or overhead cost items are those which remain relatively constant whether the machine is used or not. Of course depreciation is affected both by obsolescence and by use; hence, strictly speaking, it may vary to some extent in accordance with use. The variable-cost items are those created only by use of the machine and vary directly as the days or hours of use. One of the most important factors affecting the cost of operation of a tractor or any other machine is the number of days or hours it is used per year. The reason for this is that the total annual fixed costs remain about the same whether the machine is used 100 hr. or 1,000 hr. per year. Therefore, the greater the annual use, the lower the daily or hourly fixed cost and hence the lower the total daily or hourly operating cost.

Tractor life and depreciation. Depreciation is the decrease in value and service capacity of a machine as a result of natural wear, obsolescence, damage, corrosion, and weathering. Obviously the longer the service life of a tractor in hours, days, or years, the lower its annual depreciation rate and cost. A machine wears out with use, but the rate of wear depends upon the skill of the operator, lubrication and general maintenance, design, quality of materials, and so on. Obsolescence is an important factor in depreciation but is difficult to evaluate.

Studies and surveys indicate that tractor life varies greatly, depending upon the factors mentioned and other conditions. However, a distinct majority of farmer estimates fall within a range of 10 to 16 years. These estimates are based upon an annual use of 500 to 700 hr. Hence, in terms of total hours, it can be said that farm tractor life varies from 6,000 to 8,000 hr.

METHODS OF DETERMINING DEPRECIATION

According to Fenton and Fairbanks,[1] there are three methods of computing depreciation: (1) estimated-value, (2) straight-line, and (3) constant-percentage. They state further that the three important needs for depreciation estimates are (1) determination of resale, trade-in, or appraisal values of used machines, (2) determination of depreciation charges to be used in computing operating costs, and (3) for income tax purposes. The method used in the first case should give, as nearly as possible, throughout the machine's life, values that represent values on a used-equipment market. The second objective is the one commonly encountered in calculations to determine the cost of operation of a machine, such as cost per hour or per acre. The method of calculating depreciation for this purpose should assume that the equipment is to remain in use on the farm and perform its particular job throughout its useful life. It should give results that are uniform throughout the machine's life. Of the three methods enumerated, the estimated-value and constant-percentage methods are more suitable for determining resale values, and the straight-line method is better for calculating the cost of use of equipment.

Estimated-value method. The owner's estimate of the value of a used machine may be used to determine its depreciation. When estimates are obtained from a sufficient number of owners of similar machines ranging in age from new to worn-out, the data may be used to determine the rate of depreciation of that particular type of machine.

Straight-line method. The straight-line method of depreciation reduces the value of a machine by an equal amount each year during its useful life. As shown by Fig. 28-1, the rate per year is constant and therefore results in a straight-line graph. It is the simplest method of calculating depreciation and is widely used with farm machinery. While it is true that a machine depreciates less during the first few years by this method than its resale value would indicate, it is also true that farm machines are not bought for resale purposes but are bought to perform a given service on the farm. As long as the machine will perform this service satisfactorily, there is no legitimate reason for charging larger amounts for depreciation during the early years of its life.

In view of the large number of variables that are not, and cannot be, taken into account in any system of calculating depreciation of farm machines, the accuracy of the straight-line method is all that can be expected. Many of the other methods that have been proposed are claimed to be more accurate; however, they do not offer anything in

[1] *Kansas State Coll. Eng. Expt. Sta. Bull.* 74.

the way of accuracy that will offset their difficulty and complexity of handling. In calculating the annual depreciation by the straight-line method, if the resale value is not considered or it is assumed the machine has no value at the end of its service life, then the annual depreciation charge is simply the original cost divided by the life in years. For many purposes this gives a satisfactory answer, but since the machines usually have a trade-in value at the end of their service life and since this may be a considerable amount, it should generally be

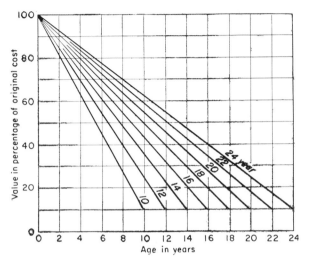

FIG. 28-1. *Depreciation curves based on straight-line depreciation.*

included. The present value of a machine can be found by obtaining its value in percentage of original cost at its present age from Table 28-1 or Fig. 28-1 and multiplying this by the original cost.

Constant-percentage method. The constant-percentage method depreciates the value of the machine at the same percentage of the value remaining each year. It results in a larger reduction of value during the early life of the machine and a decreasing amount of depreciation in its later life. It takes into consideration the original cost, the trade-in value, and the estimated service life of the machine, as does the straight-line method, but calculates the percentage that will reduce the value to the trade-in value at the end of the machine's useful life. It may be used where the value of a machine is desired for resale purposes or for making farm-machinery appraisals.

To determine the rate or percentage necessary to reduce the original value to trade-in value at the end of the estimated service life, the following formula is used:

$$r = 1 - \sqrt[L]{\frac{S}{C}}$$

where r = percentage annual rate of depreciation
  L = total service life, years
  S = trade-in value
  C = original cost of machine

The value V at any age n during the useful life is equal to $C(1 - r)^n$. The curves (Fig. 28-2) were prepared by using this formula.

Table 28-1. *Values of Machines, by Straight-line Depreciation, in Percentage of Original Cost* [1] *(10 per cent trade-in value)*

Age, years	10-year service life	12-year service life	14-year service life	16-year service life	18-year service life	20-year service life	22-year service life	24-year service life
0	100.00	100.00	100.00	100.00	100.00	100.00	100.00	100.00
1	91.00	92.50	93.57	94.37	95.00	95.50	95.91	96.25
2	82.00	85.00	87.14	88.75	90.00	91.00	91.82	92.50
3	73.00	77.50	80.72	83.12	85.00	86.50	87.73	88.75
4	64.00	70.00	74.29	77.50	80.00	82.00	83.64	85.00
5	55.00	62.50	67.86	71.87	75.00	77.50	79.54	81.25
6	46.00	55.00	61.43	66.25	70.00	73.00	75.45	77.50
7	37.00	47.50	55.00	60.62	65.00	68.50	71.36	73.75
8	28.00	40.00	48.58	55.00	60.00	64.00	67.27	70.00
9	19.00	32.50	42.15	49.37	55.00	59.50	63.18	66.25
10	10.00	25.00	35.72	43.75	50.00	55.00	59.09	62.50
11	. . . . .	17.50	29.29	38.12	45.00	50.50	55.00	58.75
12	. . . . .	10.00	22.86	32.50	40.00	46.00	50.91	55.00
13	. . . . .	. . . . .	16.43	26.87	35.00	41.50	46.82	51.25
14	. . . . .	. . . . .	10.00	21.25	30.00	37.00	42.73	47.50
15	. . . . .	. . . . .	. . . . .	15.62	25.00	32.50	38.63	43.75
16	. . . . .	. . . . .	. . . . .	10.00	20.00	28.00	34.54	40.00
17	. . . . .	. . . . .	. . . . .	. . . . .	15.00	23.50	30.45	36.25
18	. . . . .	. . . . .	. . . . .	. . . . .	10.00	19.00	26.36	32.50
19	. . . . .	. . . . .	. . . . .	. . . . .	. . . . .	14.50	22.27	28.75
20	. . . . .	. . . . .	. . . . .	. . . . .	. . . . .	10.00	18.18	25.00
21	. . . . .	. . . . .	. . . . .	. . . . .	. . . . .	. . . . .	14.09	21.25
22	. . . . .	. . . . .	. . . . .	. . . . .	. . . . .	. . . . .	10.00	17.50
23	. . . . .	. . . . .	. . . . .	. . . . .	. . . . .	. . . . .	. . . . .	13.75
24	. . . . .	. . . . .	. . . . .	. . . . .	. . . . .	. . . . .	. . . . .	10.00

[1] *Kansas State Coll. Eng. Expt. Sta. Bull. 74.*

OTHER FIXED COSTS

Interest on investment. Interest on the investment in farm equipment is usually included in operational cost estimates, since money used to buy a machine cannot be used for other purposes such as the purchase of land, livestock, bonds, or other productive enterprises.

The amount invested in a machine is greater during its early life than during the later years, since an amount is written off each year as depreciation. This is true regardless of the method used in calculating

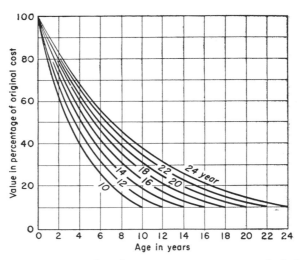

FIG. 28-2. *Depreciation curves based on constant-percentage method of depreciation.*

depreciation. Interest charges are usually desired when operating costs are being determined but not when depreciated values for resale or trade-in are being determined. In calculating interest charges where operating costs are concerned, it is desirable to use a method that results in constant or equal yearly charges throughout the machine's life; that is, the sum of the interest charge and the depreciation should be constant, for reasons that have already been discussed. When the straight-line method of depreciation is used, this is accomplished by making an annual interest charge on the average investment in the machine over its full life. The average investment is equal to one-half the sum of the first cost and the trade-in value. The annual interest charge will then be the product of the interest rate and the average investment.

Insurance—shelter—taxes. Insurance and housing expense and taxes, if incurred, must be included in any tractor operation costs. Although insurance and tax rates vary according to local conditions and other factors, Fenton and Fairbanks [1] suggest an annual tax charge of 1 per cent and an annual insurance charge of 0.25 per cent of the original cost of the machine.

Regarding shelter for farm equipment, Fenton and Fairbanks state that numerous attempts have been made by various investigators to obtain conclusive evidence of the value of a shelter for farm machinery. Most of these have failed to find such evidence but from observation have stated that, although monetary savings are not apparent, there are indeterminate values such as better management, better appearance of the farmstead, and ease of making repairs during a slack or stormy season, and have thereby justified the expense of a machine shed.

The average annual estimated repair expense is also consistently smaller for sheltered machines. Sheltering usually goes along with better care and management, and this factor alone could account for the difference in favor of sheltering.

The cost of shelter will depend upon how expensive or elaborate the structure is. Machine sheds should be built as simply and inexpensively as possible. A fair annual charge recommended for adequate shelter facilities for tractors and farm equipment is 1 per cent of the original cost of the machine.

OPERATING COSTS

Items making up the operating cost of a tractor are (1) fuel; (2) lubricants, including motor oil, transmission lubricant, and grease; and (3) repairs, including the labor required to do the work. These costs are incurred only through the use of the machine and vary to a large extent in direct proportion to hours or days of use per year.

Fuel and lubricants costs. Fuel is one of the major items affecting tractor operating costs. Factors affecting fuel cost are (1) the prevailing market price, (2) carburetor adjustment, (3) engine condition, and (4) load factor or ratio of used power to available power. A tractor uses less fuel at light loads, but the fuel consumption per unit of power developed is high; therefore, the most economical power, so far as fuel consumption is concerned, is obtained when the tractor load is at least 50 per cent of its available capacity. The load may be adjusted to the rated power of a tractor by (1) increasing the width or size of the equipment, (2) pulling more than one piece of machinery at the same time, (3) using a higher gear and doing the work faster, or (4) using a higher gear and throttling the engine down to the required speed.

Proper lubrication and the use of good-quality lubricants are very important in reducing the wear and repair expense of a tractor. The annual cost of all lubricants for a tractor is relatively small compared to

[1] *Kansas State Coll. Eng. Expt. Sta. Bull.* 74.

other costs, but neglect with respect to the recommended lubrication requirements for a tractor can be very expensive. Table 28-2 shows the

Table 28-2. Fuel and Oil Consumption of Various Size of Tractors [1]

Size of tractor	Number of tractors	Average days used per year	Average fuel used per year, gal.	Average fuel used per day, gal.	Average oil used per year, gal.	Average oil used per day, gal.
2-plow, row-crop.....	224	86	1,340	15.6	52	0.60
3-plow, row-crop.....	28	76	1,358	17.9	48	0.63
2-plow, standard.....	188	55	1,135	20.6	39	0.71
3-plow, standard.....	616	80	2,131	26.6	71	0.89
4-plow, standard.....	164	90	2,823	31.4	99	1.10

[1] *Kansas State Coll. Eng. Expt. Sta. Bull. 74.*

fuel and oil consumption of various sizes and types of tractors as reported by Fenton and Fairbanks.

Repair costs. The cost of the repairs for a tractor is an important item of expense and depends largely upon proper everyday maintenance. A survey [1] made among Kansas tractor users indicates a considerable variation in annual repair costs, but 3.50 per cent of the first cost is suggested as being representative.

Operating costs of tractors according to size and annual use. Table 28-3 has been prepared by the author in order to present a simple but representative operating cost analysis for farm tractors according to both size and annual use in hours. The values are based as nearly as possible on 1960 costs and conditions. A careful examination of the information given in this table will disclose the following general deductions relative to tractor operating costs:

1. The larger the tractor, the greater its total hourly and yearly operating costs.

2. The fixed costs remain relatively constant, regardless of the total hours of annual use.

3. The operating costs vary directly as the total hours of annual use.

4. Depreciation and fuel are the two most important cost items in tractor operation.

5. The greater the annual use in hours, the lower the total operating costs per hour.

6. The cost per horsepower-hour remains relatively constant (3 to 8 cents, depending upon drawbar horsepower rating used) regardless of

[1] *Kansas State Coll. Eng. Expt. Sta. Bull. 74.*

Table 09-3. *Operating Costs of Various Sizes of Tractors per Year and per Hour* [1]

Size of tractor and cost items	Used	
	500 hr. per year	1,000 hr. per year
A. Tractor costing $1,500, 15–20 drawbar hp.		
Fixed costs:		
Depreciation, 8⅓% of first cost...................	$ 125.00	$ 125.00
Interest, 6% of average investment ($750)..........	45.00	45.00
Shelter, taxes, and insurance, 2½% of original cost....	37.50	37.50
Total.......................................	$ 207.50	$ 207.50
Operating costs:		
Fuel, 1.50 gal. per hr..........................	$ 150.00	$ 300.00
Oil...	30.00	52.50
Grease and transmission lubricant..................	12.00	15.00
Repairs.......................................	45.00	75.00
Service labor.................................	37.50	75.00
Total.......................................	$ 274.50	$ 517.50
Grand total per year.......................	$ 482.00	$ 725.00
Cost per hour..............................	$ 0.96	$ 0.72
B. Tractor costing $2,000, 20–30 drawbar hp.		
Fixed costs:		
Depreciation, 8⅓% of first cost...................	$ 166.67	$ 166.67
Interest, 6% of average investment ($1,000)..........	60.00	60.00
Shelter, taxes, and insurance, 2½% of original cost....	50.00	50.00
Total.......................................	$ 276.67	$ 276.67
Operating costs:		
Fuel, 2.00 gal. per hr..........................	$ 200.00	$ 400.00
Oil...	41.25	67.50
Grease and transmission lubricant..................	15.00	20.00
Repairs.......................................	60.00	100.00
Service labor.................................	37.50	75.00
Total.......................................	$ 353.75	$ 662.50
Grand total per year.......................	$ 630.42	$ 939.17
Cost per hour..............................	$ 1.26	$ 0.94
C. Tractor costing $2,800, 30–40 drawbar hp.		
Fixed costs:		
Depreciation, 8⅓% of first cost...................	$ 233.33	$ 233.33
Interest, 6% of average investment ($1,400)..........	84.00	84.00
Shelter, taxes, and insurance, 2½% of original cost....	70.00	70.00
Total.......................................	$ 387.33	$ 387.33

[1] In preparing these cost data, certain assumptions were made as follows: average tractor life, 12 years; fuel cost, 20 cents per gal.; motor-oil cost, $1.50 per gal.; repair charges, 3 per cent of first cost when used 500 hr. and 5 per cent when used 1,000 hr.; maintenance service labor, $1.50 per hr.

Table 28-3. Operating Costs of Various Sizes of Tractors (Continued)

Size of tractor and cost items	Used	
	500 hr. per year	1,000 hr. per year
Operating costs:		
Fuel, 3.00 gal. per hr.	$ 300.00	$ 600.00
Oil	52.50	90.00
Grease and transmission lubricant	17.50	25.00
Repairs	84.00	140.00
Service labor	37.50	75.00
Total	$ 491.50	$ 930.00
Grand total per year	$ 878.83	$1,317.33
Cost per hour	$ 1.76	$ 1.32
D. Tractor costing $3,600, 40–50 drawbar hp.		
Fixed costs:		
Depreciation, 8⅓% of first cost	$ 300.00	$ 300.00
Interest, 6% of average investment ($1,800)	108.00	108.00
Shelter, taxes and insurance, 2½% of original cost	90.00	90.00
Total	$ 498.00	$ 498.00
Operating costs:		
Fuel, 3.50 gal. per hr.	$ 350.00	$ 700.00
Oil	60.00	100.00
Grease and transmission lubricant	20.00	25.00
Repairs	108.00	180.00
Service labor	37.50	75.00
Total	$ 575.50	$1,080.00
Grand total per year	$1,073.50	$1,578.00
Cost per hour	$ 2.15	$ 1.58
E. Tractor costing $4,400, 50–60 drawbar hp.		
Fixed costs:		
Depreciation, 8⅓% of first cost	$ 366.67	$ 366.67
Interest, 6% of average investment ($2,200)	132.00	132.00
Shelter, taxes and insurance, 2½% of original cost	110.00	110.00
Total	$ 608.67	$ 608.67
Operating costs:		
Fuel, 4.25 gal. per hr.	$ 425.00	$ 850.00
Oil	70.00	120.00
Grease and transmission lubricant	22.50	30.00
Repairs	132.00	220.00
Service labor	37.50	75.00
Total	$ 687.00	$1,295.00
Grand total per year	$1,295.67	$1,903.67
Cost per hour	$ 2.59	$ 1.90

the size of the tractor but under any conditions is greatest for a low annual use and lowest for a high annual use.

REFERENCES

Cost and Utilization of Tractor Power and Equipment on Farms in the Coastal Plain, *Georgia Agr. Expt. Sta. Bull.* 260.

Cost and Utilization of Tractor Power and Equipment on Farms in the Lower Piedmont, *Georgia Agr. Expt. Sta. Bull.* 256.

Cost of Tractor Power on Nebraska Farms, *Univ. Nebraska Agr. Expt. Sta. Bull.* 324.

Cost of Using Farm Machinery, *Kansas State Coll. Eng. Expt. Sta. Bulls.* 45 and 75.

Economics of Tractor Farming in the Piedmont Area of South Carolina, *S. Carolina Agr. Expt. Sta. Bull.* 377.

Farm Labor, Power, and Machinery Performance in East Central South Dakota, *S. Dakota State Coll. Agr. Expt. Sta. Circ.* 131.

Life, Service, and Cost of Service of Farm Machines on 400 Iowa Farms, *Iowa State Coll. Agr. Expt. Sta. Bull.* P-37.

Mechanized Production of Cotton in Texas, *Texas Agr. Expt. Sta. Bull.* 704.

Study of the Performance of Fifty Farm Tractors, *Kansas State Coll. Agr. Expt. Sta. Tech. Bull.* 99.

Trends in Farm Tractor Types, Sizes, Age, and Use, U.S. Dept. Agr., *Agr. Infor. Bull.* 231, A.R.S., 1960.

PROBLEMS AND QUESTIONS

1. Enumerate all items making up the cost of operating a tractor, and state which items are of major importance.

2. Explain the relationship of annual tractor use in total hours and the hourly operating cost.

3. Name and describe three methods of calculating tractor depreciation, and give the particular advantages of each method.

4. Calculate the hourly cost of operating a 45-hp. diesel tractor having an original cost of $4,750 and an annual utilization of 1,200 hr. Use prevailing costs of fuel, lubricants, and labor.

5. If the tractor in Prob. 4 pulls four 14-in. plow bottoms at the rate of 3.5 m.p.h., calculate the total cost per acre. This cost should include an operator at the prevailing rate and a charge of 50 cents per hour for the plow.

29

Materials of Construction—Power Transmission

A large part of the material used in the construction of internal-combustion engines consists of iron in some form or another. Therefore, some knowledge of its source, manufacture, the methods of treatment, and the characteristics and properties of the different forms is of fundamental importance. The source of all iron and steel is iron ore, which is dug from the earth's surface or from underground mines. In this ore, the iron is in the form of oxides, that is, compounds of iron and oxygen.

Pig iron. The first step in the manufacture of iron and steel is the removal of the oxygen from the iron ore by melting it in a blast furnace with a fuel, usually coke. Limestone is mixed with the ore and fuel to take up the oxygen. The process and resulting products are as follows:

Iron oxide + limestone + coke + hot-air blast = iron + slag

+ gases (carbon monoxide, carbon dioxide, nitrogen)

The iron thus obtained is cast into bars and is commonly known as *pig iron*. Pig iron is not pure iron by any means, for it contains about 3.5 per cent carbon and small amounts of silicon, manganese, phosphorus, and sulfur. From pig iron are manufactured the various kinds of iron and steel, such as gray, white, and chilled cast iron, malleable iron, wrought iron, and steel.

CAST IRON

Process of manufacture. The manufacture of cast iron from pig iron is very similar to the manufacture of pig iron from ore, except that it is more of a refining process for the purpose of securing castings of a definite composition. The process involves the melting of the pig iron with coke and a small amount of limestone in a cupola or air furnace. Sometimes scrap iron is added to secure a special grade of cast iron. The molten iron is drawn off into special molds which form the castings into their final shape for a given machine. Cast iron contains from 2.5 to 4.0 per cent carbon and very small amounts of silicon, manganese, phosphorus, and sulfur.

Kinds of cast iron. Gray-iron castings are made by allowing the metal in the molds to cool slowly so that the carbon is retained in the form of graphite. A typical gray-iron casting would have the following analysis:

	Per cent
Carbon	3.40
Silicon	2.10
Phosphorus	0.40
Manganese	0.60
Sulfur	0.10
Iron	93.40

It has the following characteristics:

1. Very brittle because of high carbon content.
2. Will not bend or twist.
3. Very soft and machines easily.
4. Easily cast into any shape.
5. Cannot be welded in a forge but only by means of an electric arc or an oxygen-acetylene flame.
6. Low tensile strength—20,000 lb. per sq. in.

Gray-iron castings are used for gas-engine cylinders, pistons, and frames.

White cast iron is made by cooling the casting rapidly so that the iron and carbon remain combined chemically as cementite (Fe_3C) and other compounds. White cast iron is harder and more brittle than gray cast iron.

Chilled cast-iron castings are produced by lining the sand molds with metal at those points where the chill is desired. The molten iron, coming in contact with this cold metal lining, cools rapidly so that those portions of the casting become very hard and resistant to wear, largely because the carbon remains in chemical combination and the crystals so form themselves that they are long and narrow and arranged perpendicular to this chilled surface. Some characteristics of this material are:

1. Chilled part very hard.
2. Very brittle and will not bend.
3. Cannot be welded except by electric arc or oxygen-acetylene flame.
4. Cannot be machined but must be ground.

The chilling process is used for moldboards, shares, and other parts of chilled plows, some bearings, cams, car-wheel treads, and brake shoes.

MALLEABLE IRON

Process of manufacture. Pig iron is first melted and cast into ordinary white-iron castings of the desired size and shape but containing only about 2.5 per cent carbon. The castings are then annealed by placing them in iron boxes, packing them with iron oxide and sand, placing the boxes in a large oven or furnace, and heating them to about 1400°F. for 3 to 5 days. They are then cooled slowly. This reduces the carbon content of the outside or skin of the casting to about 0.2 per cent, but the inside or center remains the same. The usual characteristics of malleable iron are:

1. Will bend, twist, and resist shock.

2. Is soft and easily filed or machined.

3. Cannot be welded except with electric arc or oxygen-acetylene flame.

4. Has higher tensile and compressive strength than plain cast iron.

Malleable castings are usually small in size and are used for farm machines, small pinions, pipe fittings, and various kinds of hardware.

WROUGHT IRON

Pig iron likewise forms the raw material in the manufacture of wrought iron, and the process is essentially a purifying one. The difference between this process and the manufacture of steel, as described later, is that the metal is never completely melted. The furnace used is called a reverberatory furnace. The fire is in a compartment at one end, and the flames pass over the hearth of the furnace which lies beyond. The arched roof over the hearth reflects the heat down upon the charge of pig iron and iron ore, and the products of combustion pass to the chimney.

Under the influence of the heat the oxygen from the ore oxidizes the impurities in the pig iron and the ore itself is reduced. The impurities form a slag. By constant stirring with iron rods through openings in the side of the furnace the entire charge is exposed to the heat and the impurities in the pig iron finally reduced to a very small amount.

Since the metal is heated only enough to reach a pasty condition and not enough to melt completely, the slag does not rise in a distinct layer to the top but permeates the entire mass. Near the end of the process the workmen gather the pasty mass into balls. This process is called puddling. The balls of iron are removed from the furnace, and while still hot, most of the slag is squeezed out by hydraulic presses or steam hammers.

As already stated, some of the slag remains in the mass, and the resulting network of slag in the iron, after it has been hammered and rolled, gives wrought iron its characteristic fibrous structure. This slag, which consists largely of silicates and phosphates of iron and manganese, makes up about 2.8 per cent of the material. Aside from the presence of the slag, the percentage composition of wrought iron is essentially that of low-carbon steel. Wrought iron is perhaps the purest form of iron. It is tough, malleable, and ductile and is used largely for nails, stay bolts, rivets, water and steam pipes, boiler tubes, horseshoes, and general forging purposes. It is easy to weld.

STEEL

Steel is iron containing a small amount of carbon—less than 1.5 per cent. This carbon is in a combined state called iron carbide, whereas in ordinary cast iron it is in the form of graphite and is mixed with the iron to form a physical mixture.

The general process of manufacture consists in heating the pig iron by one of four processes, in order to remove the carbon and other impurities, and then adding to the mass, or inoculating the mass with, a certain amount of an iron and carbon mixture to give the steel the correct percentage of carbon.

STEEL MANUFACTURE

There are four methods of manufacturing steel: the Bessemer process, the open-hearth process, the crucible process, and the electric process. The Bessemer process is not extensively used in the United States; by far the largest amount of steel is made by the open-hearth process.

Open-hearth process. The impurities of the pig iron are oxidized by the addition of iron oxide and diluted by the addition of scrap steel. The charge, consisting of pieces of pig iron, iron ore, and steel scrap, is melted by the flame of a blast of mixed air and gas passing over the hearth of a saucer-shaped furnace. The process takes a much longer time than the Bessemer process, and samples of the metal are taken from time to time to determine its composition. Open-hearth steel is used for bridges, armor plate, and the better class of structural work, as well as for conversion into high-grade tool steel.

Crucible steel. For uses demanding the greatest uniformity and freedom from undesirable impurities, further refining than is obtained in the process just described is necessary. The crucible and electric processes are the two most important ones in this respect.

In the crucible process wrought iron or steel is remelted in a graphite crucible. When wrought iron is used, the proper percentage of carbon is secured by the addition of charcoal to the iron before melting. As very pure wrought iron can be obtained, a high degree of purity can be secured in the steel. When steel is used as the crucible charge, it has usually been made by heating wrought-iron bars for a long time in contact with carbon. This results in the formation of iron carbide, particularly near the surface, and the object in remelting in the crucible, in this case, is to secure greater uniformity in the product. The crucible process is used chiefly to manufacture the various alloy steels but is being replaced by the electric-furnace process.

Electric process. In the electric-furnace process, the furnace proper is similar to the open-hearth furnace. The metal is placed in the furnace in a molten condition and the two graphite electrodes lowered into it. The resistance offered to the flow of the current develops an intense heat, and the sulfur and phosphorus are oxidized by the iron oxide and lime thrown in. A slab is formed on the top as a result of the oxidation of these impurities and the carbon is likewise almost entirely burned out. The proper amount of carbon is then introduced by the use of a re-carburizing material similar to that used in the open-hearth process. By the electric-furnace process, Bessemer and open-hearth steels can be quickly and cheaply converted into high-grade carbon and alloy steels of any desired composition.

Kinds of steel and their uses. Steel varies greatly in its character and properties, depending upon the carbon content, heat-treatment given, and alloying metals added to it. According to carbon content, steel may be classified as follows:

Steel	Per cent
Low-carbon, mild or soft	0.05–0.30
Medium-carbon or half	0.30–0.80
High-carbon or hard	0.80–1.50

As shown, the higher the carbon content, the harder and more brittle the steel. The following table gives the carbon content of steel used for different purposes:

Per cent	Steel products
0.05–0.10	Wire, nails, boiler plate, rivets, bolts
0.10–0.20	Rivets, screws, machine parts to be casehardened
0.20–0.25	Ordinary forgings, structural steel, cold-rolled shafting
0.25–0.40	Axles, gears, crankpins, shafts, connecting rods
0.40–0.70	Railroad rails, steel castings
0.70–0.80	Anvil facings, band saws, cold chisels, wrenches
0.80–0.90	Punches and dies, circular saws, rock drills
0.90–1.00	Springs, machinists' hammers, punches, and dies
1.00–1.10	Springs, lathe parts, taps
1.10–1.20	Ball-bearing races, wood chisels, woodworking tools, thread dies, spring steel
1.20–1.50	Files, hack saws, ball and roller bearings

HEAT-TREATMENT OF STEEL

Not only does the carbon content of steel influence its character and properties, but steel parts and tools, when subjected to certain heat-treatments, become possessed of specific properties. Some of the heat-treatments and their effects and the methods employed are described below.

Annealing. The metal is heated to 1450 to 1700°F. (depending upon the carbon content and the size of the casting) and allowed to remain at maximum temperature for one to several hours according to the size of the piece. It is then allowed to cool slowly. This treatment refines the coarse structure of the steel casting or part, removes the existing coarseness of grain, removes strains due to uneven cooling, and increases the tensile strength and resistance to shock. Wire and similar cold-rolled or cold-drawn objects are annealed to remove brittleness caused by mechanical treatment.

Hardening. The metal is heated to a high temperature (2000°F.) and cooled suddenly by quenching in water or oil. This increases the hardness, tensile strength, and brittleness. Its purpose is to adapt high-carbon steel for cutting-tool purposes.

Tempering. The hardened or quenched steel is first reheated to a temperature below the former hardening temperature for the purpose of partly restoring its ductility and softness. It is then cooled. The rate of cooling is immaterial. The piece is quenched in water when the proper heat is reached as indicated by the color.

Casehardening. This is a process of introducing additional carbon into the outer shell of the steel piece. It produces a fine-grained core and a very hard and close-grained outer shell. Stock containing 0.1 to 0.2 per cent carbon is used. The process is as follows:

1. The piece is heated, and the carbonizing material—usually charcoal, charred leather, crushed bone, horn, and so on—is applied.

2. The piece is allowed to cool to black in daylight.

3. It is reheated to critical temperature of core and quenched in oil or water.

4. It is reheated to critical temperature of shell and quenched.

For quick, superficial casehardening, the steel piece is heated to about 1700°F., and powdered potassium cyanide and potassium ferrocyanide are applied.

Gears, bearings, and parts requiring very hard external surfaces, because of exposure to high pressure, are usually casehardened.

Induction hardening. A method of heat-treatment and hardening of steel involving the use of a very high-frequency alternating electric current has been developed and used extensively in the automotive and tractor field in recent years. An induction heating circuit, fundamentally, is a transformer wherein the inductor carrying the alternating current is a primary and the substance to be heated is made the secondary by placing it within the confines of the loop formed by the inductor, there being no contact or connection between the two. The current flowing through the inductor sets up magnetic lines of force in a circular pattern which thread through the surface of the material being heated and induce a flow of energy in the latter. This substance carrying the induced current is a conductor, but it also offers a resistance to this flow of energy and this resistance, in turn, generates heat.

Basically, the necessary equipment consists of an inductor, quenching accessories for hardening, suitable transformers and capacitors, metering devices, automatic timing controls, and a source of high-frequency power. The quenching facilities are built into the inductor and permit close con-

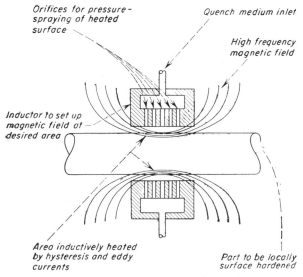

FIG. 29-1. *Schematic diagram showing induction-hardening process with integral quench.* (Courtesy of Ohio Crankshaft Company.)

trol of the heat flow and the resultant degree of hardness and specific metallurgical properties desired. Figure 29-1 shows how the operation is performed.

STEEL ALLOYS

A steel alloy is a mixture containing a high percentage of steel and a small amount of one or more of the common alloy metals, namely, manganese, nickel, chromium, vanadium, and tungsten. The common steel alloys, their characteristics, and their uses are as follows:

1. *Manganese steel.* Commercial contains 12 to 13 per cent manganese. High tensile strength, hard and resistant to wear, and ductile. Uses: rock crushers, railroad frogs and crossings, railroad curve rails, burglarproof safes.

2. *Nickel steel.* Contains 2 to 4 per cent nickel. Increases hardness, toughness, and tensile strength. Decreases ductility. Used largely with chromium. Uses: structural bridge work, railroad-curve rails, steel castings, shafting, frame and engine parts for automobiles, axles.

3. *Chrome steel.* Contains 1 to 2 per cent chromium. Gives a very hard steel. Used largely for armor-piercing projectiles. Also used for armor plate and burglarproof safes.

4. *Vanadium steel.* Contains 0.15 to 0.25 per cent vanadium. It improves the general physical properties of steel but is somewhat expensive.

5. *Chrome-vanadium steel—nickel-vanadium steel—chrome-nickel steel.* Used for ball and roller bearings, axles, crankpins, gun barrels, crankshafts.

6. *Tungsten steel.* Increases hardness. Used for high-speed cutting tools.

BEARING METALS—MISCELLANEOUS ALLOYS

Table 29-1 gives the percentage composition and uses of a number of common bearing metals, solder, and similar alloys.

Table 29-1. Composition of Bearing Metals and Other Alloys

Material or alloy	Copper, per cent	Tin, per cent	Lead, per cent	Zinc, per cent	Antimony, per cent	Phosphorus, per cent	Remarks
Babbitt (high-grade)..	4.00–5.00	90.00	0.35	......	4.00–5.00	.....	For bearings
Babbitt (low-grade)...	5.00–6.50	86.00	0.35	......	6.00–7.50	.....	For bearings, subject to heavy pressure
Babbitt (hard).......	2.25–3.75	60.00	26.00	......	9.50–11.50	.....	For light pressures
Brass (red)..........	83.00–86.00	4.50–5.50	4.50–5.50	4.50–5.50			
Brass (yellow)........	65.00–75.00	1.00	2.00	30.00			
Bronze (hard-cast)....	90.00	6.50	1.50	2.00	......	.....	General utility
Bronze (phosphor)....	79.00–82.00	9.00–11.00	9.00–11.00	......	......	0.10–0.25	For heavy loads and severe use
Solder...............	......	45.00–50.00	50.00–55.00	......	0.15		

POWER TRANSMISSION

There are a number of methods of transmitting power from the engine or other source to the driven machine. Some of the more common are (1) direct drive, (2) pulleys and belts, (3) sprocket wheel and chains, and (4) gears. Figure 29-2 shows all these methods in combination.

Direct drive. A direct power connection, although impractical for some kinds of work, offers certain advantages, such as (1) little power loss, (2) less trouble, and (3) compactness. Figure 29-3 illustrates such an application.

Pulleys and belts. The use of pulleys and belts for transmitting power is well adapted to many farm and other operations. The equipment involved is not complicated, and the power can be transmitted short or long distances, that is, from a few feet or less to 100 ft. or more, with practically the same general layout. The principal objection to this method is that it is not entirely positive and there may be some loss of power due to slippage.

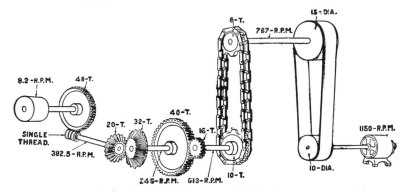

FIG. 29-2. *Sketch showing different methods of power transmission.*

The two types of belts are (1) flat and (2) V belt. The use of V belts for power transmission has expanded greatly in recent years. Some advantages of a V belt are that (1) it is simple and compact, (2) there is good pulley contact and very little slippage if the belt is given correct

FIG. 29-3. *Centrifugal pump driven direct by a gas engine.*

tension, (3) it cannot slip off pulleys, and (4) speeds can be changed without changing entire pulley.

Kinds of flat belting. The three most common flat belting materials are leather, rubber, and canvas. Leather is considered an excellent belting material for general use. It is strong, is very durable, does not stretch, and is not injured by oils and greases. On the other hand, its high first cost and inability to withstand exposure to excessive moisture and steam do not warrant its use under all conditions.

Rubber belting. Rubber belting is now used extensively for farm power transmission. It costs less than leather, withstands exposure to moisture and temperature variation, and is flexible. On the other hand, rubber belts will not stand exposure to oils and greases of any kind and should not be allowed to rub on or against any stationary object. Rubber belting really consists of two to eight layers or plies of canvas, impregnated and held together with vulcanized rubber. It can be secured in widths varying from 1 in. to 1 ft. or more.

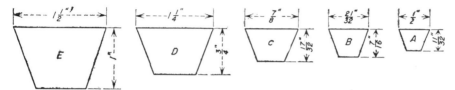

FIG. 29-4. *Standard V-belt cross-section sizes.*

Canvas belting. Canvas belting is used largely for transmitting power from tractors to threshers, silo fillers, and similar mobile machines. It is made of four to eight plies of heavy canvas duck, stitched together with strong twine and treated with a vegetable oil and a special paint.

Canvas belts are made endless for the special power jobs mentioned above. The material in various widths can be obtained in rolls and pieces cut to the desired length for any purpose. A canvas belt is strong and durable, and it withstands exposure to oil, moisture, and steam. On the other hand, it may stretch and shrink under certain conditions, it often becomes stiff, and it frays on the edges and ends, unless used with care or watched closely.

V Belts. A V belt is so named because it has a trapezoidal cross section and fits into the V slot of the pulleys. The pulley slot is usually slightly narrower than the belt; hence the latter acts as a wedge and most of the power is transmitted by the frictional contact between the side surfaces of the belt and the pulley flanges. V belts are made of cotton or synthetic fabric and cords impregnated and bonded together with rubber. V belts are made in five different cross-section sizes, as shown by Fig. 29-4. The selection of the correct section size depends upon the amount of power to be transmitted, the sheave diameters, and the speeds involved. For large machines involving the transmission of a considerable amount of power, two or more belts may be used with multiple-groove pulleys. The determination of the size, length, and number of V belts for a certain power-transmission situation must be made by the use of special formulas and tables supplied by the manufacturers.

Useful Belting Rules

To calculate the speed or size of pulleys, remember

R.p.m. of driven pulley $\times$ its diameter

$$= \text{r.p.m. of driving pulley} \times \text{its diameter}$$

Example 1. A tractor has a 16-in. pulley running at 600 r.p.m. What size pulley is required for a thresher having a cylinder speed of 1,200 r.p.m.?

Let d = diameter of thresher pulley. Then

$$1,200 \times d = 600 \times 16$$

or
$$d = \frac{600 \times 16}{1,200}$$

$$= 8 \text{ in.}$$

Example 2. Referring to Fig. 29-2, the speed of the final drive shaft, if the motor speed is 1,150 r.p.m., is computed as follows:

Speed of final drive shaft $= 1,150 \times {}^{10}\!/_{15} \times {}^{8}\!/_{10} \times {}^{16}\!/_{40} \times {}^{32}\!/_{20} \times {}^{1}\!/_{48}$

$$= 8.2 \text{ r.p.m.}$$

For a worm and worm wheel the speed ratio is the ratio of the number of separate threads on the worm to the number of teeth on the wheel. The number of separate threads on the worm may be determined by following one thread around 360 deg. The number of threads lying between the starting and finishing points indicates the number of threads on the worm.

PULLEYS

Kinds of pulleys. Pulleys are made of wood, cast iron, steel, and fiber or paper. Wood pulleys of any size are built up in sections and split, usually in two parts which are held together by long bolts. They are suitable for line shafts, especially where it is desired to remove or replace the pulley without taking down the shafting. Wood pulleys are usually held in place by means of wood bushings.

Cast-iron pulleys are often faced (lagged) with leather or heavy canvas to reduce belt slippage. They are always made to fit a certain size of shafting and are held in place by a key or setscrew or both.

Steel pulleys are either one piece like cast-iron pulleys or split similar to wood pulleys. If split, they are held in place by metal bushings.

Fiber or composition pulleys have come into extensive use on agricultural machines and for many other power purposes, especially where a small pulley is required with good belt-gripping qualities. Like cast-iron pulleys, they must fit the shaft on which they are to be used and are keyed rigidly to it.

Pulley sizes are designated by the diameter and face width. For example, a 12- by 6-in. pulley means a pulley 12 in. in diameter with a 6-in. face.

GEARS AND GEARING

A gear is a wheel, made usually of iron or steel or of certain other materials and having toothlike projections that engage directly with

FIG. 29-5. *Spur gear and pinion.*

FIG. 29-6. *Internal spur gear and pinion.*

similar projections on another gear and thereby drive it. A pinion is any small gear. Gears are said to transmit power positively, because there is no slippage as with belts. The use of gears and gearing is confined largely to the transmission of motion and power from one part to another of the same machine, rather than from one machine to another. Gears also offer a simple means of speed reduction or increase with respect to the different parts of a machine.

Spur gear. A spur gear is one on which the teeth are so arranged that its axis of rotation is parallel to the axis of rotation of the gear with which it meshes. The plain external spur gear (Fig. 29-5) has its teeth on the outer face. They are straight teeth arranged parallel to the wheel axis. An internal spur gear (Fig. 29-6), as the name implies, has its teeth arranged on an inner face of the offset rim. A spiral or helical spur gear (Fig. 29-7) has angular or twisted teeth. This arrangement permits more teeth to mesh at one time, thus producing smoother and quieter action. A rack and pinion (Fig. 29-8) is a spur-gear application for producing linear movement of some device.

Bevel gear. A bevel gear has its teeth so arranged at an angle with its rotating axis that they mesh with another similar gear and drive two

shafts that form an angle with each other. Plain bevel gears (Fig. 29-9) have straight teeth, while spiral bevel gears (Fig. 29-10) have twisted teeth. The latter are used extensively for final-drive gears in automobiles to secure smoothness and quiet action. Bevel gears always have a tendency to slide out of mesh and thereby produce end thrust on the shafts involved. Therefore, some sort of well-supported thrust bearing is always necessary behind each gear.

FIG. 29-7. *A spiral or helical spur gear.*

Hypoid gear. The hypoid gear (Fig. 29-11) is similar to the spiral bevel gear, but the individual teeth have a distinct curvature, and there is a greater contact area between the teeth. The tooth action is also more of a sliding than a rolling one. The hypoid gear is used extensively for the rear-axle drive in automobiles and trucks because the axis of the

FIG. 29-8. *Rack and pinion.*

pinion gear is located below the axis of rotation of the ring gear, thus permitting the lowering of the propeller shaft. This, in turn, makes possible a lower center of gravity for the entire vehicle.

Worm gear. A worm gear (Fig. 29-12) consists essentially of two parts, the worm and the worm wheel. The worm is nothing more or less than a coarsely threaded screw, while the worm wheel, usually larger in diameter, is very much like a spiral spur gear. The use of a worm gear permits a large speed variation between the driving and driven members without the need of large parts that require considerable space or clearance. Worm gearing has certain disad-

FIG. 29-9. *Plain bevel gear and pinion.*

vantages that make its use limited: (1) it will not usually operate in a reverse manner; that is, the worm must always drive the worm wheel rather than the worm wheel drive the worm; (2) its efficiency is considerably lower than that of other kinds of gearing; and (3) it should have continuous and thorough lubrication while in operation.

FIG. 29-10. *Spiral bevel gear and pinion.*

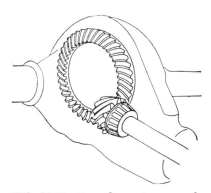

FIG. 29-11. *Hypoid gear for rear-axle drive.*

Gear materials. Plain spur gears, operating at low speeds and used where weight is not an important factor, are usually made of cast iron. This material, however, is not recommended for gears exposed to sand, grit, or other abrasives that cause rapid wear.

FIG. 29-12. *Worm and worm-wheel drive.*

Gears operating at medium to high speeds and requiring protection and good lubrication are made of steel or steel alloys and are hardened or heat-treated.

Bakelite, fiber, or similar composition materials are often used for small gears carrying light loads to reduce noise.

SPROCKET WHEELS AND CHAINS

Sprocket wheels and chains, like gears, are a positive means of power transmission and are used largely for driving different parts of a machine, particularly when these parts are several feet apart or considerable speed reduction is desired. A chain drive possesses certain distinct advantages as follows:

1. It is positive and there is no slippage.

2. It can be coupled and uncoupled readily.

3. Chains absorb shock.

4. A small variation in the distance between sprocket centers is not harmful.

Figure 29-13 illustrates an ordinary sprocket wheel. The sprockets are the projections on the wheel rim. Their size, shape, and spacing depend upon the kind of chain, speed, amount of power transmitted, and other factors.

FIG. 29-13. *Sprocket wheel.*

Kinds of chain. There are a large number of different kinds of chains used for the many applications of this method of power transmission. Likewise, the same type of chain may be made in several distinct sizes and variations. The more common kinds being used for agricultural purposes are (1) the detachable-link chain, which may be malleable (Fig. 29-14) or steel (Fig. 29-15); (2) the pintle chain (Fig. 29-16); (3) the finished steel roller chain (Fig. 29-17); and (4) the silent chain or chain belt (Fig. 10-9).

The detachable-link chain is used largely for light work and medium speeds where the chains are exposed, as on grain binders, threshers, and combines. The steel link is used more extensively because it is cheaper to manufacture and stronger.

The pintle chain is made of malleable links held together by pins. It is used largely for heavy-duty slow-speed work where the chain is exposed.

Steel roller chain is made of special steel, finished, and polished, and equipped with hardened rollers. It is more efficient, is stronger, and wears longer, even under high speeds. It is used largely for heavy-transmission installations such as the final drives of trucks and tractors. It should be well protected from dirt and grit or enclosed and run in oil.

Silent chain is a special type having built-up toothlike links running over toothed wheels similar to gear wheels. This chain is a sort of flexible, metal, corrugated belt. It is used for light, high-speed work such as driving the cam and accessory shafts of automobiles and trucks.

BEARINGS

In general, all bearings may be classed, according to construction, as either plain or antifriction.

FIG. 29-14. *Open or detachable-link chain with malleable links.*

FIG. 29-15. *Open or detachable-link chain with steel links.*

FIG. 29-16. *Pintle chain.*

FIG. 29-17. *Steel roller chain.*

PLAIN BEARINGS

For plain bearings, the most common bearing materials are wood, babbitt, and bronze.

Wood. Wood as a bearing material is used to a limited extent where a bearing is exposed to dirt and grit and therefore is subject to rapid wear and frequent replacement. Figure 29-18 shows the wood bushings used in a disk harrow. A specially treated hard wood is recommended.

Babbitt. Babbitt is an alloy containing tin, copper, lead, and antimony and is used extensively for line-shaft and general-transmission bearings, engine-crankshaft and connecting-rod bearings, generator bearings, and bearings in many agricultural machines. Babbitt is comparatively cheap and soft enough so that it does not wear the journal and at the same time hard enough to withstand excessive pressure. When a babbitt bearing wears out, it is inexpensive to replace either by means of an entirely new babbitt shell or by melting and repouring the bearing. Babbitt also possesses certain other advantages. It retains the lubricant well, even when smooth and well run in, and it melts at a temperature varying from 350 to 450°F.; consequently, danger from fires, due to excessive overheating of a bearing, is avoided.

FIG. 29-18. *Wood bushings for bearings.*

Bronze. Bronze is used extensively for small bearings subject to high speeds or excessive pressures, as piston-pin bearings, certain bearings in farm machines, transmission bearings, and the like. The bronze liner is usually in the form of a solid bushing pressed in place or anchored by a setscrew, pin, or key. The bushing should not be loose or allowed any movement. A bronze bearing wears very slowly, especially if kept well lubricated.

ANTIFRICTION BEARINGS

Antifriction bearings are bearings that are specially constructed to give less power loss and greater efficiency than plain bearings. They are classed as either (1) roller bearings or (2) ball bearings.

Roller bearings. There are four kinds of roller bearings: (1) the plain roller (Fig. 29-19), (2) the spiral roller (Fig. 29-20), (3) the tapered roller (Fig. 29-21), and (4) the needle bearing (Fig. 29-22). A plain roller bearing consists of a number of solid cylindrical steel rollers, assembled as shown. This type is used primarily in agricultural machinery.

The spiral roller bearing, better known as the Hyatt bearing, consists of a number of hollow alloy-steel rollers, assembled as illustrated. Each roller is constructed in the form of a helix. The complete bearing always includes an outer race and may or may not include an inner race.

Hyatt roller bearings are designed for both heavy-duty and light high-speed work. They are best adapted to installations producing radial loads only. If side thrust is present, thrust washers or an additional thrust ball bearing is necessary.

The tapered roller bearing, as shown by Fig. 29-21, is made up of a number of conical rollers assembled in a cage and revolving about the inner and outer races whose bearing surfaces are likewise conical. The outer race is sometimes termed the *cup*, and the inner race the *cone*. The rollers and races are made of high-carbon alloy steel.

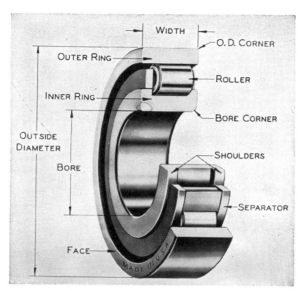

FIG. 29-19. *Plain roller-bearing construction.* (Courtesy of Anti-friction Bearing Manufacturers' Association.)

A tapered roller-bearing installation requires at least two sets of rollers assembled in such a way that they act against each other. Either one or both bearings are usually adjustable, permitting the taking up of any wear. This type of bearing will carry a radial load as well as one producing a side or angular thrust. Tapered roller bearings are used extensively in tractors, trucks, automobiles, and heavy agricultural machinery.

Ball bearings. A ball bearing (Fig. 29-23) consists of one or more rows of highly polished, hardened-steel balls held in a cage and rolling between an inner and an outer race. It may carry

FIG. 29-20. *A spiral roller bearing.*

an ordinary radial load, a combined radial and thrust load, or a straight thrust load, as shown by Fig. 29-24.

The double-row radial bearing is used for heavy-duty purposes or where the outside diameter of the bearing must be limited owing to interference of other parts.

Ball bearings are now being used very extensively for nearly every known purpose. In the agricultural field they are being used for tractor crankshaft mountings, transmissions, steering mechanisms and wheels, thresher cylinder bearings, ensilage cutters, and combines.

FIG. 29-21. *A tapered roller bearing showing parts and construction.*

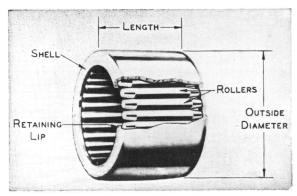

FIG. 29-22. *Needle roller bearing.* (Courtesy of Anti-friction Bearing Manufacturers' Association.)

Care of roller and ball bearings. Good antifriction bearings are made of high-quality materials and require very precise workmanship. It is, therefore, more expensive for the manufacturer of a certain machine to equip it with these bearings, but they usually assure more satisfactory service. They practically eliminate overheating of bearings; they wear very slowly and seldom produce any noise; they greatly reduce friction and power losses; and their lubrication is easier to care for.

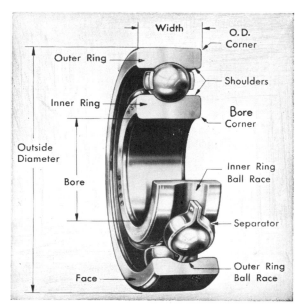

FIG. 29-23. *Ball-bearing construction.*

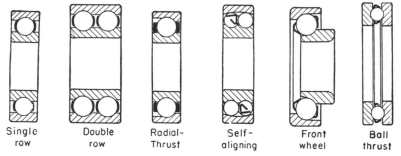

| Single row | Double row | Radial-Thrust | Self-aligning | Front wheel | Ball thrust |

FIG. 29-24. *Some common types of ball bearings.* (Courtesy of Anti-friction Bearing Manufacturers' Association.)

Any ball or roller bearing will give excellent service if the following precautions are observed:

1. It must be properly installed so that it is not subjected to any abnormal strains.

2. It must be well enclosed and completely protected from dirt, grit, or other foreign matter.

3. If it is adjustable, any wear or looseness should be taken up or removed.

4. It should be properly lubricated as often as necessary.

REFERENCES

BAINER, ROY, R. A. KEPNER, and E. L. BARGER, "Principles of Farm Machinery," John Wiley & Sons, Inc., New York, 1955.

CONFER, L. J., Standards for V-belt Drives on Farm Equipment, *Agr. Eng.*, Vol. 31, No. 5.

FIELDING, JOHN, "The Ferrous Metals," Burgess Publishing Company, Minneapolis, Minn., 1941.

KIMMICH, E. G., W. Q. ROESLER, and W. S. WORLEY, Variable-speed V-belt Drives for Farm Machines, *Agr. Eng.*, Vol. 31, No. 7.

LEIGHOU, ROBERT B., "Chemistry of Engineering Materials," 4th ed., McGraw-Hill Book Company, Inc., New York, 1942.

Lubrication Progress Paces Ball and Roller Bearing Developments, *Lubrication*, February, 1945.

MADILL, STANLEY, The Evolution of Materials for Farm Tractors, *Agr. Eng.*, Vol. 33, No. 4.

MARKS, L. S. (ed.), "Mechanical Engineers' Handbook," 6th ed. (revised by T. Baumeister), McGraw-Hill Book Company, Inc., New York, 1958.

MINER, D. F., and J. B. SEASTONE, "Handbook of Engineering Materials," John Wiley & Sons, Inc., New York, 1955.

S.A.E. Handbook, Society of Automotive Engineers, New York, 1961.

SCRANTON, C. J., V-belt Drives for Farm Machines, *Agr. Eng.*, Vol. 36, No. 9.

SCRANTON, C. J., W. C. BLIESENER, W. H. NORDENSON, and H. W. BROWALL, Farm Equipment Steels, *Agr. Eng.*, Vol. 34, No. 10.

THUERMAN, JETT, and E. A. PAUL, Recent Agricultural Chain Developments, *Agr. Eng.*, Vol. 37, No. 9.

PROBLEMS AND QUESTIONS

1. Explain the general processes involved in the manufacture of the various kinds of cast iron and steel.

2. Discuss the relationship of carbon content to the hardness of steel, the various methods of heat-treating steel, and their specific effects on the metal.

3. Name some common steel alloys, and give their specific characteristics and uses.

4. Referring to Fig. 29-2, compute the speed of the worm-wheel shaft if the diameter of the motor pulley is 13.5 in.

5. Differentiate between a plain bevel gear, a spiral bevel gear, and a hypoid gear.

6. Compare the use and adaptability of plain roller bearings and tapered roller bearings.

Appendix

TRACTOR BELT SPEED

A.S.A.E.–S.A.E. Standard

(Revised to January, 1944)

1. The standard belt speed for farm tractors shall be 3,100 feet per minute, plus or minus 100 feet per minute.

2. The minimum width of tractor belt pulleys shall be such as to provide for the use of a belt 6 inches in width.

APPLICATION OF HYDRAULIC REMOTE CONTROL TO FARM TRACTORS AND TRAILING-TYPE FARM IMPLEMENTS

A.S.A.E.–S.A.E. Standard

Foreword. This standard was developed by the Advisory Engineering Committee of the Farm Equipment Institute. Adopted originally by A.S.A.E. in March, 1949, it was later revised and expanded and approved in its present form, July, 1951, as an official A.S.A.E. Standard. It is published as an approved standard of both the American Society of Agricultural Engineers and the Society of Automotive Engineers.

Application. Hydraulic remote controls for all general-purpose and other farm tractors with a work capacity up to 6,000 lb. maximum drawbar pull shall include a cylinder with 8-in. working stroke. Trailing-type hydraulically controlled farm implements intended for use with such tractors shall provide standard mounting points and clearance space for this cylinder.

Hydraulic remote controls for farm tractors larger than the above, up to those with a work capacity of 11,000 lb. maximum drawbar pull, shall regularly include a cylinder with 8-in. working stroke. Trailing-type hydraulically controlled farm implements intended for use with such tractors and requiring an operating thrust within the capacity of an 8-in.-stroke cylinder shall provide standard mounting points and clearance space for this cylinder. Manufacturers of such tractors shall, however, make available cylinders with 16-in.

working stroke for use with implements for which an 8-in.-stroke cylinder is inadequate. Implements requiring a 16-in.-stroke cylinder include deep-tillage plows, 5-furrow moldboard plows, heavy-duty disk plows, deep-tillage tool carriers, and offset disk harrows, 9-ft. cut and over.

Hydraulic remote controls for all farm tractors with a work capacity above 11,000 lb. and up to 20,000 lb. maximum drawbar pull shall include a cylinder with 16-in. working stroke. Trailing-type hydraulically controlled farm implements intended for use with such tractors shall provide standard mounting points and clearance space for this cylinder.

Since most implements intended for use with tractors having a work capacity over 20,000 lb. maximum drawbar pull are regularly provided with one or more suitable cylinders, they impose little requirement for the interchangeable use of hydraulic cylinders. For this reason, hydraulic controls for such tractors are not considered within this standard.

Definition. The purpose of the Standard is to establish common mounting and clearance dimensions for hydraulic remote-control cylinders and trailing-type farm implements with such other specifications as are necessary to accomplish the following objectives:

1. To permit use of any make or model of trailing-type farm implement adapted for control by an 8-in.-stroke hydraulic cylinder, with the 8-in.-stroke hydraulic cylinder furnished with any make or model of farm tractor.

2. To permit use of any make or model of trailing-type farm implement adapted for control by a 16-in.-stroke hydraulic cylinder, with the 16-in.-stroke hydraulic cylinder furnished with any make or model of farm tractor, consistent with the maximum drawbar pull of the tractor normally required to operate the implement.

3. To facilitate changing the hydraulic cylinder from one implement to another and decrease the possibility of introducing dirt or other foreign material into the hydraulic system, by reducing the necessity for supplemental hose lengths or piping with certain types of implements.

STANDARD DIMENSIONS AND SPECIFICATIONS FOR HYDRAULIC REMOTE CONTROLS INCLUDING A CYLINDER WITH 8-IN. WORKING STROKE

1. The hydraulic cylinder with hose shall be considered as part of the tractor hydraulic remote control and shall be built to standard dimensions.

2. Both single and double-acting cylinders shall operate to raise the implements (or deangle disk harrows) on their extending stroke. Implements requiring actuating force in both directions should be operated by a double-acting cylinder.

3. Provision shall be made on the implement to accommodate the full stroke of the hydraulic cylinder. Variable-stroke control necessary in the application of hydraulic control to some implements shall be incorporated in the cylinder or hydraulic system and applied on the retracting stroke.

4. *Cylinder length of stroke.* 8 in.—plus ⅛ in.

                                        —minus 0 in.

5. *Distance, center to center between attaching pins.*

        Extended, 28¼ in.—plus ⅛ in.

                —minus 0 in.

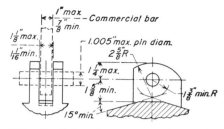

FIG. 1. *Yoke clearances—anchor end—for 8-in.-stroke hydraulic cylinder.*

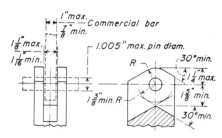

FIG. 2. *Yoke clearances—rod end—for 8-in.-stroke hydraulic cylinder.*

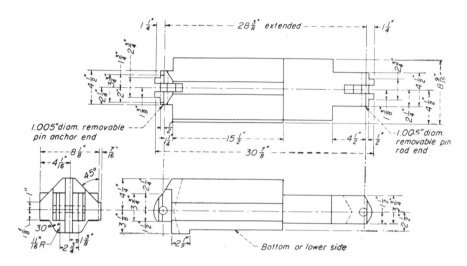

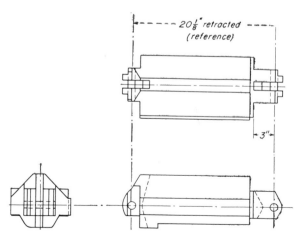

FIG. 3. *Clearance model of agricultural hydraulic cylinder with 8-in. length of stroke for tractors having up to and including 11,000 lb. maximum drawbar pull.*

6. *Size of attaching pins.* Cylinder attaching pins shall be of 1 in. nominal diameter. Oversize tolerance, 0.005 in. maximum. Implement mountings shall provide operating clearance for 1.005-in. maximum diameter pins.

7. *Type of ends.* Yoke on anchor and rod ends.

8. *Width of throat.* 1¹⁄₁₆ in. minimum and 1⅛ in. maximum for bar ⅞-in. minimum and 1-in. maximum thickness.

9. *Depth of throat.* The anchor end of the cylinder shall provide the clearance shown in Fig. 1. This affords clearance for a 1 × 2½-in. bar through a 30-deg. included angle, equally divided, and a 1 × 3-in. bar in a perpendicular position.

The rod end of the cylinder shall provide the clearance shown in Fig. 2. This affords clearance for a 1 × 2½-in. bar through a 60-deg. included angle, equally divided, and a 1 × 3-in. bar in a perpendicular position.

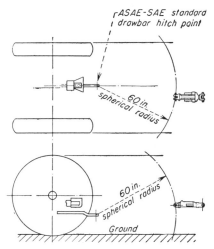

FIG. 4. *Hose-length diagram for wheel-type tractor drawbar, 60-in. spherical radius.*

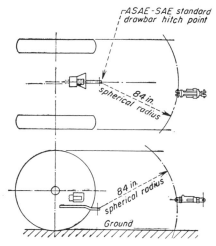

FIG. 5. *Hose-length diagram for wheel-type tractor drawbar, 84-in. spherical radius.*

10. *Clearance area on implement.* Hydraulic cylinders shall operate within the composite volume specified in Fig. 3. Implements designed for remote-cylinder operation shall provide clearance for a cylinder of the composite volume specified in Fig. 3.

11. *Standard hose lengths for remote hydraulic cylinders.* The tractor manufacturer shall provide sufficient lengths of hose so that the hydraulic cylinder, provided with tractors having a work capacity up to 6,000 lb. maximum drawbar pull, is operable when the front anchor pin is located at a maximum 60-in. spherical radius from a center which is the A.S.A.E.–S.A.E. Standard Drawbar Hitch Point (Fig. 4).

Tractors with a work capacity between 6,000 and 11,000 lb. maximum drawbar pull shall be provided by the manufacturer with sufficient lengths of hose so that the hydraulic cylinder is operable when the front anchor pin is located at a maximum 84-in. spherical radius from the drawbar hitch point.

On such tractors, for which the A.S.A.E.-S.A.E. Standard Power Take-off Shaft is available, the A.S.A.E.-S.A.E. Standard Drawbar Hitch Point shall be used, as shown in Fig. 5. On all other track-type tractors, the S.A.E. Standard Track-type Drawbar Hitch Point shall apply as shown in Fig. 6.

The implement manufacturer shall locate the hydraulic cylinder on the implement to provide allowance for cushion spring hitches, maneuverability and turning so that the implement can be operated safely without stretching or breaking the hose under any circumstances.

12. *Hose supports.* Support required for remote cylinder hose shall be considered as part of the implement.

13. *Hose connections to cylinders.* Hose connections shall be such that the hose will not interfere with bars extending through the yoke on either end of the hydraulic cylinder.

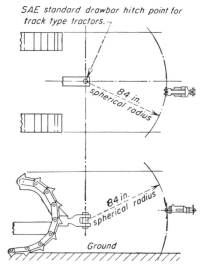

FIG. 6. *Hose-length diagram for track-type tractor drawbar, 84-in. spherical radius.*

14. *Operating time at rated engine speed.* 1½ to 2 sec. per 8-in. stroke at rated hydraulic pressure.

RECOMMENDED PRACTICE: SUPPLEMENTAL HOSE LENGTHS

(*Not a part of the Standard*)

As built at present, the position of the hydraulic cylinder on some large disk implements requires additional hose beyond that necessary for the specified spherical radius from center of drawbar hitch point. For implements requiring additional hose length, two supplemental hose lengths increasing the spherical radius by 60-in. and 96-in. increments shall be made available by the tractor manufacturer on special orders. When supplemental hose lengths are used, self-sealing couplings shall be provided for each of the hose lines leading from the tractor and for the supplemental hose lengths.

STANDARD DIMENSIONS AND SPECIFICATIONS FOR HYDRAULIC REMOTE CONTROLS INCLUDING A CYLINDER WITH 16-IN. WORKING STROKE

1. The hydraulic cylinder with hose shall be considered as part of the tractor hydraulic remote control and shall be built to standard dimensions.

2. All hydraulic cylinders shall be double acting and shall operate to raise the implements (or deangle disk harrows) on their extending stroke.

3. Provision shall be made on the implement to accommodate the full stroke of the hydraulic cylinder. Variable-stroke control necessary in the application of hydraulic control to some implements shall be incorporated in the cylinder or hydraulic system and applied on the retracting stroke.

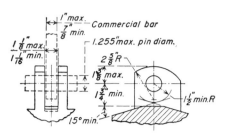

FIG. 7. *Yoke clearances—anchor end—for 16-in.-stroke hydraulic cylinder.*

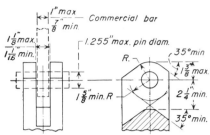

FIG. 8. *Yoke clearances—rod end—for 16-in.-stroke hydraulic cylinder.*

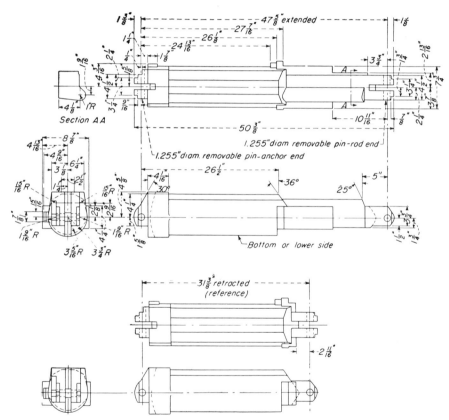

FIG. 9. *Clearance model of agricultural hydraulic cylinder with 16-in. length of stroke for tractors having up to and including 11,000 lb. maximum drawbar pull.*

4. *Cylinder length of stroke.* 16 in.—plus ⅛ in.
                                                     —minus 0 in.
5. *Distance, center to center between attaching pins.*
      Extended, 47½ in.—plus ⅛ in.
                                      —minus 0 in.
6. *Size of attaching pins.* Cylinder attaching pins shall be of 1¼ in. nominal diameter. Oversize tolerance, 0.005 in. maximum. Implement mountings shall provide operating clearance for 1.255-in. maximum diameter pins.

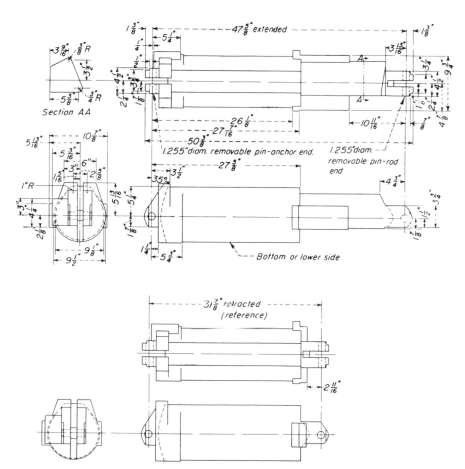

FIG. 10. *Clearance model of agricultural hydraulic cylinder with 16-in. length of stroke for tractors having above 11,000 lb. and up to 20,000 lb. maximum drawbar pull.*

7. *Type of ends.* Yoke on anchor and rod ends.
8. *Width of throat.* 1¹⁄₁₆ in. minimum and 1⅛ in. maximum for bar ⅞-in. minimum and 1-in. maximum thickness.
9. *Depth of throat.* The anchor end of the cylinder shall provide the clearance as shown in Fig. 7. This affords clearance for a 1 × 2¾-in. bar

through a 30-deg. included angle, equally divided, and a $1 \times 3\frac{1}{4}$-in. bar in a perpendicular position.

The rod end of the cylinder shall provide the clearance as shown in Fig. 8. This affords clearance for a 1×3-in. bar through a 70-deg. included angle, equally divided, and a 1×4-in. bar in a perpendicular position.

10. *Clearance area on implements.* Hydraulic cylinders for tractors, up to and including those with a working capacity of 11,000 lb. maximum drawbar pull, shall operate within the composite volume specified in Fig. 9. Hydraulic cylinders for larger tractors, up to and including those with a work capacity

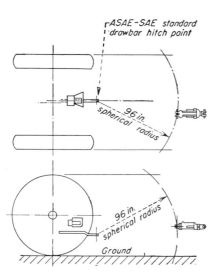

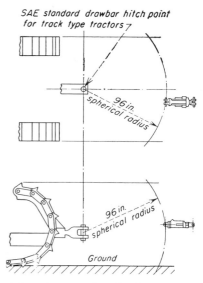

FIG. 11. *Hose length diagram for wheel-type tractor drawbar, 96-in. spherical radius.*

FIG. 12. *Hose-length diagram for track-type tractor drawbar, 96-in. spherical radius.*

of 20,000 lb. maximum drawbar pull, shall operate within the composite volume specified in Fig. 10. Implements designed for remote-cylinder operation shall provide clearance for a cylinder of the composite volume specified in Fig. 9 or 10 consistent with maximum drawbar pull of the tractor normally required to operate the implement.

11. *Hose lengths for remote hydraulic cylinders.* The tractor manufacturer shall provide sufficient hose, including a self-sealing coupling in each line, so that the hydraulic cylinder is operable when the front anchor pin is located at a maximum 96-in. spherical radius from the drawbar hitch point. On tractors for which the A.S.A.E.–S.A.E. Standard Power Take-off Shaft is available, the A.S.A.E.–S.A.E. Standard Drawbar Hitch Point shall be used as shown in Fig. 11. On all other track-type tractors, the S.A.E. Standard Track-type Drawbar Hitch Point will apply as shown in Fig. 12.

To provide for the hydraulic control of implements on which the cylinder is positioned outside of the specified 96-in. spherical radius, two lengths of supplemental hose, each including a self-sealing coupling and increasing the spherical radius by 60-in. and 96-in. increments, shall be made available by the tractor manufacturer.

The implement manufacturer shall locate the hydraulic cylinder on the implement to provide allowance for cushion spring hitches, maneuverability, and turning so that the implement can be operated safely without stretching or breaking the hose under any circumstances.

12. *Hose supports.* Support required for remote cylinder hose shall be considered as part of the implement.

13. *Hose connections to cylinders.* Hose connections shall be such that the hose will not interfere with bars extending through the yoke on either end of the hydraulic cylinder.

14. *Operating time at rated engine speed.* 3 to 5 sec. per 16-in. stroke at rated hydraulic pressure.

FARM TRACTOR POWER TAKE-OFF: DEFINITIONS AND TERMINOLOGY

A.S.A.E.–S.A.E. Standard

(Adopted March, 1955)

This Recommendation deals only with the definitions and terminology pertaining to the power shafts of farm tractors in which the power take-off rotational speed is proportional to the engine speed. This is the type that prevails in the United States, Canada, England, and generally throughout the world. The following recommendations will facilitate a clear understanding for engineering discussions, comparisons, and the preparation of technical papers.

The term "master clutch" is generally used to describe a clutch which transmits all power from the engine and controls both travel and the power take-off. Likewise, when disengaged, both stop.

Transmission-driven power take-off. Power to operate both the transmission and the power take-off is transmitted through a master clutch, which serves primarily as a traction clutch. The power take-off operates only when the master clutch is engaged. The transmission-driven power take-off ceases to operate at any time the master clutch is disengaged.

Continuous-running power take-off. Power to operate both the transmission and the power take-off is transmitted through a master clutch. Both operate only when the master clutch is engaged. Auxiliary means are provided for stopping the travel of the tractor without stopping the power take-off. The continuous-running power take-off ceases to operate at any time when the master clutch is disengaged.

Independent power take-off. Power to operate the transmission and power take-off is transmitted through independent transmission and power take-off clutches. Travel of the tractor may be started or stopped by operation of the transmission clutch without affecting operation of the independent power take-off. Likewise, the power take-off may be started or stopped by the power take-off clutch without affecting tractor travel.

540-R.P.M. POWER TAKE-OFF FOR FARM TRACTORS

A.S.A.E.–S.A.E. Standard

(Revised 1961)

This Standard establishes the specifications that are essential in order that any 540-r.p.m. power take-off-driven machine may be operated with any make of tractor having a 540-r.p.m. power take-off drive.

1. The diameter of the hitch hole (Fig. 13) at the end of the tractor drawbar shall be not less than 1¾₆ in., and, in addition, an 1¹⁄₁₆-in. hole shall be provided in the drawbar 4 in. ahead of the hitch hole.

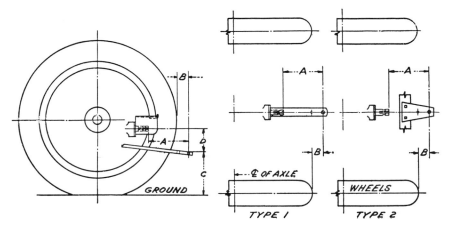

FIG. 13. *Drawbar hitch and power take-off locations for farm tractors.*

2. The material in the tractor drawbar shall clear an implement clevis (3 in. wide and having a 3-in. throat clearance) through a 90-deg. swing right or left of the tractor drawbar center line.

3. The horizontal distance (*B*, Fig. 13) between the hitch point on the tractor drawbar and the rearmost point on the standard-sized rubber tire, steel wheel rim lug, or fender of the tractor shall be not less than 4 in.

4. The position of the tractor drawbar, for power take-off work, shall be such that the vertical distance (*C*, Fig. 13) from the ground line to the top of the drawbar at the hitch point shall be 15 in. ± 2 in. when the tractor is equipped with regular-sized tires.

5. The horizontal distance (*A*, Fig. 13) between the hitch point on the tractor drawbar and the end of the splined shaft of the power take-off shall be 14 in. The hitch point shall be directly in line with the center line of the power take-off shaft, and provision shall be made on the tractor for locking the drawbar in this position.

6. The vertical distance (*D*, Fig. 13) between the top of the drawbar at the hitch point and the center line of the power take-off splined shaft shall be not less than 6 in. or more than 15 in., 8 in. being the recommended dimension.

7. The location of the tractor power take-off shaft shall be within the limits

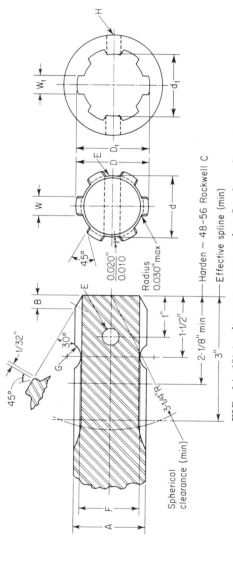

FIG. 14. *1⅜-in.-diameter power take-off spline dimensions.*

Table 1. Shaft and hub spline dimensions

A Nom diam	Spline on shaft									Spline in hub									
	D Large diam		d Small diam		W Spline width			D₁ Large diam		d₁ Small diam		W₁ Spline width	
	max	min	max	min	max	min					max	min	max	min	max	min	max	min
1-3/8	1.373	1.366	1.108	1.098	0.340	0.338					1.375	1.374	1.170	1.168	0.344	0.342

Table 2. General shaft and hub dimensions

Shaft							H Hub pin hole diam
G Radius	E Hole diam	F Groove bottom diam		B Chamfer		Pin diam	
		max	min	Length			
17/64	21/64	1.160	1.155	9/32		5/16	21/64 (0.328)

Harden – 48–56 Rockwell C

Effective spline (min)

Radius 0.030″ max

Spherical clearance (min)

499

of 3 in. to the right or left of the center line of the tractor, the tractor center line being the recommended location.

8. The tractor drawbar shall be strong enough to carry vertical loads at the PTO drawbar hitch point in accordance with the schedule shown in Table 3, and implements designed for each class of tractor shall not impose loads in excess of these values. In Table 3 the maximum drawbar pull (P) is based on test 2.5, Maximum Drawbar Power with Ballast, of the Agricultural Tractor Test Code; the dynamic load (W_d) is the maximum vertical load imposed on the drawbar when operating under field conditions; and the static load (W_s) is the maximum vertical load imposed on the drawbar with the implement and tractor combination at rest on level ground.

Table 3. Tractor Drawbar Vertical Load Limitations

Tractor class	Maximum drawbar pull (P), lb.	Maximum vertical dynamic load (W_d), lb.	Maximum vertical static load (W_s), lb.
A	0–2,000	1,250	500
B	2,000–3,500	1,875	750
C	3,500–6,000	2,500	1,000
D	6,000 and up	3,750	1,500

9. The tractor power take-off shaft (except belt-pulley shafts) for power take-off drives extending from the tractor to the rear shall have the dimensions shown in Fig. 14 and Tables 1 and 2 if a 1⅜-in.-diameter shaft is employed, and shall have the dimensions shown in Fig. 15 if a 1¾-in.-diameter shaft is employed. A minimum clearance of 3¼ in. between the end of the spline shaft and any stationary part of the tractor shall be provided, this clearance to be a spherical radius from the center of the spline shaft end. The spline shaft groove shown in Figs. 14 and 15 is provided for use where additional retaining means is desired. On the 1¾-in.-diameter power take-off shaft, the option of the major diameter fit is recommended for applications encountering greater radial load than can successfully be transmitted with the option of a tooth side fit; also, hubs incorporating a clamping means along with the option of the tooth side fit are recommended for applications encountering reversal of torsional load of sufficient magnitude so that hubs without clamping means are found inadequate.

10. The normal speed of the rear power take-off shaft, when operating under load, shall be 540 r.p.m. ± 10 r.p.m. The direction of rotation is to be clockwise when facing in the direction of forward travel. It is recommended that an instrument indicating the normal speed of the power take-off shaft, when operating under load, be made available for farm tractors. Such an instrument shall be provided as part of any farm tractor capable of driving the rear power take-off in excess of 600 r.p.m., when operating under load.

11. The tractor shall be equipped with a power take-off master shield (Fig. 16), incorporating the attaching point for the shield of the driven machine as dimensioned.

12. The strength of the master shield shall be sufficient to support the weight of the operator without taking a permanent set.

13. Both towed and integral-type power take-off-driven machines shall be equipped with adequate shielding for that portion of the power line that is furnished as a part of the driven machines. This shielding shall prevent the operator from coming in contact with positively driven rotating members of the power line. The shield for the power line between the implement and tractor shall be integral with and journaled on the rotating member. Where integral power take-off-driven implements are of a design requiring removal of the tractor master shield, such implements shall also include adequate protection for that portion of the tractor power shaft which protrudes from the tractor.

1,000-R.P.M. POWER TAKE-OFF FOR FARM TRACTORS

A.S.A.E.–S.A.E. Standard

(Approved 1958, revised 1961)

This Standard established the specifications that are essential in order that any 1,000-r.p.m. power take-off-driven machine may be operated with any make of tractor having a 1,000-r.p.m. power take-off drive:

1. The diameter of the hitch hole (Fig. 13) at the end of the tractor drawbar shall be not less than 1¾₆ in., and, in addition, an 1¼₆-in. hole shall be provided in the drawbar 4 in. ahead of the hitch hole.

2. The material in the tractor drawbar shall clear an implement clevis (3 in. wide and having a 3-in. throat clearance) through a 90-deg. swing right or left of the tractor drawbar center line.

3. The horizontal distance (B, Fig. 13) between the hitch point on the tractor drawbar and the rearmost point on the standard-sized rubber tire, steel wheel rim lug, or tractor fender shall not be less than 3 in.

4. The position of the tractor drawbar for power take-off work shall be such that the vertical distance (C, Fig. 13) from the ground line to the top of the drawbar at the hitch point shall be 15 in. ± 2 in. when the tractor is equipped with regular-sized tires.

5. The horizontal distance (A, Fig. 13) between the hitch point on the tractor drawbar and the end of the splined shaft of the power take-off shall be 16 in. The hitch point shall be directly in line with the center line of the power take-off shaft, and provision shall be made on the tractor for locking the drawbar in this position.

6. The vertical distance (D, Fig. 13) between the top of the drawbar at the hitch point and the center line of the power take-off splined shaft shall not be less than 6 in. or more than 12 in., 8 in. being the recommended dimension.

7. The location of the tractor power take-off shaft shall be within the limits of 1 in. to the right or left of the center line of the tractor, the tractor center line being the recommended location.

8. The tractor drawbar shall be strong enough to carry vertical loads at the

1-3/4 involute PTO spline

Hub
0.1010 max actual
0.1000 min actual (ref)
0.0992 max effective (ref)
0.0982 min effective (with gage)

0.013 R
APP

0.006 Max ht

0.0900

1.5896
Max between pins

1.7520
1.7500
Major dia for
option of major
dia fit

1.739
TIF diameter

Tooth form shall
be a true involute
inside this dia

1.6275
1.6250
Minor dia

Internal spline

Base circle dia   1.4614
Max involute profile error   0.0005
Max cumulative pitch error
(Any two teeth)   0.0015
Max out of roundness   0.0012
Max eccentricity of major
dia with pitch dia   0.0010

Ref only

Shaft
0.0952 max effective (with gage)
0.0942 min effective (ref)
0.0930 max actual (ref)
0.0920 min actual

0.015
0.007

0.015
Min

1.5408
Min minor dia

1.6075
Max minor dia

1.8125
Max major dia for
option of tooth
side fit

0.1200

0.006 R
Max

Tooth form shall
be a true involute
outside this dia

1.616
TIF diameter

1.6875
Pitch diameter
(ref)

1.7480
1.7470
Major diameter

1.8611 min
over pins

External spline

Base circle dia   1.4614
Max involute profile error   0.0005
Max cumulative pitch error
(Any two teeth)   0.0015
Max out of roundness   0.0013
Max eccentricity of major
dia with pitch dia   0.0015

Ref only

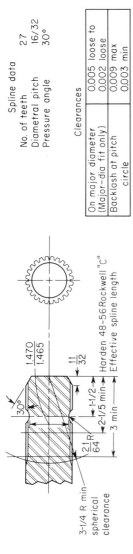

Spline data

No. of teeth	27
Diametral pitch	16/32
Pressure angle	30°

Clearances

On major diameter (Major–dia fit only)	0.005 loose to	0.002 loose
Backlash at pitch circle	0.009 max	0.003 min

Drawing labels: 1.470/1.465 · 11/32 · 30° · 1-1/2 min · 2-1/5 min · 3 min · 21/64 R · 3-1/4 R min spherical clearance · Harden 48–56 Rockwell "C" · Effective spline length

FIG. 15. 1¾-in.-diameter power take-off spline dimensions.

PTO drawbar hitch point in accordance with the schedule shown in Table 3, and implements designed for each class of tractor shall not impose loads in excess of these values. In Table 3, the maximum drawbar pull (P) is based on test 2.5, Maximum Drawbar Power with Ballast, of the Agricultural Tractor Test Code; the dynamic load (W_d) is the maximum vertical load imposed on the drawbar when operating under field conditions; and the static load (W_s) is the maximum vertical load imposed on the drawbar with the implement and tractor combination at rest on level ground.

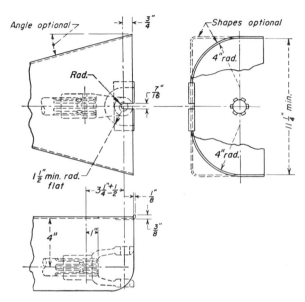

FIG. 16. *Power take-off master shield for the tractor with 540-r.p.m. shaft.*

9. The tractor power take-off shaft (except belt-pulley shafts) for power take-off drives extending from the tractor to the rear shall have the dimensions shown in Fig. 17. A minimum clearance spherical radius of 3¼ in. as illustrated in Fig. 17 shall be provided. The spline shaft groove shown in Fig. 17 is provided for a retaining means where required. The option of the major diameter fit is recommended for applications encountering greater radial load than can successfully be transmitted with the option of a tooth side fit; also, hubs incorporating a clamping means along with the option of the tooth side fit are recommended for applications encountering loads of sufficient magnitude so that hubs without clamping means are found inadequate.

10. The normal speed of the rear power take-off shaft, when operating under normal load, shall be 1,000 r.p.m. ± 25 r.p.m. The direction of the rotation shall be clockwise when facing in the direction of forward travel. It is recommended that an instrument indicating the normal speed of the power take-off shaft, when operating under normal load, be made available for farm tractors. Such an instrument shall be provided as a part of any farm tractor capable of

driving the rear power take-off shaft in excess of 1,100 r.p.m. when operating under load.

11. The tractor shall be equipped with a power take-off master shield (Fig. 18), incorporating the attaching point for the shield of the driven machine as dimensioned.

12. The strength of the master shield shall be sufficient to support the weight of the operator without taking a permanent set.

13. Both towed and integral-type power take-off-driven machines shall be equipped with adequate shielding for that portion of the power line that is furnished as a part of the driven machines. This shielding shall prevent the operator from coming in contact with positively driven rotating members of the power line. The shield for the power line between the implement and tractor shall be integral with and journaled on the rotating member. Where integral power take-off-driven implements are of a design requiring removal of the tractor master shield, such implements shall also include adequate protection for that portion of the tractor power shaft which protrudes from the tractor.

OPERATING REQUIREMENTS FOR POWER TAKE-OFF DRIVES

(Adopted March, 1953; revised January, 1958)

(This A.S.A.E. Recommendation was prepared and approved by the Advisory Engineering Committee of the Farm Equipment Institute to assist manufacturers of tractors and PTO-driven machines in providing suitable means of power transmission from the tractor to the driven machine.)

The A.S.A.E. standards for 1,000-r.p.m. and 540-r.p.m. power take-off drives specify the essential dimensions of tractor components necessary to enable manufacturers of driven machines to provide for the satisfactory hitching of their machines to any make of tractor. The successful performance of all tractor and driven-machine combinations likely to be met in field service requires consideration of many factors other than the dimensional relationships established in the forementioned Standard. Some of the more important of these factors are as follows:

1. Instructions for the operator. The tractor manufacturer shall provide a safety instruction in a prominent place on the tractor specifying:

(*a*) The normal operating speed of the rear power take-off shaft (540 or 1,000 r.p.m.)

(*b*) That the tractor drawbar is to be adjusted and locked in a position so that the drawbar hitch point is located

(1) On the longitudinal center line of the tractor power take-off shaft

(2) With the center of the implement hitch pin 14 in. to the rear of the end of the power take-off shaft for an implement and tractor combination operating at 540 r.p.m., and 16 in. to the rear of the end of the power take-off shaft for an implement and tractor combination operating at 1,000 r.p.m.

(3) With the vertical distance between the top of the tractor drawbar and the center line of the power take-off shaft being as close to 8 in. as possible

(*c*) That power-line safety shields are to be kept in place

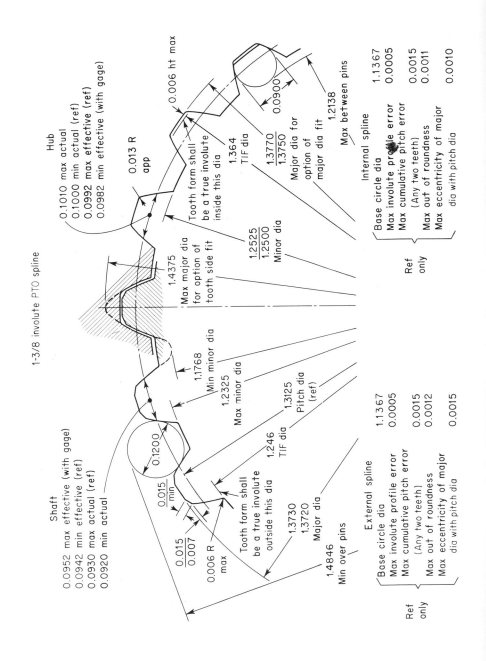

1-3/8 involute PTO spline

Hub

0.1010 max actual
0.1000 min actual (ref)
0.0992 max effective (ref)
0.0982 min effective (with gage)

0.006 ht max

0.013 R
app

Tooth form shall
be a true involute
inside this dia

1.364
TIF dia

$\dfrac{1.3770}{1.3750}$
Major dia for
option of
major dia fit

$\dfrac{1.2525}{1.2500}$
Minor dia

0.0900

1.2138
Max between pins

Internal spline

Base circle dia   1.1367
Max involute profile error   0.0005
Max cumulative pitch error   0.0015
(Any two teeth)   0.0011
Max out of roundness
Max eccentricity of major
dia with pitch dia   0.0010

Ref
only

Shaft

0.0952 max effective (with gage)
0.0942 min effective (ref)
0.0930 max actual (ref)
0.0920 min actual

0.1200

0.1768
Min minor dia

1.2325
Max minor dia

1.4375
Max major dia
for option of
tooth side fit

$\dfrac{0.015}{\text{min}}$

$\dfrac{0.015}{0.007}$

0.006 R
max

Tooth form shall
be a true involute
outside this dia

1.3730
1.3720
Major dia

1.3125
Pitch dia
(ref)

1.246
TIF dia

1.4846
Min over pins

External spline

Base circle dia   1.1367
Max involute profile error   0.0005
Max cumulative pitch error   0.0015
(Any two teeth)   0.0012
Max out of roundness
Max eccentricity of major
dia with pitch dia   0.0015

Ref
only

506

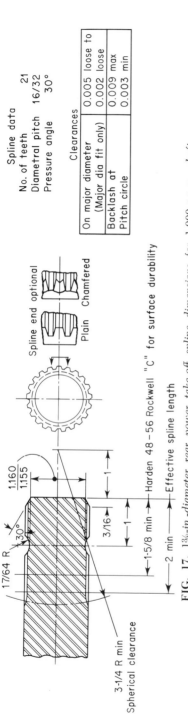

Spline data

No. of teeth   21
Diametral pitch   16/32
Pressure angle   30°

Clearances

On major diameter (Major dia fit only)	0.005 loose to 0.002 loose
Backlash at Pitch circle	0.009 max 0.003 min

Spline end optional

Plain   Chamfered

Harden 48–56 Rockwell "C" for surface durability

Effective spline length

1.160 / 1.155

3/16

1-5/8 min

2 min

17/64 R

30°

3-1/4 R min
Spherical clearance

FIG. 17. 1⅜-in.-diameter rear power take-off spline dimensions for 1,000-r.p.m. shaft.

The implement manufacturer shall provide an instruction in a prominent place on the implement specifying:

(*a*) The normal operating speed of the power take-off drive to the implement (540 or 1,000 r.p.m.)

(*b*) That the power-line safety shields are to be kept in place

The operator's manuals for both tractors and power take-off-driven implements shall also include the above information.

If a conversion assembly is made available for changing tractors or implements from the 540- to the 1,000-r.p.m. power take-off standard, or from the

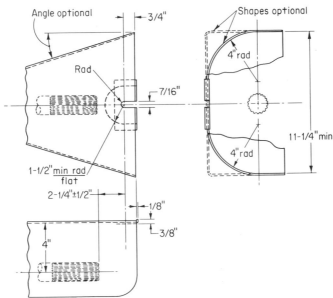

FIG. 18. *Power take-off master shield for tractor with 1,000-r.p.m. shaft.*

1,000- to the 540-r.p.m. power take-off standard, these conversion assemblies shall include an instruction plate or sticker specifying the power take-off speed and the corresponding drawbar adjustments.

2. Driven-machine hitch and power-line design requirements. The hitch and power line of any PTO-driven machine, when the machine is hitched to any tractor that conforms to the A.S.A.E. Standard: "Power Take-off for Farm Tractors," should provide satisfactory operation over any terrain the machine is likely to encounter. To meet any such operating conditions, provision should be made in the power line and hitch of the driven machine to prevent any of the following from occurring:

(*a*) The universal joints in the power line from reaching a locking angle

(*b*) The telescoping section of the power line from separating beyond the point where there is sufficient bearing to provide for proper operation, or

(*c*) The telescoping section of the power line from shortening to a solid position

In normal forward operation the universal joints in the power line of the driven machine should be in straight alignment as nearly as possible, and should be properly indexed with respect to each other so as to maintain the torsional-load fluctuations at the lowest possible value. Extreme care should be taken to determine load fluctuations or load reversals when one or three universal joints are employed in a power line.

3. *Maximum bending load limitations for power take-off shaft drives employing V belts or chains.* The power take-off drive of tractors is designed primarily to transmit torsional loads. When V-belt or chain drives with the driving sheave or sprocket mounted directly on the power take-off shaft are used, bending loads on the shaft should be checked carefully. The total bending load imposed on the tractor power take-off shaft by drives of this type should not be in excess of values shown in the following table:

Position of load application	1⅜-diameter power take-off	1¾-diameter power take-off
At the end of power take-off shaft..................	500 lb.	800 lb.
Between the power take-off shaft rear bearing and/or at the groove in the outside diameter of the power take-off shaft splines...........................	600 lb.	1,000 lb.

The tractor power take-off shaft and bearing mountings should successfully withstand the magnitude of bending loads indicated in this table.

4. *Power-line protective couplings and maximum torsional-load limitations for power take-off shafts.* The dynamic torsional loads on power take-off drives should be checked carefully. Because of the large amount of kinetic energy available at the power take-off shaft, instantaneous torsional loads and fluctuating operating loads far in excess of the average rated horsepower of the tractor may be transmitted. Transmittal of these excessive loads can result in premature failure of the driving parts.

Implements subject to high starting loads or plugging should be equipped with an overload protective device in the power line which will protect the drive against torsional overloads of sufficient magnitude to cause mechanical failure of either tractor or implement parts.

In consideration of the foregoing factors it is desirable for implements to conform to the following conditions:

(*a*) The instantaneous operating loads should not exceed 7,500 lb.-in. for the 1⅜-diameter shaft or 12,000 lb.-in. for the 1¾-diameter shaft under conditions where there is no reversal of load. When a repetitive reversal of load is encountered, the aforementioned load limitations must be reduced by the amount of the reverse load.

(*b*) When the frequency of the instantaneous load does not exceed 10 cycles per hr., implements imposing loads greater than 7,500 lb.-in. for the 1⅜-diameter shaft or 12,000 lb.-in. for the 1¾-diameter shaft should have a power-line protective device which does not exceed a maximum instantaneous slip value of 13,000 lb.-in. for the 1⅜-diameter shaft or 26,000 lb.-in. for the 1¾-diameter shaft.

(c) The requirements in paragraphs (a) and (b) above will generally be met with a smooth-surface frictional type of power-line protective device which does not exceed a breakaway value of 4,000 lb.-in. for the 1⅜-diameter shaft or 6,400 lb.-in. for the 1¾-diameter shaft when checked under static conditions. Snap-type spring-loaded jaw clutches should not be evaluated under static conditions, and therefore must comply with paragraphs (a) and (b) above.

Tractors capable of imposing inertia loads on the power line as high as those mentioned above should have a power take-off drive capable of transmitting a torque equivalent to that described in paragraphs (a) and (b) without failure. Tractors which are not capable of transmitting a torque of this magnitude should have a drive of sufficient strength to transmit the maximum torque they are capable of delivering to the power take-off drive.

Index